CONTENTS

Preliminary Edition Notice

You have been selected to receive a copy of this book in the form of a preliminary edition. A preliminary edition is used in a classroom setting to test the overall value of a book's content and its effectiveness in a practical course prior to its formal publication on the national market.

As you use this text in your course, please share any and all feedback regarding the volume with your professor. Your comments on this text will allow the author to further develop the content of the book, so we can ensure it will be a useful and informative classroom tool for students in universities across the nation and around the globe. If you find the material is challenging to understand, or could be expanded to improve the usefulness of the text, it is important for us to know. If you have any suggestions for improving the material contained in the book or the way it is presented, we encourage you to share your thoughts.

This text is not available in wide release on the market, as it is actively being prepared for formal publication. Accordingly, the book is offered to you at a discounted price to reflect its preliminary status.

If you would like to provide notes directly to the publisher, you may contact us by e-mailing studentreviews@cognella.com. Please include the book's title, author, and 7-digit SKU reference number (found below the barcode on the back cover of the book) in the body of your message.

Stress Analysis

with an Introduction to

Finite Element Methods

REVISED PRELIMINARY EDITION

M. Oussama Safadi

University of Southern California

Bassim Hamadeh, CEO and Publisher
Mieka Portier, Senior Acquisitions Editor
Tony Paese, Senior Project Editor
Susana Christie, Senior Developmental Editor
Alia Bales, Production Editor
Emely Villavicencio, Senior Graphic Designer
Greg Isales, Licensing Coordinator
Natalie Piccotti, Director of Marketing
Kassie Graves, Senior Vice President of Editorial
Jamie Giganti, Director of Academic Publishing

Printed in the United States of America.

PREFACE

Introduction

The first course students take when studying applied mechanics is Statics. This course, together with Dynamics, is the foundation of classical Newtonian mechanics. Both are based on 17th-century Newtonian laws. After Statics, which is a must-take course prior to reading my textbook, college students who want to study solid applied mechanics take Strength of Materials. The term is a translation from the French, "Résistance des Matériaux," and was coined in France. Nowadays, Strength of Materials is more likely to be called Mechanics of Materials or Introduction to Mechanics of Deformable Bodies. In this elementary class, students move from idealistic rigid mechanics (assuming that the body is 100% rigid) to a more practical deformable body mechanics (taking into consideration the deformability of the material). Strength of Materials is elementary and relatively simple. It is preferred by engineers. It does not require advanced mathematics; however, it has its limitations. It only covers simple structures with simple loadings. For instance, we do not cover complex structures such as plates and shells in Strength of Materials.

The topics in this textbook are usually covered in an advanced Strength of Materials course (Strength of Materials II). It also includes introductions to several advanced important (graduate) courses. It has an introduction to the theory of elasticity, an introduction to structural stability, an introduction to theory of plates, and an introduction to finite element analysis. Readers, after being exposed to these several introductions, can take more advanced specific graduate courses, depending on their interest and need. This textbook can be used by advanced undergraduate (senior) students, by graduate (MS and PhD) students, as well as by professional engineers working in industry. The textbook benefits students studying aerospace; civil, mechanical, and biomedical engineering; as well as practicing engineers.

I believe the textbook is unique in its approach to its topics. The intent is to make the topics easier and more appealing to the reader. The emphasis is on understanding the physics and on practical applications needed in the industry. Certain detailed rigorous explanations were skipped but without any compromise on quality, accuracy, and professionalism. Like in any effort such as mine, many readers, whether students or professional engineers, are going to appreciate such an approach and find it useful and appealing. Yet, my approach will likely draw some criticism, which I am open to. If I have succeeded in making the topics more appealing to our students and making Stress Analysis a "stress free course!" that should be great. Any shortcoming in this work will be my responsibility, and I will accept it.

Learning is a continuous perpetual effort. It takes time and struggle. It does not occur instantly. Like any topic in mathematics, physics, or engineering, you cannot digest the material by simply reading it. You need to work out practice problems and additional supplementary problems. Some of these problems are simple, while others are much more challenging. You learn the material by trying challenging problems (no pain, no gain!). When a student approaches a problem and works on it for hours without ending up with the correct answer, they are not wasting time. Indeed, the student in this case will be investing a very valuable time. It is the best investment in their life! This is the way to master a topic. We learn from our mistakes. When you read the stories and biographies of famous mathematicians and scientists in the world, often you encounter one of them literally spent half of their lifespan on one single problem. They end up discovering many outstanding and interesting results while working on such a single problem.

Occasionally, you might notice a slight overlapping among the various chapters of the textbook. This was done to emphasize essential concepts and to render each chapter to be, whenever possible, read and understood independently.

I am going to end this brief introduction one a humorous note. I started teaching at a very young age, and one of the first classes I started teaching was Statics. In my social circle back then, and when people around me became aware that I was teaching Statics, often, they used to ask me if they could take my course. Knowing their background and major, I had to explain to them that they needed to take Statistics, not Statics!

Text Arrangement

The textbook consists of 10 chapters and five appendices. The contents in the textbook are similar to the contents of a popular textbook in the United States by A. C. Ugural and S. K. Fenster: *Advanced Mechanics of Materials and Applied Elasticity*. My textbook is much influenced by the Ugural and Fenster book, since I used it as an undergraduate student and later adopted it for several years when I taught AME 403 Stress Analysis at USC.

It is recommended to study chapters 1 and 2 of my textbook first. At USC, chapters 1, 2, 3, 4, 5, 6, and 7 were used in teaching AME 403 (Stress Analysis), while chapters 1, 2, 3, 8, 9, and 10 were used as part of a more advanced course AME 529 (Aircraft Structures Analysis).

Supplement

This textbook is accompanied by a complete solution manual available to instructors.

CHAPTER 1

Stress Tensor

1.1 Definition of Stress and Strain

Consider a prismatic bar loaded axially with a load P as shown in **figure 1.1.**

Let A be the area of the cross section of the bar.

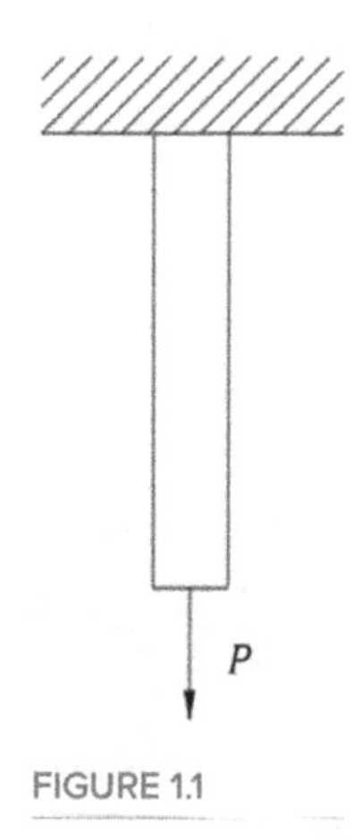

FIGURE 1.1

Let:

$$\sigma = \frac{P}{A}. \tag{1.1}$$

σ is called the engineering (or conventional) axial (or normal) stress. If the cut is made not close to the point of application of P, it is safe to assume that σ is uniform over the cross section of the bar.

Notice that σ has the dimension of force per area. Its unit in SI system is $\frac{N}{m^2}$ or Pa (Pascal[1]).

One Pascal is very small in structural engineering. We often use:

$$1\,kPa = 10^3\,Pa \text{ (kilo Pascal)}$$

or

$$1\,MPa = 10^6\,Pa \text{ (mega Pascal)}$$

or

$$1\,GPa = 10^9\,Pa \text{ (giga Pascal).}$$

In the CGS system, the unit of stress is $\frac{\text{dyne}}{\text{cm}^2}$.

$$1Pa = 1\frac{N}{m^2} = \frac{10^5\,dyne}{10^4\,cm^2} = 10\frac{dyne}{cm^2}$$

In the technical English system, the unit of stress is $\frac{\text{lb}_f}{\text{ft}^2}$.

Instead, we often use $1\,psi = 1\frac{lb_f}{in^2} = 144\frac{lb_f}{ft^2}$ or $1\,ksi = 1\frac{kip}{in^2} = 10^3\,psi$. 1 *psi* is very small in structural engineering. To get a feeling of what 1 *psi* is: The pressure in the tire of your small car is 32 *psi*. The pressure in the spare tire in the trunk of your car might be 60 *psi*.

Since the material is assumed to be deformable (non-rigid), there will be deformation in the bar.

Let:

$$\varepsilon = \frac{\Delta l}{l_0}. \tag{1.2}$$

l_0 is the original (initial) length of the bar before deformation and $\delta = \Delta l$ is the amount of axial deformation of the bar. Δl can be positive (elongation) or negative (contraction), depending on whether P is tensile or compressive. ε is called the engineering (or conventional) axial (or normal) strain. Notice that ε is a dimensionless or unitless quantity ($\frac{m}{m}$, $\frac{cm}{cm}$, or $\frac{in}{in}$...).

1.2 Stress-Strain Relationship

Having defined σ (the engineering or conventional axial or normal stress) and ε (the engineering or conventional axial or normal strain), a natural question comes up: is there a relationship between σ and ε? The answer is yes.

1 Named after the 17th-century French polymath Blaise Pascal (1623–1662).

A ductile material (e.g., steel, aluminum, and copper) is one capable of sustaining large amount of deformation. The opposite of ductile is brittle (e.g., most cast iron and glass).

If we increase the axial load P in **figure 1.1** slowly (gradually), obviously σ will increase and so will ε. For a ductile material subject to a uniaxial tensile stress, the following graph depicts a typical relationship between σ and ε.

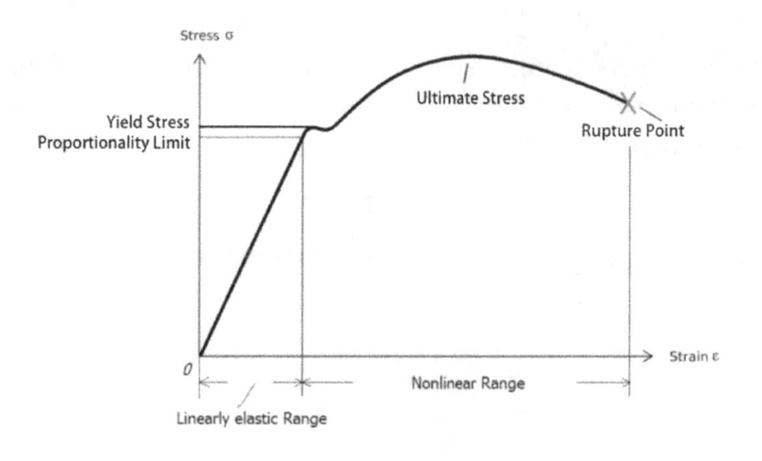

FIGURE 1.2

Notice that the relationship between σ and ε at the beginning is nice and smooth (linear). Later, such a relationship becomes more complex (nonlinear).

We usually consider the yield strength (σ_{yield}) to be the proportionality limit.

In the linearly elastic range, the relationship between σ and ε is linear. Therefore, we can write:

$$\frac{\sigma}{\varepsilon} = E. \tag{1.3}$$

The proportionality constant E is called Young's modulus of elasticity.[2] The unit of E is the same as that of stress (*Pa, MPa, psi, ksi,* etc.). E is a mechanical property of the material. It is tabulated. A typical value of E:

$$E_{steel} = 30 \times 10^6 \; psi = 30{,}000 \; ksi.$$

2 This was named after the 18th-century English physicist Thomas Young (1773–1829). Young was also a noted physician and Egyptologist. He was credited with deciphering the Rosetta Stone. He was incredibly gifted at learning foreign languages. He was acquainted with a dozen of them. "Modulus" means "measurement" in Latin.

(1.3) is called Hooke's law.[3] Using $\sigma = \frac{P}{A}$ and $\varepsilon = \frac{\delta}{l}$, Hooke's law can be written as

$$\delta = \frac{Pl}{AE}$$

or

$$\delta = \frac{P}{\frac{AE}{l}} \tag{1.4}$$

The first time the author encountered Hooke's law was in an elementary physics course when a linear spring was presented with spring constant k (dimension: $\frac{\text{force}}{\text{length}}$. Unit in SI system: $\frac{N}{m}$) loaded with a load P:

$$\delta = \frac{P}{k}. \tag{1.5}$$

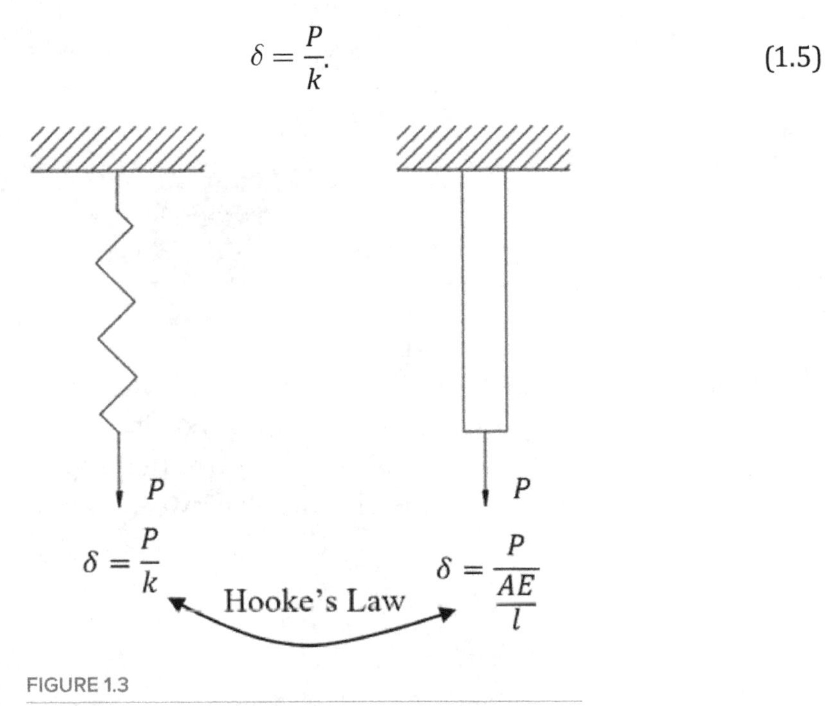

FIGURE 1.3

Notice the similarity between equations (1.4) and (1.5). It's no wonder why both are called Hooke's law!

Notice also that $\frac{AE}{l}$ has the same dimension as k. In SI system, the unit of $\frac{AE}{l}$ is: $\frac{m^{\square}N}{m^{\square}m} = \frac{N}{m}$, which is the same unit for k.

---

3 After the English physicist Robert Hooke (1635–1703). Hooke was a contemporary and rival of Isaac Newton. His relationship with Newton was not very cordial because he competed with him.

Indeed, a prismatic bar loaded axially with a load P, as long as it is still in the linearly elastic range, will behave like a linear spring with spring constant (or stiffness) k.

$$k = \frac{AE}{l} \tag{1.6}$$

k depends on the mechanical property of the material (E) and the geometric properties of the prismatic bar (A and l).

We will visit this concept again and see its applications later in the textbook in Chapter 7: Energy Methods and Chapter 10: Introduction to Finite Element Analysis.

It should be noted that **figure 1.2** depicts the relationship between σ and ε for a ductile material subject to uniaxial tensile stress. Brittle materials do not behave the same. Below are typical graphs depicting the relationship between σ and ε for brittle materials.

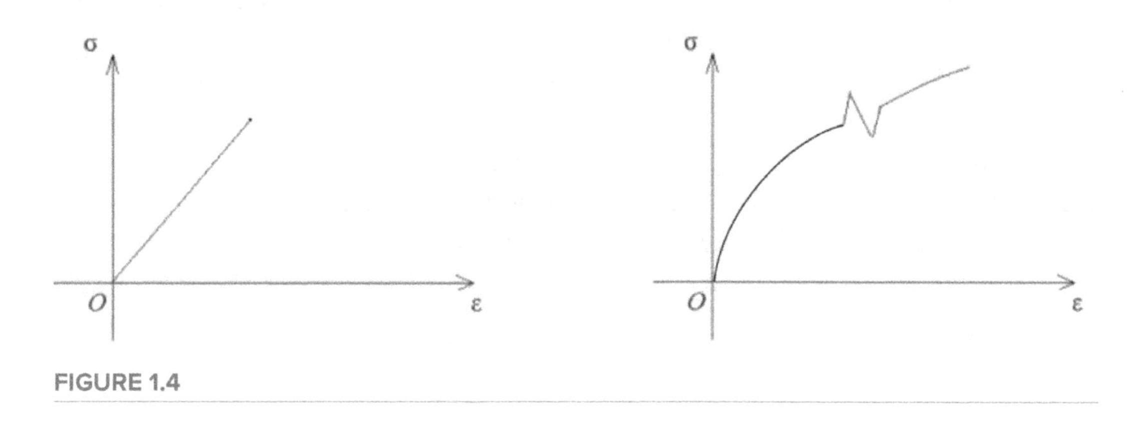

FIGURE 1.4

"σ versus ε for cast iron" "σ versus ε for glass"

Notice that for brittle cast iron proportionality limit, yield strength, ultimate stress, and rupture point are the same. The material ruptures suddenly without any warning (brittle fracture). For this reason, decades ago, steel was preferred over cast iron in manufacturing car engines.

For glass, which is another brittle material, its behavior does not show any linear relationship between σ and ε at any stage.

1.3 Poisson's Ratio

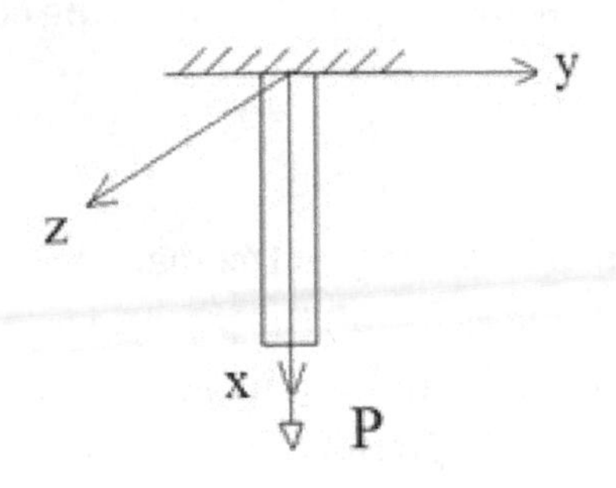

FIGURE 1.5

Let us associate with the three-dimensional space an *xyz* Cartesian coordinate system as shown in **figure 1.5**. When the prismatic bar is loaded axially with a load *P*, we defined $\sigma = \frac{P}{A}$ as the axial (or normal) conventional (or engineering) stress. Indeed, σ is here σ_x: an axial stress in the *x*-direction. In this case, there is no σ_y and there is no σ_z. We also defined $\varepsilon = \frac{\Delta l}{l_0}$ and called it the axial (or normal) conventional (or engineering) strain. Indeed, ε is here ε_x (axial strain in the *x*-direction). However, it is observed that an axial elongation will be accompanied by lateral contraction. An axial contraction will be accompanied by lateral expansion. Although, in this uniaxial state of stress only σ_x is applied (no σ_y and no σ_z), yet we have ε_x, ε_y and ε_z. It can be shown that ε_y and ε_z are directly proportional to ε_x:

$$\varepsilon_y \propto \varepsilon_x.$$

In order to switch from a proportionality sign to an equality sign, we need to introduce a proportionality constant:

$$\varepsilon_y = -\nu\varepsilon_x$$

Similarly, we can also write that:

$$\varepsilon_z = -\nu\varepsilon_x$$

ν is a positive proportionality constant called Poisson's[4] ratio. This is a unitless (dimensionless) quantity. $0 < \nu < \frac{1}{2}$. Typical values: $\nu_{steel} = 0.3$ and $\nu_{rubber} = 0.499$.

Therefore, Hooke's laws for a uniaxial state of stress can be written as:

$$\varepsilon_x = \frac{\sigma_x}{E}$$
$$\varepsilon_y = -\frac{\nu\sigma_x}{E} \tag{1.7}$$
$$\varepsilon_z = -\frac{\nu\sigma_x}{E} \cdot$$

1.4 True Stress and True Strain

In section 1.1, σ and ε were called engineering (conventional) stress and engineering (conventional) strain, respectively, in order to distinguish them from true stress and true strain. When we define σ to be $\frac{P}{A}$, which area are we referring to? Are we referring to the original cross-sectional area (before deformation) or the actual area (after deformation)? In most engineering applications, it is conventional and sufficient to use the original area. If, however, we use the actual area, the stress is called true stress, which is slightly different from the conventional one.

Similarly, we can distinguish between engineering strain and true strain. Engineering strain ε was defined by dividing Δl over l_0 in one shot. In defining the true strain ε_1, we consider an elementary differential strain and then add these elementary differential strains. In the limit, this summation becomes Riemann integration:

$$\varepsilon_1 = \int_{l_0}^{l} \frac{dl}{l} = [\ln l]_{l_0}^{l} = \ln l - \ln l_0 = \ln\left(\frac{l}{l_0}\right) = \ln\left(\frac{l_0 + \Delta l}{l_0}\right).$$

$\Rightarrow$

$$\varepsilon_1 = \ln(1 + \varepsilon) \tag{1.8}$$

---

4 Named after Simeon Poisson (1781–1840). He was a great French mathematician who contributed to the theory of elasticity and applied mechanics. He was a student of Laplace. Poisson taught at École Polytechnique in Paris—the first modern school of engineering, established in Paris in 1794.

In most engineering applications, ε is very small (of the order of 10^{-3} or 10^{-4}). In this case ε_1 is very close to ε. To demonstrate that,

$$\frac{1}{1+\varepsilon} = 1 - \varepsilon + \varepsilon^2 - \varepsilon^3 \ldots$$

$$\Rightarrow \quad \int \frac{1}{1+\varepsilon} d\varepsilon = \varepsilon - \frac{\varepsilon^2}{2} + \frac{\varepsilon^3}{3} - \frac{\varepsilon^4}{4} \ldots$$

$$\Rightarrow \quad \varepsilon_1 = \ln(1+\varepsilon) = \int \frac{1}{1+\varepsilon} d\varepsilon = \varepsilon - \frac{\varepsilon^2}{2} + \frac{\varepsilon^3}{3} - \frac{\varepsilon^4}{4} \ldots.$$

When ε is of the order of 10^{-3}, ε^2 will be of the order of 10^{-6}, and ε^3 will be of the order of 10^{-9}. The engineering (conventional) strain is a very good approximation of the true strain when it is very small (by ignoring higher order terms).

1.5 Shear Stress and Shear Angle

σ and ε were called axial (or normal) stress and axial (or normal) strain, respectively, in order to distinguish them from other types of stress called shear stress and shear strain. Shear stress causes angular deformation.

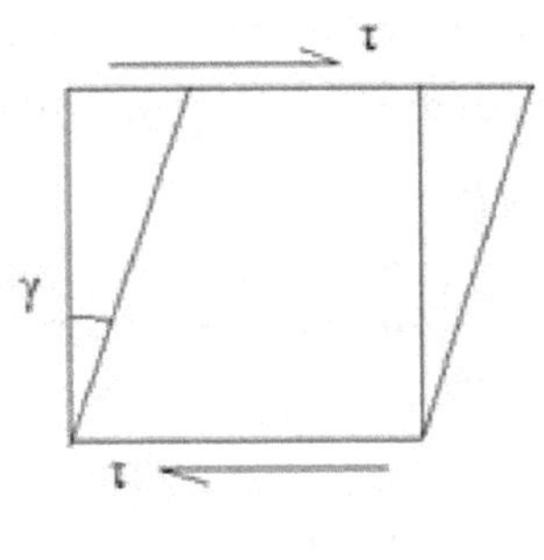

FIGURE 1.6

The very thin rectangular plate shown in **figure 1.6** is subject to shear stress τ, which results in shear angle Υ. It can be observed that in the linearly elastic range τ and Υ are directly proportional to each other. Therefore, we can write:

$$\frac{\tau}{\gamma} = G.$$

The proportionality constant G is called shear modulus of elasticity or modulus of rigidity. τ has the dimension of stress, and the units include *Pa, MPa,* and *ksi*. Υ is unitless or dimensionless (radian). Therefore, G has the dimension of stress. It is measured, like E, in *MPa* or *ksi*.

Hooke's laws for the state of plane stress are the following:

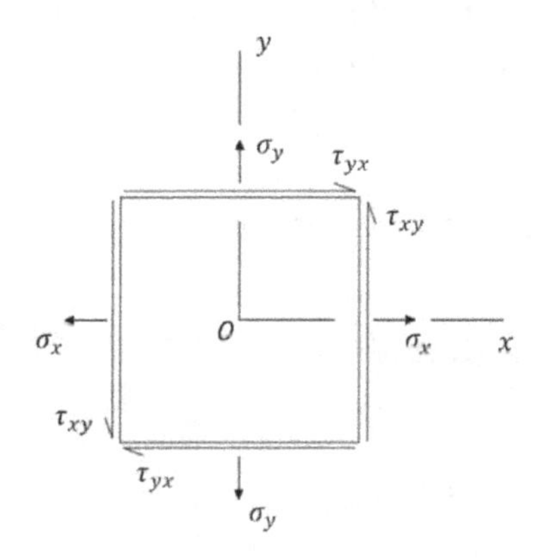

FIGURE 1.7

$$\begin{aligned} \varepsilon_x &= \frac{\sigma_x}{E} - \frac{\nu}{E}\sigma_y \\ \varepsilon_y &= \frac{\sigma_y}{E} - \frac{\nu}{E}\sigma_x \\ \gamma_{xy} &= \frac{\tau_{xy}}{G}. \end{aligned} \tag{1.9}$$

1.6 Stress and Strain Tensors

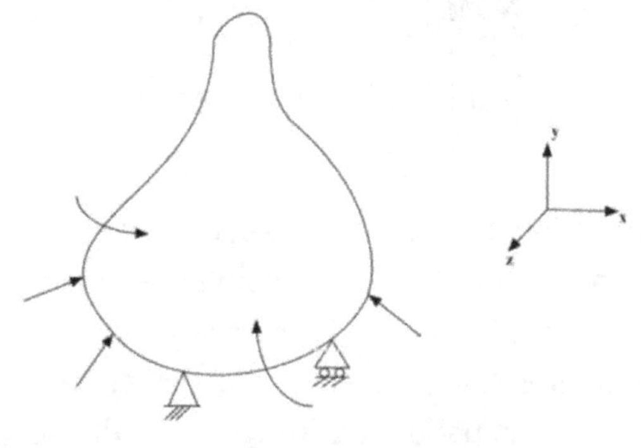

FIGURE 1.8

In the most general case, consider a body (such a body can be any structure, including a beam, frame, plate, shell, truss, or three-dimensional part) subject to a system of forces (in mechanics, such forces can be linear, and measured in *N*, *kN*, *kip*, etc., or moments or torques, measured in $N \times m$, $kip \times in$, etc.).

At a specific point *P* of the body, we can define σ_x (axial or normal stress in the *x*-direction), σ_y (axial or normal stress in the *y*-direction), σ_z (axial or normal stress in the *z*-direction), τ_{xy} (shear stress in the *xy* plane), τ_{xz} (shear stress in the *xz* plane), and τ_{yz} (shear stress in the *yz* plane).

To organize ourselves, we put these quantities in a rectangular array called a matrix. We say that the state of stress at point *P* is completely defined by the (3×3) real symmetric matrix:

$$\left[\sigma_{ij}\right] = \begin{bmatrix} \sigma_x & \tau_{xy} & \tau_{xz} \\ \tau_{yx} & \sigma_y & \tau_{yz} \\ \tau_{zx} & \tau_{zy} & \sigma_z \end{bmatrix}_{(3\times3)} \tag{1.10}$$

$\left[\sigma_{ij}\right]$ is real and symmetric. In other words,

$$\sigma_{ij} = \sigma_{ji}.$$

Indeed, $\left[\sigma_{ij}\right]$ must be symmetric in order to satisfy Newton's equilibrium equations. It can be shown using statics that:

$$\sum M_x = 0 \Rightarrow \tau_{yz} = \tau_{zy}$$

$$\sum M_y = 0 \Rightarrow \tau_{xz} = \tau_{zx}$$

$$\sum M_z = 0 \Rightarrow \tau_{xy} = \tau_{yx}.$$

$\left[\sigma_{ij}\right]$ is a second rank (or second order) tensor called the stress tensor.

A scalar quantity (i.e., a real number is a tensor of the zero order). A vector quantity, such as a force, is a tensor of the first order. Stress is a tensor of the second order.

Figure 1.9 below illustrates the general case of a three-dimensional state of stress at a point. Notice that τ_{xy} acts perpendicular to *x* and parallel to *y*, whereas τ_{yx} acts perpendicular to *y* and parallel to *x*. However, $\tau_{xy} = \tau_{yx}$.

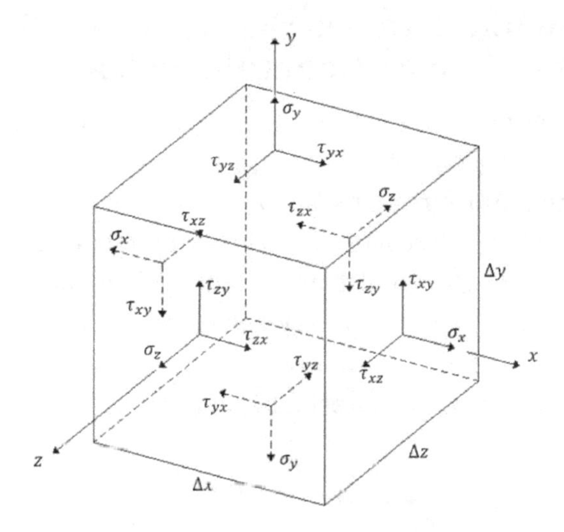

FIGURE 1.9

Since the material is not assumed to be rigid (rather, it is deformable), we can also define ε_x (axial or normal strain in the x-direction), ε_y, ε_z, ε_{xy} (shear strain in the xy plane), ε_{xz}, and ε_{yx}.

We say that the state of strain at the same specific point P is completely defined by the (3×3) real symmetric matrix

$$\left[\varepsilon_{ij}\right] = \begin{bmatrix} \varepsilon_x & \varepsilon_{xy} & \varepsilon_{xz} \\ \varepsilon_{yx} & \varepsilon_y & \varepsilon_{yz} \\ \varepsilon_{zx} & \varepsilon_{zy} & \varepsilon_z \end{bmatrix}_{(3\times 3)} \tag{1.11}$$

$\left[\varepsilon_{ij}\right]$ is real and symmetric. In other words,

$$\varepsilon_{ij} = \varepsilon_{ji.}$$

$\left[\varepsilon_{ij}\right]$ is a second rank (or second order) tensor called the strain tensor.

1.7 Relationship Between the Stress and Strain Tensors—Hooke's Generalized Laws

A homogeneous[5] material is one that has the same properties throughout. Opposite of homogeneous is heterogeneous or nonhomogeneous. An isotropic[6] material is one that has the same properties in all directions. Opposite of isotropic is anisotropic. An anisotropic material is one that has different properties in different directions. Wood is a natural anisotropic material. Fiberglass is also anisotropic. When fiberglass is loaded parallel to the fiber, its behavior is not the same as when loaded perpendicular to the fiber. (For instance, for fiberglass, we have two different Young's moduli of elasticity $E_{\parallel}$ and $E_{\perp}$.)

For a homogeneous isotropic material behaving in the linearly elastic range, we can write:

$$\varepsilon_x = \frac{\sigma_x}{E} - \frac{\nu}{E}\left(\sigma_y + \sigma_z\right);\ \gamma_{xy} = \frac{\tau_{xy}}{G}$$

$$\varepsilon_y = \frac{\sigma_y}{E} - \frac{\nu}{E}\left(\sigma_x + \sigma_z\right);\ \gamma_{xz} = \frac{\tau_{xz}}{G}$$

$$\varepsilon_z = \frac{\sigma_z}{E} - \frac{\nu}{E}\left(\sigma_x + \sigma_y\right);\ \gamma_{yz} = \frac{\tau_{yz}}{G}. \tag{1.12}$$

The above six relationships are called Hooke's generalized laws.

1.8 Special Cases

Case (i): $\sigma_y = \sigma_z = \tau_{xy} = \tau_{xz} = \tau_{yz} = 0$

This is the simplest case in stress analysis. It is called uniaxial state of stress.

$$\left[\sigma_{ij}\right] = \begin{bmatrix} \sigma_x & 0 & 0 \\ 0 & 0 & 0 \\ 0 & 0 & 0 \end{bmatrix}_{(3\times3)}$$

---

5 The etymology of homogeneous comes from "homos," which means "same" in Greek, and "gene," meaning "kind" or "born".

6 The etymology of isotropic comes from "isos", which means "equal" in Greek, and "tropic," meaning "to turn".

An example of a uniaxial state of stress is when we have a prismatic bar loaded axially with a load P (**figure 1.10**).

Case (ii): $\sigma_z = \tau_{xy} = \tau_{xz} = \tau_{yz} = 0$

This is called biaxial state of stress.

$$[\sigma_{ij}] = \begin{bmatrix} \sigma_x & 0 & 0 \\ 0 & \sigma_y & 0 \\ 0 & 0 & 0 \end{bmatrix}_{(3\times3)}$$

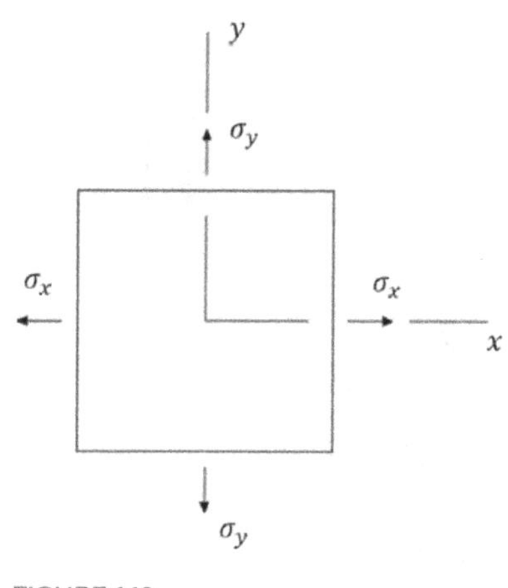

FIGURE 1.10

Case (iii): $\tau_{xy} = \tau_{xz} = \tau_{yz} = 0$

It is called triaxial state of stress.

$$[\sigma_{ij}] = \begin{bmatrix} \sigma_x & 0 & 0 \\ 0 & \sigma_y & 0 \\ 0 & 0 & \sigma_z \end{bmatrix}_{(3\times3)}$$

Notice that in a triaxial state of stress, shear stress is suppressed, and $[\sigma_{ij}]$ becomes a diagonal matrix.

Case (iv): $\sigma_z = \tau_{xz} = \tau_{yz} = 0$

It is called state of plane stress.

$$\left[\sigma_{ij}\right] = \begin{bmatrix} \sigma_x & \tau_{xy} & 0 \\ \tau_{yx} & \sigma_y & 0 \\ 0 & 0 & 0 \end{bmatrix}_{(3\times3)}$$

Notice that in a state of plane stress, the third row and third column in $\left[\sigma_{ij}\right]_{(3x3)}$ are suppressed. For this reason, the state of plane stress at a point P can now be defined by the (2×2) real symmetric matrix:

$$\left[\sigma_{ij}\right] = \begin{bmatrix} \sigma_x & \tau_{xy} \\ \tau_{yx} & \sigma_y \end{bmatrix}_{(2\times2)}.$$

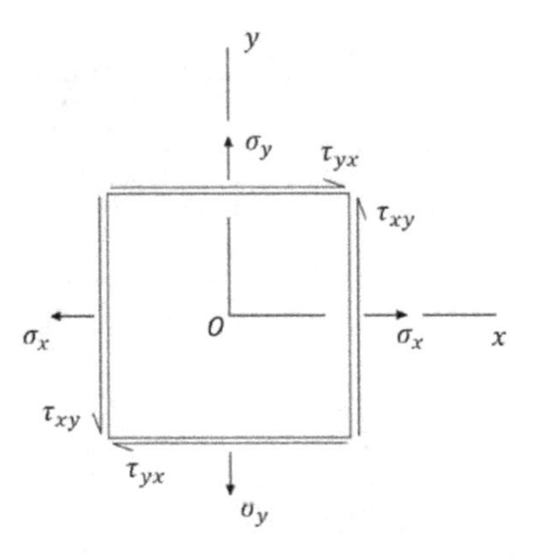

FIGURE 1.11

Case (v): $\varepsilon_z = \varepsilon_{xz} = \varepsilon_{yz} = 0$

This is called state of plane strain.

$$\left[\varepsilon_{ij}\right] = \begin{bmatrix} \varepsilon_x & \varepsilon_{xy} & 0 \\ \varepsilon_{yx} & \varepsilon_y & 0 \\ 0 & 0 & 0 \end{bmatrix}_{(3\times3)}$$

Notice that in a state of plain strain, the third row and third column in $\left[\varepsilon_{ij}\right]_{(3x3)}$ are suppressed. In this case, the state of plane strain at a point P can be defined by the (2×2) real symmetric matrix

$$\left[\varepsilon_{ij}\right]=\begin{bmatrix}\varepsilon_{x} & \varepsilon_{xy}\\ \varepsilon_{yx} & \varepsilon_{y}\end{bmatrix}_{(2\times2)}$$

Case (vi): $\sigma_{x}=\sigma_{y}=\sigma_{z}=-p\ (p>0)$ and $\tau_{xy}=\tau_{xz}=\tau_{yz}=0$
This is called hydrostatic pressure.

$$\left[\sigma_{ij}\right]=\begin{bmatrix}-p & 0 & 0\\ 0 & -p & 0\\ 0 & 0 & -p\end{bmatrix}_{(3x3)}$$

Notice that hydrostatic pressure is a special case of triaxial state of stress when $\sigma_{x}=\sigma_{y}=\sigma_{z}$. Also, p does not have to be positive.

The term "hydrostatic pressure" is borrowed from fluid mechanics even though this topic and the entire textbook deals with solid mechanics. Hydrostatic means fluid at rest. It can be shown that the hydrostatic pressure ($\rho gh=\gamma h$) at a point in a tank filled with liquid at rest is the same in all directions. Also, there is no shear stress in a fluid at rest. Shear stress is what makes a fluid flow.

1.9 State of Plane Stress

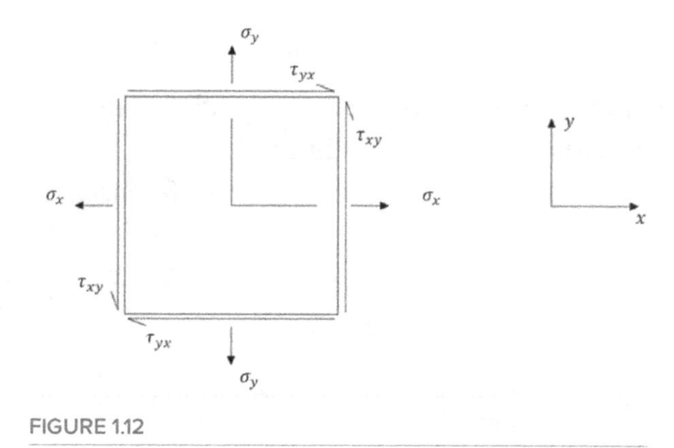

FIGURE 1.12

In the state of plane stress, we suppress the third row (and third column) of the (3 × 3) real symmetric matrix

$$\left[\sigma_{ij}\right] = \begin{bmatrix} \sigma_x & \tau_{xy} & \tau_{xz} \\ \tau_{yx} & \sigma_y & \tau_{yz} \\ \tau_{zx} & \tau_{zy} & \sigma_z \end{bmatrix}_{(3\times3)},$$

and the state of plane stress at a point P can now be completely defined by the (2 × 2) real symmetric matrix

$$\left[\sigma_{ij}\right] = \begin{bmatrix} \sigma_x & \tau_{xy} \\ \tau_{yx} & \sigma_y \end{bmatrix}_{(2\times2)},$$

and this makes analyzing the state of plane stress mathematically much simpler.

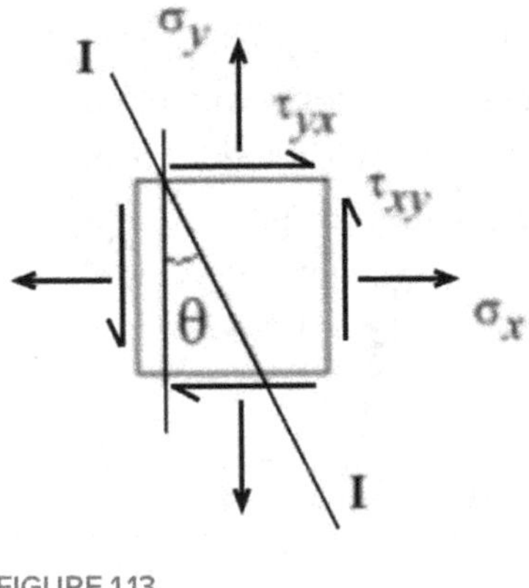

FIGURE 1.13

Our objective is to investigate the normal stress σ_n and the tangential stress σ_t that will pop up on an oblique plane I-I as shown in **figure 1.13**.

Consider the free body diagram of an elementary differential element shown in the figure before.

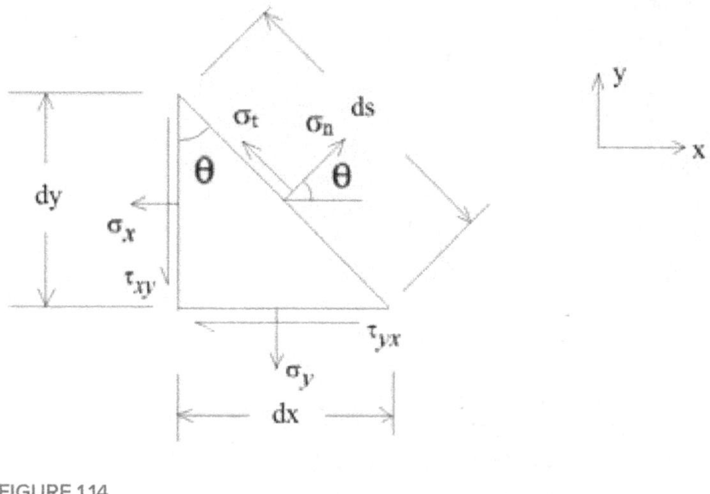

FIGURE 1.14

We have two unknowns σ_n and σ_t. We need two equations. We get them from statics.

$$\sum \vec{F} = \vec{0} \Rightarrow \begin{cases} \Sigma F_x = 0 \\ \Sigma F_y = 0 \end{cases}$$

However, in the free body diagram shown in **figure 1.14**, we have stresses $\left(\frac{Force}{area}\right)$, while Newton's equilibrium equations relate forces. Thus, we need to convert stress into force by multiplying it by the appropriate area.

$$\sum F_x = 0$$

$$\Rightarrow \qquad \sigma_n dsdz \cos\theta - \sigma_t dsdz \sin\theta - \sigma_x dydz - \tau_{yx} dxdz = 0 \tag{1.13}$$

$$\sum F_y = 0$$

$$\Rightarrow \qquad \sigma_n dsdz \sin\theta + \sigma_t dsdz \cos\theta - \sigma_y dxdz - \tau_{xy} dydz = 0 \tag{1.14}$$

Dividing the right-hand side and left-hand side by $dsdz$ and noticing that

$$sin\theta = \frac{dx}{ds}; \ cos\theta = \frac{dy}{ds},$$

we obtain:

$$\Rightarrow \quad \begin{aligned} \sigma_n \cos\theta - \sigma_t \sin\theta &= \sigma_x \cos\theta + \tau_{xy} \sin\theta \\ \sigma_n \sin\theta + \sigma_t \cos\theta &= \sigma_y \sin\theta + \tau_{xy} \cos\theta. \end{aligned} \tag{1.15}$$

Multiplying the first equation in (1.15) by $\cos\theta$ and the second equation by $\sin\theta$, then adding them up member to member:

$$\sigma_n \cos^2\theta - \sigma_t \sin\theta\cos\theta = \sigma_x \cos^2\theta + \tau_{xy} \sin\theta\cos\theta$$

$$\sigma_n \sin^2\theta + \sigma_t \sin\theta\cos\theta = \sigma_y \sin^2\theta + \tau_{xy} \sin\theta\cos\theta$$

$$\sigma_n = \sigma_x \cos^2\theta + \sigma_y \sin^2\theta + 2\tau_{xy} \sin\theta\cos\theta$$

$$\Rightarrow \quad \sigma_n = \sigma_x \left(\frac{1+\cos 2\theta}{2}\right) + \sigma_y \left(\frac{1-\cos 2\theta}{2}\right) + \tau_{xy} \sin 2\theta$$

$$= \frac{\sigma_x + \sigma_y}{2} + \frac{\sigma_x - \sigma_y}{2} \cos 2\theta + \tau_{xy} \sin 2\theta.$$

Multiplying the first equation in (1.15) by $\sin\theta$, the second equation by $\cos\theta$ and subtracting the first equation from the second:

$$\sigma_n \cos\theta\sin\theta - \sigma_t \sin^2\theta = \sigma_x \cos\theta\sin\theta + \tau_{xy} \sin^2\theta$$

$$\sigma_n \sin\theta\cos\theta + \sigma_t \cos^2\theta = \sigma_y \sin\theta\cos\theta + \tau_{xy} \cos^2\theta$$

$$\Rightarrow \quad \sigma_t = \tau_{xy}(\cos^2\theta - \sin^2\theta) + (\sigma_y - \sigma_x)\sin\theta\cos\theta$$

$$\Rightarrow \quad \sigma_t = \tau_{xy} \cos 2\theta - \frac{\sigma_x - \sigma_y}{2} \sin 2\theta$$

In reality, this is equivalent to rotating the original unprimed coordinate system xy counterclockwise through an angle θ.

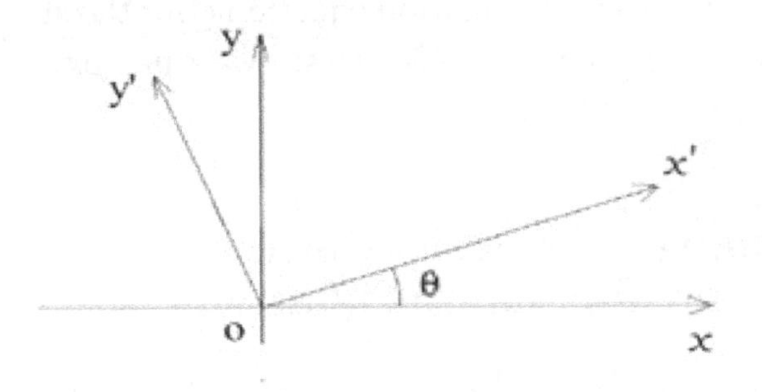

FIGURE 1.15

Renaming σ_n to be $\sigma_{x'}$ and σ_t to be $\tau_{x'y'}$, we obtain:

$$\sigma_{x'} = \frac{\sigma_x + \sigma_y}{2} + \frac{\sigma_x - \sigma_y}{2} cos2\theta + \tau_{xy} sin2\theta$$

$$\tau_{x'y'} = \tau_{xy} cos2\theta - \frac{\sigma_x - \sigma_y}{2} sin2\theta. \tag{1.16}$$

We can obtain by $\sigma_{y'}$ substituting θ with $\theta + \frac{\pi}{2}$ in the expression for $\sigma_{x'}$ in (1.16):

$$\sigma_{y'} = \frac{\sigma_x + \sigma_y}{2} - \frac{\sigma_x - \sigma_y}{2} cos\,2\theta - \tau_{xy}\, sin\,2\theta.$$

Finally, we end up with the following equations:

$$\sigma_{x'}(\theta) = \frac{\sigma_x + \sigma_y}{2} + \frac{\sigma_x - \sigma_y}{2} cos\,2\theta + \tau_{xy}\, sin\,2\theta \tag{1.17}$$

$$\sigma_{y'}(\theta) = \frac{\sigma_x + \sigma_y}{2} - \frac{\sigma_x - \sigma_y}{2} cos\,2\theta - \tau_{xy}\, sin\,2\theta$$

$$\tau_{x'y'}(\theta) = \tau_{xy}\, cos\,2\theta - \frac{\sigma_x - \sigma_y}{2} sin\,2\theta$$

or in matrix form:

$$\begin{Bmatrix} \sigma_{x'} \\ \sigma_{y'} \\ \tau_{x'y'} \end{Bmatrix} = \begin{bmatrix} cos^2\theta & sin^2\theta & 2sin\theta cos\theta \\ sin^2\theta & cos^2\theta & -2sin\theta cos\theta \\ -sin\theta cos\theta & sin\theta cos\theta & cos^2\theta - sin^2\theta \end{bmatrix} \begin{Bmatrix} \sigma_x \\ \sigma_y \\ \tau_{xy} \end{Bmatrix}.$$

(1.17) are called the stress transformation equations (for the state of plane stress). Indeed, these equations are characteristic of a second rank (or second order) tensor when rotating the coordinate system.

1.10 Discussion of and Reflection on the Stress Transformation Equations

i. The state of plane stress at a point P in reference to a man-made xy-coordinate system is completely defined by the (2 × 2) real symmetric matrix

$$\left[\sigma_{ij}\right] = \begin{bmatrix} \sigma_x & \tau_{xy} \\ \tau_{yx} & \sigma_y \end{bmatrix}_{(2\times2)}.$$

The state of plane stress at the same point P in the new primed coordinate system $x'y'$ is completely defined by the (2 × 2) real symmetric matrix $\left[\sigma'_{ij}\right] = \begin{bmatrix} \sigma_{x'} & \tau_{x'y'} \\ \tau_{y'x'} & \sigma_{y'} \end{bmatrix}_{(2\times2)}$.

The components of $\left[\sigma'_{ij}\right]$ are not the same as the components of $\left[\sigma_{ij}\right]$. Equations (1.17) show how these components are transformed. Obviously, $\sigma_{x'}$, $\sigma_{y'}$, and $\tau_{x'y'}$ depend on the angle of rotation θ. They are here functions of one single variable θ.

ii. Add $\sigma_{x'}(\theta)$ to $\sigma_{y'}(\theta)$ in equations (1.17):

$$\sigma_{x'} + \sigma_{y'} = \sigma_x + \sigma_y.$$

Therefore, the trace (sum of diagonal elements) of $[\sigma_{ij}]$ is the same as the trace of $\left[\sigma'_{ij}\right]$. This is what we call a stress invariant.

iii. $\sigma_{x'}(\theta)$ is a function of one single variable θ. Let us find θ that will extremize $\sigma_{x'}$. In order to extremize $\sigma_{x'}$, we set $\frac{d\sigma_x'(\theta)}{d\theta} = 0$:

$$2\tau_{xy}\cos 2\theta - (\sigma_x - \sigma_y)\sin 2\theta = 0$$

$$\Rightarrow \qquad \tan 2\theta = \frac{2\tau_{xy}}{\sigma_x - \sigma_y}. \qquad (1.18)$$

iv. Let us look for angle θ that will extremize $\sigma_{y'}$. In order to extremize $\sigma_{y'}$, we set $\frac{d\sigma_y'(\theta)}{d\theta} = 0$:

$$(\sigma_x - \sigma_y)sin2\theta - 2\tau_{xy} cos 2\theta = 0$$

$$\Rightarrow \qquad tan2\theta = \frac{2\tau_{xy}}{\sigma_x - \sigma_y},$$

which is identical to (1.18).

v. Let us find angle θ that will make the shear stress $\tau_{x'y'}$ vanish (become zero):

$$\tau_{x'y'}(\theta) = 0 \ \Rightarrow \ \tau_{xy} cos2\theta - \frac{\sigma_x - \sigma_y}{2} sin2\theta = 0$$

$$\Rightarrow \qquad tan2\theta = \frac{2\tau_{xy}}{\sigma_x - \sigma_y}.$$

Notice that the same angle θ defined by (1.18) will extremize both $\sigma_{x'}$ and $\sigma_{y'}$. Indeed, this angle θ will maximize one while minimizing the other. Furthermore, such an angle will suppress the shear stress. The axes corresponding to such an angle are called the principal axes (or principal directions), and the corresponding stresses are called the principal stresses. In order to obtain the principal stresses, we need to substitute (1.18) in (1.17):

$$sec^2 2\theta = \frac{1}{cos^2 2\theta} = 1 + tan^2 2\theta = 1 + \frac{4\tau_{xy}^2}{(\sigma_x - \sigma_y)^2} = \frac{(\sigma_x - \sigma_y)^2 + 4\tau_{xy}^2}{(\sigma_x - \sigma_y)^2}$$

$$\Rightarrow \qquad cos2\theta = \mp \frac{\sigma_x - \sigma_y}{\sqrt{(\sigma_x - \sigma_y)^2 + 4\tau_{xy}^2}}$$

$$\frac{sin2\theta}{cos2\theta} = tan2\theta$$

$$\Rightarrow \qquad sin2\theta = (cos2\theta)(tan2\theta) = \mp \frac{2\tau_{xy}}{\sqrt{(\sigma_x - \sigma_y)^2 + 4\tau_{xy}^2}}$$

$$\Rightarrow \qquad \sigma_{max}^{min} = \frac{\sigma_x + \sigma_y}{2} \mp \frac{1}{2}\sqrt{(\sigma_x - \sigma_y)^2 + 4\tau_{xy}^2}. \qquad (1.19)$$

Therefore, the expressions for principal stresses and principal directions in a state of plane stress:

$$\sigma_{max}^{min} = \frac{\sigma_x + \sigma_y}{2} \mp \frac{1}{2}\sqrt{(\sigma_x - \sigma_y)^2 + 4\tau_{xy}^2}$$

$$tan2\theta = \frac{2\tau_{xy}}{\sigma_x - \sigma_y}. \tag{1.20}$$

1.11 An Alternative Way of Deriving the Principal Stresses and Directions

The procedure we followed in order to obtain the principal stresses and the principal directions is equivalent to diagonalization of a matrix. Therefore, an alternative way to compute the principal stresses is by determining the eigenvalues of $\left[\sigma_{ij}\right]_{(2\times2)}$.

The principal stresses are the eigenvalues of the (2 × 2) real symmetric matrix $\left[\sigma_{ij}\right] = \begin{bmatrix} \sigma_x & \tau_{xy} \\ \tau_{yx} & \sigma_y \end{bmatrix}_{(2\times2)}$. The principal directions are the corresponding eigenvectors.

In order to compute the eigenvalues of $\left[\sigma_{ij}\right] = \begin{bmatrix} \sigma_x & \tau_{xy} \\ \tau_{yx} & \sigma_y \end{bmatrix}_{(2\times2)}$, we set

$$\begin{vmatrix} (\sigma_x - \sigma) & \tau_{xy} \\ \tau_{yx} & (\sigma_y - \sigma) \end{vmatrix} = 0$$

$$\Rightarrow \qquad (\sigma_x - \sigma)(\sigma_y - \sigma) - \tau_{xy}^2 = 0$$

$$\Rightarrow \qquad \sigma^2 - (\sigma_x + \sigma_y)\sigma + \sigma_x\sigma_y - \tau_{xy}^2 = 0.$$

The above quadratic equation is the characteristic equation,

$$\Delta = (\sigma_x + \sigma_y)^2 - (4)(1)(\sigma_x\sigma_y - \tau_{xy}^2)$$

$$= (\sigma_x - \sigma_y)^2 + 4\tau_{xy}^2$$

$$\Rightarrow \qquad \sigma = \frac{\sigma_x + \sigma_y}{2} \mp \frac{1}{2}\sqrt{(\sigma_x - \sigma_y)^2 + 4\tau_{xy}^2},$$

which is exactly the same result in (1.20).

1.12 An Alternative Way of Writing the Stress Transformation Equations

Equations (1.17) can be written in a more elegant way using matrices. Such a matrix notation will be very useful when we jump later into the three-dimensional case.

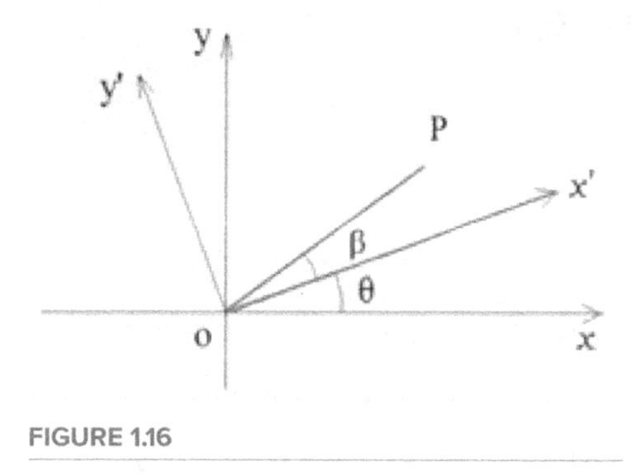

FIGURE 1.16

Our objective is to find a relationship between (x,y) the old unprimed rectangular coordinates of a point P in the plane and (x',y') the new primed rectangular coordinates of the same point P.

$$x = \overline{OP}\cos(\theta+\beta) = \overline{OP}(\cos\theta\cos\beta - \sin\theta\sin\beta)$$

$$= x'\cos\theta - y'\sin\theta$$

$$y = \overline{OP}\sin(\theta+\beta) = \overline{OP}(\sin\theta\cos\beta + \sin\beta\cos\theta)$$

$$= x'\sin\theta + y'\cos\beta$$

Therefore:

$$\begin{pmatrix} x \\ y \end{pmatrix} = \begin{pmatrix} \cos\theta & -\sin\theta \\ \sin\theta & \cos\theta \end{pmatrix} \begin{pmatrix} x' \\ y' \end{pmatrix}. \tag{1.21}$$

The above equations will take us from the new (primed) system to the old (unprimed) system.

The (2×2) matrix $\begin{pmatrix} \cos\theta & -\sin\theta \\ \sin\theta & \cos\theta \end{pmatrix}$ is called an orthonormal transformation matrix. It is an orthogonal matrix. A non-singular square matrix A is said to be orthogonal if $A^{-1} = A^{T}$.

Notice also that the determinant of the above matrix is 1.

Inverting equations (1.21) is therefore simple.

We can write:

$$\begin{pmatrix} x \\ y \end{pmatrix} = \begin{pmatrix} \cos\theta & -\sin\theta \\ \sin\theta & \cos\theta \end{pmatrix} \begin{pmatrix} x' \\ y' \end{pmatrix} <=> \begin{pmatrix} x' \\ y' \end{pmatrix} = \begin{pmatrix} \cos\theta & \sin\theta \\ -\sin\theta & \cos\theta \end{pmatrix} \begin{pmatrix} x \\ y \end{pmatrix}.$$

Let $$[M] = \begin{bmatrix} \cos\theta & \sin\theta \\ -\sin\theta & \cos\theta \end{bmatrix}.$$

It can be easily verified that equations (1.17) can be written in matrix notation as:

$$\underset{(2\times 2)}{\left[\sigma'_{ij}\right]} = \underset{(2\times 2)}{[M]} \; \underset{(2\times 2)}{\left[\sigma_{ij}\right]} \; \underset{(2\times 2)}{[M]^T}. \tag{1.22}$$

Again, $\left[\sigma_{ij}\right] = \begin{bmatrix} \sigma_x & \tau_{xy} \\ \tau_{yx} & \sigma_y \end{bmatrix}$ is the (2 × 2) real symmetric matrix that completely defines the state of plane stress at point P in the old (unprimed) coordinate system.

$\left[\sigma'_{ij}\right] = \begin{bmatrix} \sigma_{x'} & \tau_{x'y'} \\ \tau_{y'x'} & \sigma_{y'} \end{bmatrix}$ is the (2 × 2) real symmetric matrix that completely defines the state of plane stress at the same point P in the new (primed) coordinate system.

$[M] = \begin{bmatrix} \cos\theta & \sin\theta \\ -\sin\theta & \cos\theta \end{bmatrix}$ is a (2 × 2) orthonormal transformation matrix.

It can be shown that such matrix multiplication in (1.22) preserves symmetry. Both $\left[\sigma_{ij}\right]$ and $\left[\sigma'_{ij}\right]$ are symmetric. The stress matrix is always symmetric.

EXAMPLE 1.1

The state of plane stress at a point in a loaded beam is defined by the following (2 × 2) real symmetric matrix:

$$\left[\sigma_{ij}\right] = \begin{bmatrix} \sigma_x & \tau_{xy} \\ \tau_{yx} & \sigma_y \end{bmatrix} = \begin{bmatrix} 100 & -60 \\ -60 & -50 \end{bmatrix} (MPa).$$

Determine the following:

a) the maximum and minimum principal stresses and the maximum shearing stress
b) the orientation of the principal and maximum shear planes

SOLUTION

a)
$$\sigma_{max}^{min} = \frac{\sigma_x + \sigma_y}{2} \mp \frac{1}{2}\sqrt{(\sigma_x - \sigma_y)^2 + 4\tau_{xy}^2}$$

Here:
$$\sigma_x = 100MPa;\ \sigma_y = -50MPa;\ \tau_{xy} = -60MPa$$

$\Rightarrow$
$$\sigma_{max} = \frac{100-50}{2} + \frac{1}{2}\sqrt{(100+50)^2 + (4)(-60)^2} = 121.05MPa$$

$$\sigma_{min} = \frac{100-50}{2} - \frac{1}{2}\sqrt{(100+50)^2 + (4)(-60)^2} = -71.05MPa$$

Therefore, the principal stresses are:

$$\sigma_{max} = 121.05MPa$$

$$\sigma_{min} = -71.05MPa.$$

Notice that:

$$\sigma_{max} + \sigma_{min} = \sigma_x + \sigma_y = 50MPa.$$

This is not a matter of coincidence. It is a stress invariant.

In order to determine the maximum shearing stress, we set

$$\frac{d\tau_{x'y'}(\theta)}{d\theta} = 0 \ \Rightarrow \ -2\tau_{xy} sin2\theta - (\sigma_x - \sigma_y)cos2\theta = 0$$

$\Rightarrow$
$$\frac{sin2\theta}{cos2\theta} = \frac{\sigma_y - \sigma_x}{2\tau_{xy}}$$

$\Rightarrow$
$$tan2\theta = \frac{\sigma_y - \sigma_x}{2\tau_{xy}}$$

$$sec^2 2\theta = \frac{1}{cos^2 2\theta} = 1 + tan^2 2\theta = 1 + \frac{(\sigma_x - \sigma_y)^2}{4\tau_{xy}^2} = \frac{(\sigma_x - \sigma_y)^2 + 4\tau_{xy}^2}{4\tau_{xy}^2}$$

$\Rightarrow$
$$cos2\theta = \mp\frac{2\tau_{xy}}{\sqrt{(\sigma_x - \sigma_y)^2 + 4\tau_{xy}^2}}$$

$$sin2\theta = (cos2\theta)(tan2\theta)$$

$$= \mp\left[\frac{2\tau_{xy}}{\sqrt{(\sigma_x - \sigma_y)^2 + 4\tau_{xy}^2}}\right]\left(\frac{\sigma_y - \sigma_x}{2\tau_{xy}}\right)$$

$$= \mp \frac{\sigma_y - \sigma_x}{\sqrt{(\sigma_x - \sigma_y)^2 + 4\tau_{xy}^2}}$$

$$\Rightarrow \qquad \tau_{x'y'}(\theta) = (\tau_{xy})\left[\mp \frac{2\tau_{xy}}{\sqrt{(\sigma_x - \sigma_y)^2 + 4\tau_{xy}^2}}\right] \mp \left(\frac{\sigma_x - \sigma_y}{2}\right)\left[\frac{\sigma_x - \sigma_y}{\sqrt{(\sigma_x - \sigma_y)^2 + 4\tau_{xy}^2}}\right]$$

$$= \mp \frac{1}{2}\sqrt{(\sigma_x - \sigma_y)^2 + 4\tau_{xy}^2}.$$

Therefore, the maximum in-plane shearing stress is:

$$\tau_{max} = \frac{1}{2}\sqrt{(\sigma_x - \sigma_y)^2 + 4\tau_{xy}^2}.$$

In our problem:

$$\tau_{max} = \frac{1}{2}\sqrt{(100+50)^2 + (4)(-60)^2} = 96.05MPa.$$

b) In order to determine the orientation of the principal directions, we use:

$$tan2\theta = \frac{2\tau_{xy}}{\sigma_x - \sigma_y} = \frac{2(-60)}{100-(-50)} = -0.8$$

$$\Rightarrow \qquad 2\theta = -38.66° \;\Rightarrow\; \theta = -19.3°$$

$$\text{or} \qquad 2\theta = 141.34° \;\Rightarrow\; \theta = 70.7°.$$

Notice that: $70.7° - (-19.3°) = 90°$.

To find out whether $\theta = -19.3°$ corresponds to σ_{max} or to σ_{min}, we evaluate $\sigma_{x'}$ at $\theta = -19.3°$:

$$\sigma_{x'}(\theta) = \frac{\sigma_x + \sigma_y}{2} + \frac{\sigma_x - \sigma_y}{2}cos2\theta + \tau_{xy}sin2\theta$$

$$\sigma_{x'}(-19.3°) = \frac{100-50}{2} + \left(\frac{100+50}{2}\right)(0.78087) - (60)(-0.62470) = 121.05MPa$$

Therefore, we conclude that:

$$\sigma_{max} = 121.05MPa \quad \leftrightarrow \quad \theta = -19.3°$$

$$\sigma_{min} = -71.05MPa \quad \leftrightarrow \quad \theta = 70.7°.$$

In order to determine the orientation of the maximum in-plane shearing stress:

$$tan2\theta = \frac{\sigma_y - \sigma_x}{2\tau_{xy}} = \frac{-50-100}{2(-60)} = 1.25$$

$$\Rightarrow \qquad 2\theta = 51.34° \;\Rightarrow\; \theta = 25.7°$$

$$\text{or} \qquad 2\theta = 231.34° \;\Rightarrow\; \theta = 115.7°.$$

Notice that: $115.7^\circ - 25.7^\circ = 90^\circ$.
Also, notice that: $25.7^\circ - (-19.3^\circ) = 45^\circ$ and $115.7^\circ - 70.7^\circ = 45^\circ$.
The maximum in-plane shear planes always make a 45° angle with the principal planes.

1.13 Principal Stresses and Principal Directions for the (3 × 3) Stress Matrix

We said that the state of stress at a point P in a loaded structure is completely defined by the (3 × 3) real symmetric matrix

$$\left[\sigma_{ij}\right] = \begin{bmatrix} \sigma_x & \tau_{xy} & \tau_{xz} \\ \tau_{yx} & \sigma_y & \tau_{yz} \\ \tau_{zx} & \tau_{zy} & \sigma_z \end{bmatrix}_{(3\times3)}$$

The principal stresses are the eigenvalues of $[\sigma_{ij}]$. The principal directions are the corresponding eigenvectors. In order to compute the eigenvalues of $[\sigma_{ij}]$, we set:

$$\begin{vmatrix} (\sigma_x - \sigma) & \tau_{xy} & \tau_{xz} \\ \tau_{yx} & (\sigma_y - \sigma) & \tau_{yz} \\ \tau_{zx} & \tau_{zy} & (\sigma_z - \sigma) \end{vmatrix} = 0$$

$$\Rightarrow \quad (\sigma_x - \sigma)\left[(\sigma_y - \sigma)(\sigma_z - \sigma) - \tau_{yz}^2\right] - \tau_{xy}\left[\tau_{xy}(\sigma_z - \sigma) - \tau_{xz}\tau_{yz}\right]$$

$$+\tau_{xz}[\tau_{xy}\tau_{yz} - \tau_{zx}(\sigma_y - \sigma)] = 0$$

$$\Rightarrow \quad -\sigma^3 + \left(\sigma_x + \sigma_y + \sigma_z\right)\sigma^2 - \left(\sigma_x\sigma_y + \sigma_x\sigma_z + \sigma_y\sigma_z - \tau_{xy}^2 - \tau_{xz}^2 - \tau_{yz}^2\right)\sigma$$

$$+(\sigma_x\sigma_y\sigma_z + 2\tau_{xy}\tau_{xz}\tau_{yz} - \sigma_x\tau_{yz}^2 - \sigma_y\tau_{xz}^2 - \sigma_z\tau_{xy}^2) = 0$$

$$\Rightarrow \quad \sigma^3 - I_1\sigma^2 + I_2\sigma - I_3 = 0 \tag{1.23}$$

where:

$$I_1 = \sigma_x + \sigma_y + \sigma_z = Tr\left[\sigma_{ij}\right]$$

$$I_2 = \sigma_x\sigma_y + \sigma_x\sigma_z + \sigma_y\sigma_z - \tau_{xy}^2 - \tau_{xz}^2 - \tau_{yz}^2$$

$$I_3 = det\left[\sigma_{ij}\right]. \tag{1.24}$$

I_1, I_2, and I_3 are called the stress invariants, and the third-degree polynomial (cubic) algebraic equation (1.23) is called the stress characteristic equation. The roots of this equation will be always real, since $[\sigma_{ij}]$ is real and symmetric.

EXAMPLE 1.2

The state of stress at a point *P* in a loaded structure is defined, in reference to an *xyz*-coordinate system by the (3 × 3) real symmetric matrix

$$\left[\sigma_{ij}\right] = \begin{bmatrix} 2 & -1 & 1 \\ -1 & 0 & 1 \\ 1 & 1 & 2 \end{bmatrix} (ksi).$$

Determine the principal stresses and their orientation with respect to the original coordinate system.

SOLUTION

The principal stresses are the eigenvalues of $[\sigma_{ij}]$. The principal directions are the corresponding eigenvectors.

In order to determine the eigenvalues of $[\sigma_{ij}]$, we set:

$$\begin{vmatrix} (2-\sigma) & -1 & 1 \\ -1 & (0-\sigma) & 1 \\ 1 & 1 & (2-\sigma) \end{vmatrix} = 0$$

$$\Rightarrow \qquad \sigma^3 - 4\sigma^2 + \sigma + 6 = 0.$$

The above cubic equation is the characteristic equation. Alternatively, the above characteristic equation can be obtained using (1.24):

$$I_1 = \sigma_x + \sigma_y + \sigma_z = Tr\left[\sigma_{ij}\right] = 4ksi$$

$$I_2 = \sigma_x\sigma_y + \sigma_x\sigma_z + \sigma_y\sigma_z - \tau_{xy}^2 - \tau_{xz}^2 - \tau_{yz}^2 = 1(ksi)^2$$

$$I_3 = det\left[\sigma_{ij}\right] = -6(ksi)^3.$$

It is easily verified that $\sigma = -1$ is a root of the characteristic equation. We can then use synthetic division to factor out the equation.

$$(\sigma + 1)(\sigma^2 - 5\sigma + 6) = 0$$

$$\Rightarrow \qquad \text{Either } (\sigma + 1) = 0 \Rightarrow \sigma = -1$$

$$\text{or} \qquad \sigma^2 - 5\sigma + 6 = 0 \Rightarrow (\sigma - 2)(\sigma - 3) = 0$$

$$\Rightarrow \qquad \text{Either } \sigma = 2 \text{ or } \sigma = 3$$

Therefore, the three principal stresses are:

$$\sigma_1 = 3\ ksi$$

$$\sigma_2 = 2\ ksi$$

$$\sigma_3 = -1\ ksi.$$

Notice that we arranged them such that $\sigma_1 \geq \sigma_2 \geq \sigma_3$.

Notice also that:

$$I_1 = \sigma_x + \sigma_y + \sigma_z = \sigma_1 + \sigma_2 + \sigma_3 = 4ksi$$

$$I_2 = \sigma_x\sigma_y + \sigma_x\sigma_z + \sigma_y\sigma_z - \tau_{xy}^2 - \tau_{xz}^2 - \tau_{yz}^2 = \sigma_1\sigma_2 + \sigma_1\sigma_3 + \sigma_2\sigma_3 = 1(ksi)^2$$

$$I_3 = det\left[\sigma_{ij}\right] = \sigma_1\sigma_2\sigma_3 = -6(ksi)^3.$$

In order to find an eigenvector corresponding to the eigenvalue $\sigma_1 = 3ksi$, we set

$$\begin{pmatrix} -1 & -1 & 1 \\ -1 & -3 & 1 \\ 1 & 1 & -1 \end{pmatrix}\begin{pmatrix} x \\ y \\ z \end{pmatrix} = \begin{pmatrix} 0 \\ 0 \\ 0 \end{pmatrix}$$

$$\Rightarrow \quad \begin{aligned} -x - y + z &= 0 \\ -x - 3y + z &= 0 \\ x + y - z &= 0. \end{aligned} \tag{1.25}$$

The above system is a homogeneous system of linear algebraic equations. Furthermore, the equations are linearly dependent. Notice that the first equation is identical to the third equation. Indeed, because the system is linearly dependent we are able to find a nontrivial solution.

System (1.25) becomes:

$$-x - y + z = 0$$

$$-x - 3y + z = 0.$$

Adding the above two equations member to member, we obtain $y = 0$. Arbitrarily, choose $x = 1 \Rightarrow z = 1$. Therefore:

$\begin{pmatrix} 1 \\ 0 \\ 1 \end{pmatrix}$ is an eigenvector corresponding to the eigenvalue $\sigma_1 = 3ksi$, and

$\begin{pmatrix} \frac{1}{\sqrt{2}} \\ 0 \\ \frac{1}{\sqrt{2}} \end{pmatrix}$ is a normalized eigenvector corresponding to the eigenvalue $\sigma_1 = 3ksi$.

In order to find an eigenvector corresponding to the eigenvalue $\sigma_2 = 2ksi$, we set:

$$\begin{pmatrix} 0 & -1 & 1 \\ -1 & -2 & 1 \\ 1 & 1 & 0 \end{pmatrix}\begin{pmatrix} x \\ y \\ z \end{pmatrix} = \begin{pmatrix} 0 \\ 0 \\ 0 \end{pmatrix}$$

$\Rightarrow$

$$-y + z = 0$$

$$-x - 2y + z = 0$$

$$x + y = 0.$$

The above system of equations is also linearly dependent.

$\begin{pmatrix} 1 \\ -1 \\ -1 \end{pmatrix}$ is an eigenvector corresponding to the eigenvalue $\sigma_2 = 2ksi$.

$\begin{pmatrix} \frac{1}{\sqrt{3}} \\ -\frac{1}{\sqrt{3}} \\ -\frac{1}{\sqrt{3}} \end{pmatrix}$ is a normalized eigenvector corresponding to the eigenvalue $\sigma_2 = 2ksi$.

In order to find an eigenvector corresponding to the eigenvalue $\sigma_3 = -1ksi$, we set

$$\begin{pmatrix} 3 & -1 & 1 \\ -1 & 1 & 1 \\ 1 & 1 & 3 \end{pmatrix}\begin{pmatrix} x \\ y \\ z \end{pmatrix} = \begin{pmatrix} 0 \\ 0 \\ 0 \end{pmatrix}.$$

$\begin{pmatrix} 1 \\ 2 \\ -1 \end{pmatrix}$ is an eigenvector corresponding to the eigenvalue $\sigma_3 = -1ksi$.

$\begin{pmatrix} \frac{1}{\sqrt{6}} \\ \frac{2}{\sqrt{6}} \\ -\frac{1}{\sqrt{6}} \end{pmatrix}$ is a normalized eigenvector corresponding to the eigenvalue $\sigma_3 = -1ksi$.

To summarize our results, below are the principal stresses and corresponding principal directions:

$$\sigma_1 = 3ksi \quad \leftrightarrow \quad \begin{pmatrix} \frac{1}{\sqrt{2}} \\ 0 \\ \frac{1}{\sqrt{2}} \end{pmatrix}$$

$$\sigma_2 = 2ksi \quad \leftrightarrow \quad \begin{pmatrix} \frac{1}{\sqrt{3}} \\ -\frac{1}{\sqrt{3}} \\ -\frac{1}{\sqrt{3}} \end{pmatrix}$$

$$\sigma_3 = -1ksi \quad \leftrightarrow \quad \begin{pmatrix} \frac{1}{\sqrt{6}} \\ \frac{2}{\sqrt{6}} \\ -\frac{1}{\sqrt{6}} \end{pmatrix}.$$

Notice that the above vectors are three-unit vectors that are mutually perpendicular to each other.

1.14 3-D Stress Transformation Equations

We found that the stress transformation equations in the state of plane stress can be written in matrix form:

$$\underset{(2\times 2)}{[\sigma'_{ij}]} = \underset{(2\times 2)}{[M]} \; \underset{(2\times 2)}{[\sigma_{ij}]} \; \underset{(2\times 2)}{[M]^T}$$

where [M] is the (2×2) orthonormal transformation matrix:

$$[M] = \begin{bmatrix} cos\theta & sin\theta \\ -sin\theta & cos\theta \end{bmatrix} = \begin{bmatrix} \vec{e_1}' \cdot \vec{e_1} & \vec{e_1}' \cdot \vec{e_2} \\ \vec{e_2}' \cdot \vec{e_1} & \vec{e_2}' \cdot \vec{e_2} \end{bmatrix}.$$

When $[\sigma_{ij}]$ is a (3×3) matrix, the stress transformation equations in matrix form take the same form:

$$\underset{(3\times 3)}{[\sigma'_{ij}]} = \underset{(3\times 3)}{[M]} \; \underset{(3\times 3)}{[\sigma_{ij}]} \; \underset{(3\times 3)}{[M]^T}. \tag{1.26}$$

Obviously, $[\sigma_{ij}]$, $[\sigma'_{ij}]$and $[M]$ are now (3×3) matrices.

The orthonormal transformation matrix $[M]$ becomes

$$[M] = \begin{bmatrix} \vec{e_1'} \cdot \vec{e_1} & \vec{e_1'} \cdot \vec{e_2} & \vec{e_1'} \cdot \vec{e_3} \\ \vec{e_2'} \cdot \vec{e_1} & \vec{e_2'} \cdot \vec{e_2} & \vec{e_2'} \cdot \vec{e_3} \\ \vec{e_3'} \cdot \vec{e_1} & \vec{e_3'} \cdot \vec{e_2} & \vec{e_3'} \cdot \vec{e_3} \end{bmatrix}_{(3\times3)}$$

where $\vec{e_1}$, $\vec{e_2}$, and $\vec{e_3}$ are the three-unit vectors along the x, y, and z axes respectively. $\vec{e_1'}$, $\vec{e_2'}$, and $\vec{e_3'}$ are the three-unit vectors along the x', y', and z' axes respectively.

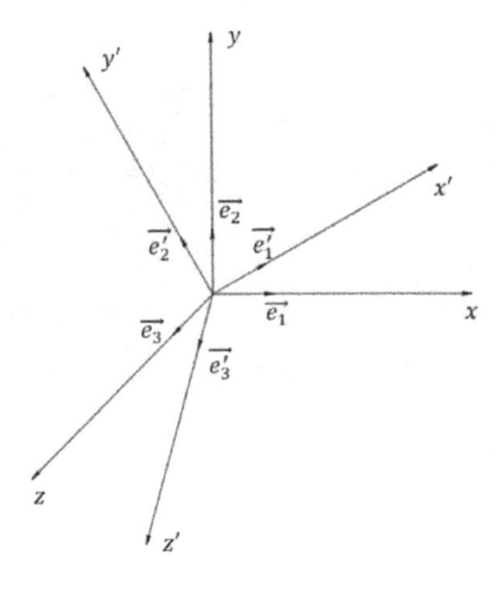

FIGURE 1.17

It can be shown in linear algebra that the matrix multiplication in (1.26) preserves symmetry. Thus, both $[\sigma_{ij}]$ and $[\sigma'_{ij}]$ will be symmetric.

EXAMPLE 1.3

The state of stress at a point in a machine element, with respect to a Cartesian coordinate system *xyz*, is defined by the following matrix:

$$\left[\sigma_{ij}\right] = \begin{bmatrix} 5 & 1 & 0 \\ 1 & 2 & 4 \\ 0 & 4 & 3 \end{bmatrix} (ksi).$$

Determine the state of stress for an $x'y'z'$-coordinate system defined by rotating xy through an angle of 30° counterclockwise about the z-axis.

SOLUTION

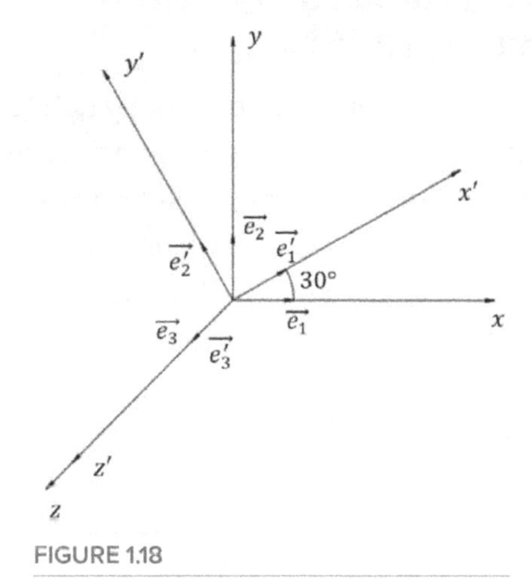

FIGURE 1.18

$$[M] = \begin{bmatrix} \vec{e_1'} \cdot \vec{e_1} & \vec{e_1'} \cdot \vec{e_2} & \vec{e_1'} \cdot \vec{e_3} \\ \vec{e_2'} \cdot \vec{e_1} & \vec{e_2'} \cdot \vec{e_2} & \vec{e_2'} \cdot \vec{e_3} \\ \vec{e_3'} \cdot \vec{e_1} & \vec{e_3'} \cdot \vec{e_2} & \vec{e_3'} \cdot \vec{e_3} \end{bmatrix}_{3\times 3} = \begin{bmatrix} \frac{\sqrt{3}}{2} & \frac{1}{2} & 0 \\ -\frac{1}{2} & \frac{\sqrt{3}}{2} & 0 \\ 0 & 0 & 1 \end{bmatrix}$$

Notice that the determinant of $[M]$ is: $(1)\left(\frac{3}{4} + \frac{1}{4}\right) = 1$.
Therefore,

$$\left[\sigma_{ij}'\right] = \begin{bmatrix} \frac{\sqrt{3}}{2} & \frac{1}{2} & 0 \\ -\frac{1}{2} & \frac{\sqrt{3}}{2} & 0 \\ 0 & 0 & 1 \end{bmatrix} \begin{bmatrix} 5 & 1 & 0 \\ 1 & 2 & 4 \\ 0 & 4 & 3 \end{bmatrix} \begin{bmatrix} \frac{\sqrt{3}}{2} & -\frac{1}{2} & 0 \\ \frac{1}{2} & \frac{\sqrt{3}}{2} & 0 \\ 0 & 0 & 1 \end{bmatrix} = \begin{bmatrix} \frac{17+2\sqrt{3}}{4} & \frac{2-3\sqrt{3}}{4} & 2 \\ \frac{2-3\sqrt{3}}{4} & \frac{11-2\sqrt{3}}{4} & 2\sqrt{3} \\ 2 & 2\sqrt{3} & 3 \end{bmatrix} (ksi).$$

$$(3\times 3) \qquad (3\times 3) \qquad (3\times 3) \qquad (3\times 3)$$

Notice that $[\sigma'_{ij}]$ is also symmetric. We can verify our work by checking the stress invariants.
Notice that:

$$I_1 = \sigma_x + \sigma_y + \sigma_z = \sigma_{x'} + \sigma_{y'} + \sigma_{z'} = 10ksi$$

$$I_2 = \sigma_x\sigma_y + \sigma_x\sigma_z + \sigma_y\sigma_z - \tau_{xy}^2 - \tau_{xz}^2 - \tau_{yz}^2$$

$$= \sigma_{x'}\sigma_{y'} + \sigma_{x'}\sigma_{z'} + \sigma_{y'}\sigma_{z'} - \tau_{x'y'}^2 - \tau_{x'z'}^2 - \tau_{y'z'}^2 = 14(ksi)^2$$

$$I_3 = \det\left[\sigma_{ij}\right] = \det\left[\sigma_{ij}'\right] = -53(ksi)^3.$$

1.15 Stresses on an Arbitrary Plane Passing Through a Point

We said that the state of stress at a point P is completely defined by the (3×3) real symmetric matrix $[\sigma_{ij}]$ in reference to a man-made arbitrary xyz-coordinate system. Once $[\sigma_{ij}]$ is known, we can then determine the normal stress σ_n and shear stress τ_n that will pop up on any arbitrary oblique plane passing through point P.

The orientation in space of the oblique plane is defined by a unit normal vector $\vec{n}$. σ_n and τ_n can then be determined using the following relations:

$$\vec{T} = \left[\sigma_{ij}\right]\vec{n}$$

$$\sigma_n = \vec{T} \bullet \vec{n} \tag{1.27}$$

$$\sigma_n = \left|\vec{n} \times (\vec{T} \times \vec{n})\right| = \sqrt{\left|\vec{T}\right|^2 - \sigma_n^2}.$$

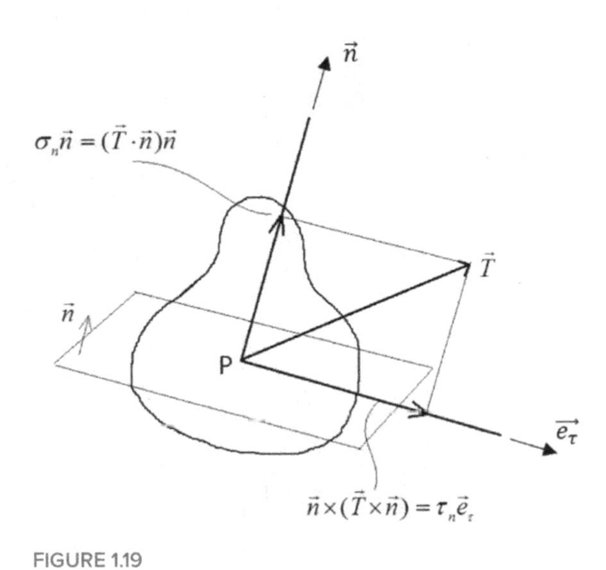

FIGURE 1.19

Obviously, we can write that:

$$\vec{T} = \sigma_n\vec{n} + \tau_n\overrightarrow{e_\tau}.$$

$\vec{T}$ is called the traction vector. It has the dimension of stress. $\vec{T}$ is resolved into two components $\sigma_n\vec{n}$ perpendicular to the plane in the direction of $\vec{n}$ and $\sigma_n\overrightarrow{e_\tau}$ in the plane.

Equations (1.27), which can be written in detailed as

$$\begin{pmatrix} T_x \\ T_y \\ T_z \end{pmatrix} = \begin{bmatrix} \sigma_x & \tau_{xy} & \tau_{xz} \\ \tau_{yx} & \sigma_y & \tau_{yz} \\ \tau_{zx} & \tau_{zy} & \sigma_z \end{bmatrix} \begin{pmatrix} n_x \\ n_y \\ n_z \end{pmatrix} \quad \text{or} \quad \begin{aligned} T_x &= \sigma_x n_x + \tau_{xy} n_y + \tau_{xz} n_z \\ T_y &= \tau_{yx} n_x + \sigma_y n_y + \tau_{yz} n_z \\ T_z &= \tau_{zx} n_x + \tau_{zy} n_y + \sigma_z n_z, \end{aligned}$$

are called Cauchy stress formulas after Augustin-Louis Cauchy*.

It is clear that when the plane passing through point P changes its orientation $\vec{n}$ will change. σ_n and τ_n will follow such a change. We can continue changing the orientation of the plane until the traction vector $\vec{T}$ becomes parallel to $\vec{n}$. In this case, there will be only normal component of stress, and the shear stress is suppressed, and this corresponds to the principal direction.

EXAMPLE 1.4

The state of stress at a point, in reference to an *xyz*-coordinate system, is defined by the following matrix:

$$\left[\sigma_{ij}\right] = \begin{bmatrix} 36 & 27 & 0 \\ 27 & -36 & 0 \\ 0 & 0 & 18 \end{bmatrix} (ksi).$$

Find:

a) the rectangular components of the traction vector $\vec{T}$ acting on a plane passing through the point and with a unit normal vector $\vec{n}$ (2/3, -2/3, 1/3)
b) the magnitude of the traction vector in (*a*)
c) its component in the direction of the normal
d) the angle between the traction vector and the normal

SOLUTION

a) First notice that

$$\left(\frac{2}{3}\right)^2 + \left(-\frac{2}{3}\right)^2 + \left(\frac{1}{3}\right)^2 = 1,$$

---

* Augustin-Louis Cauchy (1789–1857) was a French mathematician who also contributed to theory of elasticity. Cauchy taught at École Polytechnique in Paris. Newton and Leibniz are credited with establishing calculus in the 17th century. However, Cauchy is the one credited with establishing, in the 19th century (two centuries later), the rigorous treatment of the subject (real analysis). He also founded complex analysis.

which emphasizes that $\vec{n}$ is a unit vector.

$$\vec{T} = [\sigma_{ij}]\vec{n} = \begin{bmatrix} 36 & 27 & 0 \\ 27 & -36 & 0 \\ 0 & 0 & 18 \end{bmatrix} \begin{pmatrix} 2/3 \\ -2/3 \\ 1/3 \end{pmatrix} = \begin{pmatrix} 6 \\ 42 \\ 6 \end{pmatrix} (ksi)$$

Notice that $\vec{T}$ has the dimension of stress.

b) $|\vec{T}| = \sqrt{T_x^2 + T_y^2 + T_z^2} = \sqrt{(6)^2 + (42)^2 + (6)^2} = 42.85\ ksi$

c) $\sigma_n = \vec{T} \cdot \vec{n} = (6)\left(\frac{2}{3}\right) + (42)\left(-\frac{2}{3}\right) + (6)\left(\frac{1}{3}\right) = -22\ ksi$

d) $cos\theta = \frac{\vec{T} \cdot \vec{n}}{|\vec{T}||\vec{n}|} = \frac{-22}{42.85} \Rightarrow \theta = 120.9°$

1.16 Maximum Shear Stress and Octahedral Stresses

In order to evaluate the maximum shear stress τ_{max} in the 3D case, first, we need to establish a formula for the shear stress τ. To do that, we can start with Cauchy stress formula written in an arbitrary *xyz* Cartesian coordinate system.

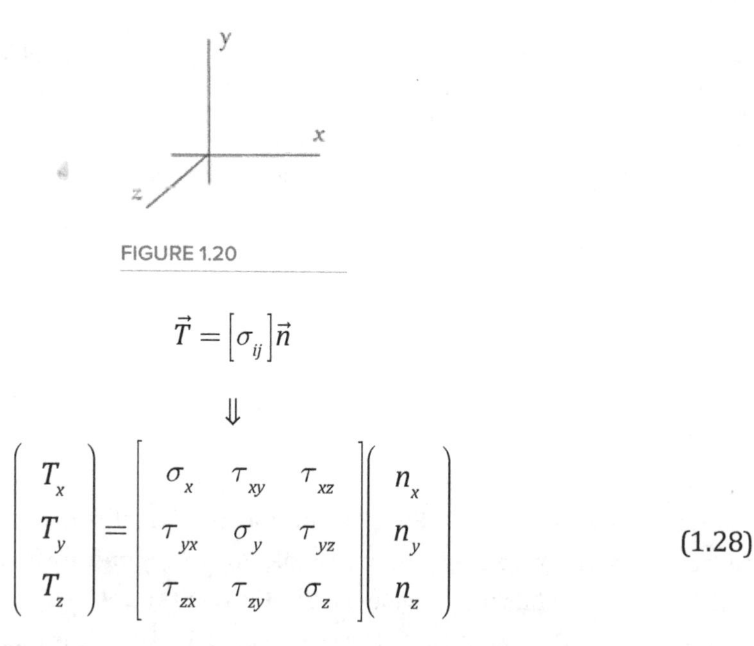

FIGURE 1.20

$$\vec{T} = [\sigma_{ij}]\vec{n}$$

$$\Downarrow$$

$$\begin{pmatrix} T_x \\ T_y \\ T_z \end{pmatrix} = \begin{bmatrix} \sigma_x & \tau_{xy} & \tau_{xz} \\ \tau_{yx} & \sigma_y & \tau_{yz} \\ \tau_{zx} & \tau_{zy} & \sigma_z \end{bmatrix} \begin{pmatrix} n_x \\ n_y \\ n_z \end{pmatrix} \tag{1.28}$$

$$\Downarrow$$

$$T_x = \sigma_x n_x + \tau_{xy} n_y + \tau_{xz} n_z$$

$$T_y = \tau_{yx} n_x + \sigma_y n_y + \tau_{yz} n_z$$

$$T_z = \tau_{zx} n_x + \tau_{zy} n_y + \sigma_z n_z$$

If, instead of using an arbitrary *xyz*-coordinate system, the principal *123*-coordinate system is used, the above equations will take the following form:

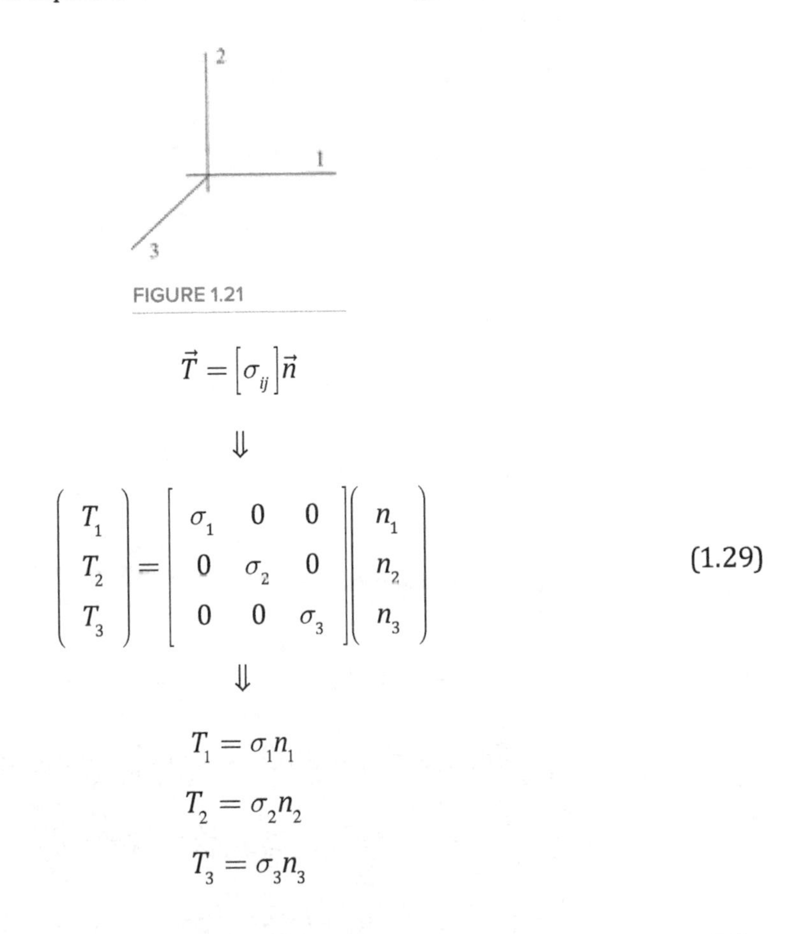

FIGURE 1.21

$$\vec{T} = \left[\sigma_{ij}\right]\vec{n}$$

$$\Downarrow$$

$$\begin{pmatrix} T_1 \\ T_2 \\ T_3 \end{pmatrix} = \begin{bmatrix} \sigma_1 & 0 & 0 \\ 0 & \sigma_2 & 0 \\ 0 & 0 & \sigma_3 \end{bmatrix} \begin{pmatrix} n_1 \\ n_2 \\ n_3 \end{pmatrix} \tag{1.29}$$

$$\Downarrow$$

$$T_1 = \sigma_1 n_1$$

$$T_2 = \sigma_2 n_2$$

$$T_3 = \sigma_3 n_3$$

Notice that equations (1.29) are much simpler than (1.28). For this reason, it will be much simpler and more convenient to work out the problem in the *123* principal coordinate system. Using the algorithm outlined in the previous section:

$$\sigma_n = \vec{T} \bullet \vec{n} = \sigma_1 n_1^2 + \sigma_2 n_2^2 + \sigma_3 n_3^2$$

$$\Rightarrow \qquad \tau_n^2 = \left|\vec{T}\right|^2 - \sigma_n^2$$

$$= \sigma_1^2 n_1^2 + \sigma_2^2 n_2^2 + \sigma_3^2 n_3^2 - \left(\sigma_1 n_1^2 + \sigma_2 n_2^2 + \sigma_3 n_3^2\right)^2$$

$$= \sigma_1^2 n_1^2 \left(1 - n_1^2\right) + \sigma_2^2 n_2^2 \left(1 - n_2^2\right) + \sigma_3^2 n_3^2 \left(1 - n_3^2\right)$$

$$-2\sigma_1\sigma_2 n_1^2 n_2^2 - 2\sigma_1\sigma_3 n_1^2 n_3^2 - 2\sigma_2\sigma_3 n_2^2 n_3^2.$$

However, $\vec{n}$ is a unit vector. Therefore,

$$\left|\vec{n}\right| = 1$$

$\Rightarrow$

$$n_1^2 + n_2^2 + n_3^2 = 1$$

$\Rightarrow$

$$1 - n_1^2 = n_2^2 + n_3^2$$

$$1 - n_2^2 = n_1^2 + n_3^2$$

$$1 - n_3^2 = n_1^2 + n_2^2.$$

Therefore,

$$\tau_n^2 = \sigma_1^2 n_1^2 \left(n_2^2 + n_3^2\right) + \sigma_2^2 n_2^2 \left(n_1^2 + n_3^2\right) + \sigma_3^2 n_3^2 \left(n_1^2 + n_2^2\right)$$

$$-2\sigma_1\sigma_2 n_1^2 n_2^2 - 2\sigma_1\sigma_3 n_1^2 n_3^2 - 2\sigma_2\sigma_3 n_2^2 n_3^2$$

$$\Rightarrow \qquad \tau_n^2 = \sigma_1^2 n_1^2 n_2^2 + \sigma_1^2 n_1^2 n_3^2 + \sigma_2^2 n_2^2 n_1^2 + \sigma_2^2 n_2^2 n_3^2 + \sigma_3^2 n_3^2 n_1^2 + \sigma_3^2 n_3^2 n_2^2$$

$$-2\sigma_1\sigma_2 n_1^2 n_2^2 - 2\sigma_1\sigma_3 n_1^2 n_3^2 - 2\sigma_2\sigma_3 n_2^2 n_3^2$$

$$\Rightarrow \qquad \tau_n^2 = (\sigma_1 - \sigma_2)^2 n_1^2 n_2^2 + (\sigma_1 - \sigma_3)^2 n_1^2 n_3^2 + (\sigma_2 - \sigma_3)^2 n_2^2 n_3^2$$

$$\Rightarrow \qquad \tau_n = \sqrt{(\sigma_1 - \sigma_2)^2 n_1^2 n_2^2 + (\sigma_1 - \sigma_3)^2 n_1^2 n_3^2 + (\sigma_2 - \sigma_3)^2 n_2^2 n_3^2}. \qquad (1.30)$$

We want to extremize τ_n in (1.30). Notice that τ_n in the 3D case is a function of three variables: n_1, n_2, and n_3. In the 2D case, τ was a function of one single variable θ. Instead of extremizing τ_n, we will extremize τ_n^2 to get rid of the radical root. Our objective is to extremize

$$f(n_1, n_2, n_3) = (\sigma_1 - \sigma_2)^2 n_1^2 n_2^2 + (\sigma_1 - \sigma_3)^2 n_1^2 n_3^2 + (\sigma_2 - \sigma_3)^2 n_2^2 n_3^2,$$

subject to the following constraint:

$$g(n_1, n_2, n_3) = n_1^2 + n_2^2 + n_3^2 - 1 = 0.$$

We will use Lagrange multipliers technique.[7]
We set

$$\vec{\nabla} f = \lambda \vec{\nabla} g \qquad \text{or} \qquad \begin{pmatrix} \dfrac{\partial f}{\partial n_1} \\ \dfrac{\partial f}{\partial n_2} \\ \dfrac{\partial f}{\partial n_3} \end{pmatrix} = \lambda \begin{pmatrix} \dfrac{\partial g}{\partial n_1} \\ \dfrac{\partial g}{\partial n_2} \\ \dfrac{\partial g}{\partial n_3} \end{pmatrix},$$

subject to the constraint $n_1^2 + n_2^2 + n_3^2 - 1 = 0$

$\Rightarrow$

$$2n_1 n_2^2 (\sigma_1 - \sigma_2)^2 + 2n_1 n_3^2 (\sigma_1 - \sigma_3)^2 = 2n_1 \lambda$$

$$2n_2 n_1^2 (\sigma_1 - \sigma_2)^2 + 2n_2 n_3^2 (\sigma_2 - \sigma_3)^2 = 2n_2 \lambda$$

$$2n_3 n_1^2 (\sigma_1 - \sigma_3)^2 + 2n_3 n_2^2 (\sigma_2 - \sigma_3)^2 = 2n_3 \lambda$$

$$n_1^2 + n_2^2 + n_3^2 = 1. \tag{1.31}$$

---

7 Lagrange was a famous French mathematician who enormously contributed to mechanics. Poisson was a student of Laplace, who was, in turn, a student of Lagrange. They all taught at École Polytechnique in Paris. Indeed, Lagrange founded what is now called Lagrangian mechanics, which deals with energy quantities (scalars), as opposed to Newtonian or vector mechanics, which relates two vector quantities (force and acceleration).

The above equations consist of a system of (nonlinear) equations: four equations and four unknowns.

We notice that $n_1 = n_2 = \frac{1}{\sqrt{2}}; n_3 = 0$ is a solution that leads to $\tau_n = \frac{1}{2}\left|\sigma_1 - \sigma_2\right|$.

Also, $n_1 = n_3 = \frac{1}{\sqrt{2}}; n_2 = 0$ is a solution that leads to $\tau_n = \frac{1}{2}\left|\sigma_1 - \sigma_3\right|$.

Also, $n_2 = n_3 = \frac{1}{\sqrt{2}}; n_1 = 0$ is a solution that leads to $\tau_n = \frac{1}{2}\left|\sigma_2 - \sigma_3\right|$.

It is customary to arrange the principal stresses in descending order, such that $\sigma_1 \geq \sigma_2 \geq \sigma_3$. In this case, the absolute maximum shear stress becomes:

$$\tau_{max} = \frac{1}{2}(\sigma_1 - \sigma_3). \tag{1.32}$$

Notice that there is no need to place the absolute value sign in (1.32), since arranging the principal stresses in descending order guarantees that $(\sigma_1 - \sigma_3)$ becomes nonnegative. Notice also that τ_{max} takes place in a plane that bisects the one and three principal axes (i.e., in a plane that makes $45° = cos^{-1}\left(\frac{1}{\sqrt{2}}\right)$ with the one and three principal axes).

An important plane in design problems and failure by yielding theories is the octahedral plane. It is the plane that makes equal angles with the three principal axes. The shear stress and normal stress on the octahedral plane are denoted by τ_{oct} and σ_{oct}, respectively.

Using equation (1.30) with

$$n_1 = n_2 = n_3 = \frac{1}{\sqrt{3}},$$

we obtain:

$$\tau_{oct} = \frac{1}{3}\sqrt{\left(\sigma_1 - \sigma_2\right)^2 + \left(\sigma_1 - \sigma_3\right)^2 + \left(\sigma_2 - \sigma_3\right)^2}. \tag{1.33}$$

Also, from the expression for σ_n, we conclude that:

$$\sigma_{oct} = \frac{\sigma_1 + \sigma_2 + \sigma_3}{3} = \frac{1}{3}I_1 = \frac{1}{3}T_r[\sigma_{ij}]. \tag{1.34}$$

The octahedral normal stress is the arithmetic mean of the three principal stresses. The word "octahedral" is related to "octa," which means eight in Latin. An *xy*-coordinate system in the plane splits the plane into $2^2 = 4$ quadrants. The *123*-coordinate system splits the space into $2^3 = 8$ octants.

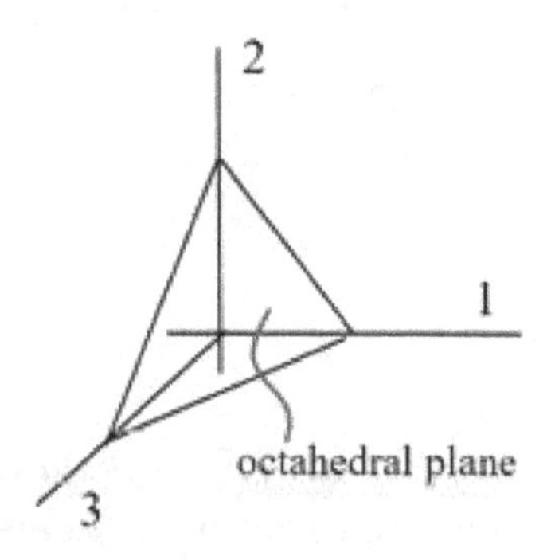

FIGURE 1.22

EXAMPLE 1.5

The state of stress at a point in a loaded structure, in reference to a Cartesian coordinate system, is defined by the following (3 × 3) real symmetric matrix:

$$[\sigma_{ij}] = \begin{bmatrix} 50 & 0 & 0 \\ 0 & 60 & 0 \\ 0 & 0 & -70 \end{bmatrix} (MPa).$$

a) Compute the maximum shear stress τ_{max}.
b) Compute the octahedral shear stress τ_{oct} and the octahedral normal stress σ_{oct}.

SOLUTION

$[\sigma_{ij}]$ is diagonal. This means that the state of stress is defined in the principal coordinate system *123*.

The principal stresses are the diagonal elements:

$$\sigma_1 = 60\ MPa$$

$$\sigma_2 = 50\ MPa$$

$$\sigma_3 = -70\ MPa.$$

Notice that the principal stresses were arranged such that:

$$\sigma_1 \geq \sigma_2 \geq \sigma_3$$

$$(a)\ \tau_{max} = \frac{1}{2}(\sigma_1 - \sigma_3) = 65\ MPa$$

$$(b)\ \tau_{oct} = \frac{1}{3}\sqrt{(\sigma_1 - \sigma_2)^2 + (\sigma_1 - \sigma_3)^2 + (\sigma_2 - \sigma_3)^2}$$

$$= \frac{1}{3}\sqrt{(60 - 50)^2 + (60 + 70)^2 + (50 + 70)^2}$$

$$= 59.07\ MPa$$

$$\sigma_{oct} = \frac{1}{3}(\sigma_1 + \sigma_2 + \sigma_3)$$

$$= 13.3\ MPa.$$

1.17 Mohr's Circle

Mohr's circle is a graphical solution to the stress problem and other similar problems. It is named after Otto Mohr, a German professor of engineering, who came up with a graphical solution in 1905. The method was popular and very useful in the early 20th century when engineers had to perform hand calculations and occasionally use the sliding ruler. The method is not useful in the 21st century when we have access to very cheap and powerful electronic calculators.

1.18 What Did We Learn in Chapter 1?

- Stress is a point function. It is defined at a point and can vary from one point to the other.
- To completely define the state of stress at a point, a scalar quantity (a real number) is not enough. Also, a vector quantity is inadequate. Rather, a (3 × 3) real symmetric matrix is needed. Stress is a second rank (or second order) tensor.
- Once we establish the (3 × 3) real symmetric matrix, defining the state of stress at a point in reference to an arbitrary *xyz*-coordinate system, we can know everything about the stress at this particular point, including the normal and shear stresses that pop up on any plane passing through the point.
- Using vector algebra and matrix notation for 3D problems is recommended to make the formulas more compact, elegant, and simple. For 2D problems, we do not have to use vector algebra or matrix notation. Indeed, it is customary not to use such notation when dealing with 2D problems.

Problems

1.1. The state of plane stress at a point in a loaded beam is defined by the following (2 × 2) real symmetric matrix:

$$\left[\sigma_{ij}\right] = \begin{bmatrix} \sigma_x & \tau_{xy} \\ \tau_{yx} & \sigma_y \end{bmatrix} = \begin{bmatrix} 150 & -50 \\ -50 & -40 \end{bmatrix} (MPa).$$

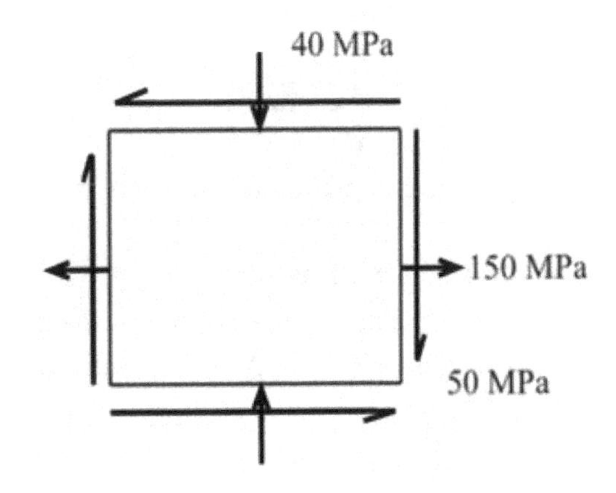

FIGURE 1.23

Determine the following: *(a)* the maximum and minimum principal stresses and the maximum in-plane shearing stress and *(b)* the orientation of the principal and maximum shear planes.

1.2. For the given state of plane stress, determine the normal and shear stresses after the element shown has been rotated 30° counterclockwise.

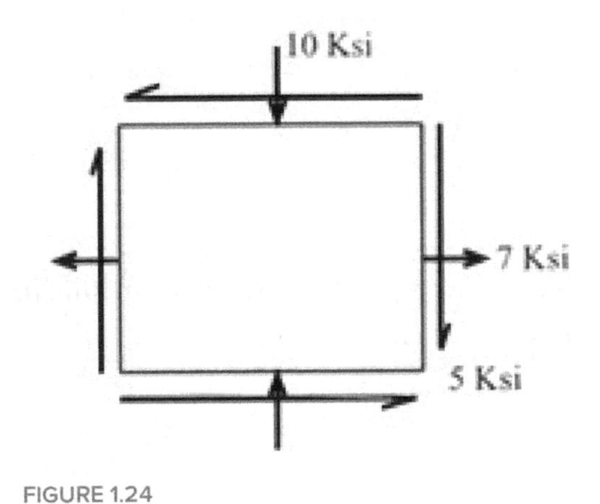

FIGURE 1.24

1.3. For the state of plane stress shown, determine the largest value of σ_y for which the maximum in-plane shearing stress is equal to or less than 70 *Mpa*.

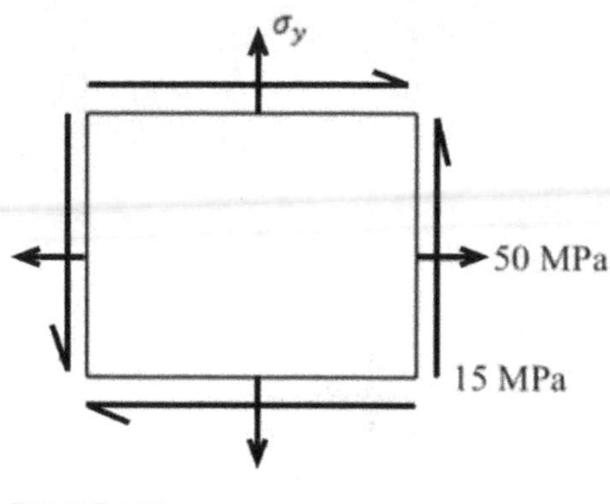

FIGURE 1.25

1.4. In a state of plane stress, it is known that $\tau_{xy} = 40\ MPa$ and that σ_x is compressive. Also, it is known that the principal stresses are $\sigma_{max} = 40\ MPa$ and $\sigma_{min} = -60\ MPa$. Determine σ_x and σ_y. Also, indicate the direction in which the principal stresses and maximum in-plane shearing stresses act.

1.5. The state of plane stress on an element oriented at $\theta = 30°$ is shown in the figure below. Calculate the normal and shearing stresses on an element oriented at $\theta = 0°$.

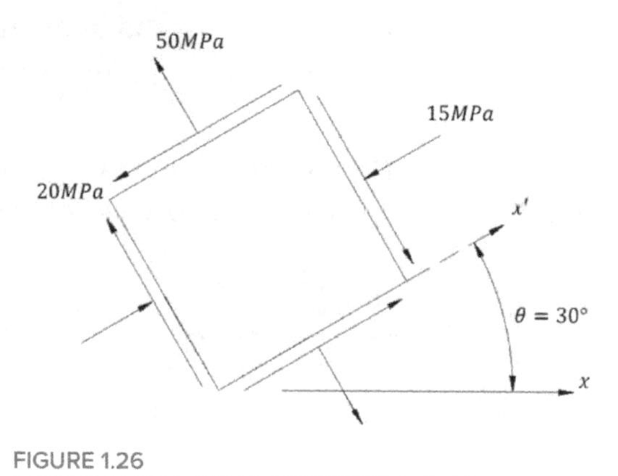

FIGURE 1.26

1.6. Assume that the stress at a point measured in an unprimed coordinate system in a plane stress analysis is:

$$\left[\sigma_{ij}\right] = \begin{bmatrix} 1 & -1 \\ -1 & 1 \end{bmatrix} (ksi).$$

a. Establish the components of the stress tensor in the primed coordinate system in terms of angle θ, knowing that the primed coordinate system results from rotating the unprimed coordinate system through an angle θ counterclockwise.

b. Make $\theta = 45^\circ$ (special case), and establish the components of the stress tensor in the primed coordinate system.

1.7. The state of stress at a point P in a loaded structure is defined, in reference to an xyz-coordinate system, by the following (3 × 3) real symmetric matrix:

$$\left[\sigma_{ij}\right] = \begin{bmatrix} 10 & 5 & 7 \\ 5 & 8 & 4 \\ 7 & 4 & 15 \end{bmatrix} (MPa).$$

Determine the principal stresses and their orientation with respect to the original coordinate system.

1.8. The state of stress at a point in a loaded machine is defined, in reference to an xyz-coordinate system, by the following (3 × 3) real symmetric matrix:

$$\left[\sigma_{ij}\right] = \begin{bmatrix} 40 & 0 & 0 \\ 0 & 52 & 0 \\ 0 & 0 & -78 \end{bmatrix} (MPa).$$

Determine *(a)* the maximum shearing stress; *(b)* the octahedral shearing stress; and *(c)* the octahedral normal stress.

1.9. The state of stress at a point in a machine element, with respect to a Cartesian coordinate system xyz, is defined by the following (3 × 3) real symmetric matrix:

$$\left[\sigma_{ij}\right] = \begin{bmatrix} 7 & 1 & 0 \\ 1 & 3 & 5 \\ 0 & 5 & 4 \end{bmatrix} (ksi).$$

Determine the state of stress for an $x'y'z'$-coordinate system defined by rotating x,y through an angle of 30° counterclockwise about the z-axis.

1.10. The state of stress at a point in a loaded body is defined by the following (3 × 3) matrix:

$$\left[\sigma_{ij}\right] = \begin{bmatrix} 40 & 29 & 0 \\ 29 & -38 & 0 \\ 0 & 0 & 19 \end{bmatrix} (ksi).$$

Determine *(a)* the three rectangular components of the traction vector acting on a plane through the point with unit normal (2/3, –2/3, 1/3); *(b)* the magnitude of the traction vector of *(a)*; *(c)* its component in the direction of the normal; and *(d)* the angle between the traction vector and the normal.

1.11. The state of stress at a point in a structure is defined, in reference to a Cartesian coordinate system *xyz*, by the following (3 × 3) real symmetric matrix:

$$\left[\sigma_{ij}\right] = \begin{bmatrix} 0 & 2 & 1 \\ 2 & 1 & 0 \\ 1 & 0 & 2 \end{bmatrix} \times 10^7 \ N / m^2.$$

Determine *(a)* the traction vector $\vec{T}$ acting on the plane passing through this point and defined by the equation $x + 2y + 4z = 4$; *(b)* the normal σ_n and shearing τ_n components of $\vec{T}$.

1.12. At a point in a loaded member, the stress relative to an *xyz*-coordinate system is defined by the following stress tensor

$$\left[\sigma_{ij}\right] = \begin{bmatrix} 35 & 30 & 25 \\ 30 & 15 & 0 \\ 25 & 0 & 20 \end{bmatrix} (MPa)$$

Calculate the normal stress σ_n and the shearing stress τ_n on a plane passing through the point and whose outward normal is oriented at angles $35^\circ, 70^\circ$, and 62.58° with the *x*-, *y*-, and *z*-axes, respectively.

1.13. Find an expression in terms of the principal stresses for the magnitude T_0 of the traction vector on an octahedral plane—that is, a plane whose normal makes equal angles with the three principal directions.

1.14. The state of stress at a point in a loaded member is defined, relative to an *xyz*-coordinate system, by the (3 × 3) real symmetric matrix

$$\left[\sigma_{ij}\right] = \begin{bmatrix} 85 & 25 & 45 \\ 25 & 65 & 15 \\ 45 & 15 & 25 \end{bmatrix} (MPa).$$

Calculate the normal stress σ_n and the shearing stress τ_n on a plane passing through the point and perpendicular to vector $\vec{V} = \vec{i} + 2\vec{j} + \vec{k}$.

1.15. Show that the octahedral shear stress τ_{oct} is another stress invariant. (Hint: express τ_{oct} in terms of the stress invariants I_1, I_2, and I_3.)

1.16. At a point in a loaded structure, the state of stress in reference to an *xyz*-coordinate system is given by

$$\left[\sigma_{ij}\right] = \begin{bmatrix} 30 & 0 & 20 \\ 0 & 0 & 0 \\ 20 & 0 & 0 \end{bmatrix} (MPa).$$

Determine *(a)* the principal stresses and *(b)* the direction cosines that correspond to the maximum principal stress.

1.17. The state of stress at a point in a structure is defined by the following (3 × 3) real and symmetric matrix

$$\left[\sigma_{ij}\right] = \begin{bmatrix} 0 & a & a \\ a & 0 & a \\ a & \mathrm{a} & 0 \end{bmatrix},$$

where a is a positive real number. Compute the principal stresses and the direction of the maximum principal stress.

1.18. The state of stress at a point is defined by the following (3 × 3) real symmetric matrix. Choose σ_y so that there will be a traction-free plane through the point. Also, determine the unit normal vector $\vec{n}$ of the traction-free plane.

$$\left[\sigma_{ij}\right] = \begin{bmatrix} 3 & 2 & 1 \\ 2 & \sigma_y & 2 \\ 1 & 2 & 0 \end{bmatrix} (ksi)$$

1.19. The state of stress at a point is defined by the following (3 × 3) real symmetric matrix. Determine a unit normal vector $\vec{n}$ such that the traction vector on a plane normal to $\vec{n}$ has $T_y = T_z = 0$. Also, determine T_x on the plane.

$$\left[\sigma_{ij}\right] = \begin{bmatrix} 1 & 0 & 2 \\ 0 & 3 & 6 \\ 2 & 6 & 0 \end{bmatrix} (ksi)$$

1.20. The state of stress at a point in a machine element is defined, relative to an *xyz*-coordinate system, by the following real symmetric matrix:

$$\left[\sigma_{ij}\right] = \begin{bmatrix} -100 & 0 & -80 \\ 0 & 20 & 0 \\ -80 & 0 & 20 \end{bmatrix} (MPa).$$

a) Determine the principal stresses $\sigma_1 \geq \sigma_2 \geq \sigma_3$.
b) Determine the octahedral shear stress τ_{oct}.
c) Determine the maximum shear stress τ_{max}.

1.21. The state of stress at a point in a loaded structure is defined, in reference to a rectangular Cartesian coordinate system *x*, *y*, and *z*, by the following stress tensor:

$$\left[\sigma_{ij}\right] = \begin{bmatrix} 1 & 2 & 3 \\ 2 & 4 & 6 \\ 3 & 6 & 1 \end{bmatrix} (ksi).$$

a) Find the principal stresses σ_1, σ_2, and σ_3.
b) Determine the stress invariants I_1, I_2, and I_3.
c) Find the maximum shear stress τ_{max}.
d) Find the octahedral shear stress τ_{oct}.
e) Find the normal stress σ_n and shear stress τ_n on a plane passing through the point and whose orientation in the space is defined by the equation $2x + \sqrt{5}y + 4z = 1$.

Further Reading

Beer, Ferdinand P., E. Russell Johnston, Jr., John T. DeWolf, and David. F. Mazurek. *Mechanics of Materials.* 7th ed. New York City: McGraw-Hill, 2015.

Budynas, Richard G. *Advanced Strength and Applied Stress Analysis.* New York City: McGraw-Hill, 1977.

Curtis, H. D. *Fundamentals of Aircraft Structural Analysis.* New York City: McGraw-Hill, 1997.

Donaldson, Bruce K. *Analysis of Aircraft Structures—An Introduction.* New York City: McGraw-Hill, 1993.

Roylance, David. *Mechanics of Materials.* Hoboken: Wiley, 1996.

Ugural, Ansel. C. *Mechanical Design: An Integrated Approach.* New York City: McGraw-Hill, 2004.

Ugural, Ansel C., and Saul K. Fenster. *Advanced Mechanics of Materials and Applied Elasticity.* 5th ed. Upper Saddle River: Prentice Hall, 2012.

CHAPTER 2

Strain Tensor

2.1 Strain Tensor

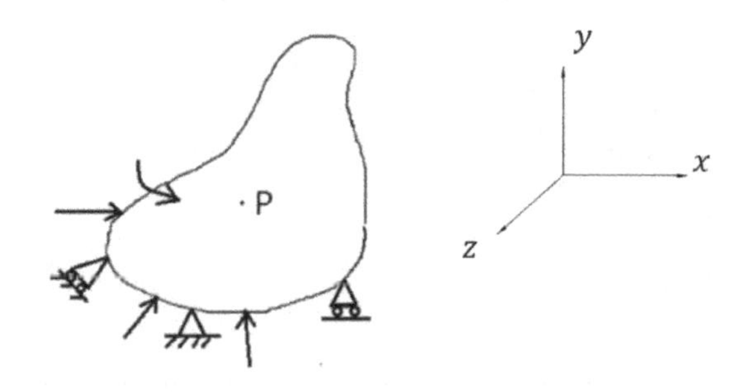

FIGURE 2.1

We defined the strain tensor in chapter 1. Consider a deformable body subject to a system of forces as shown in **figure 2.1**. The state of strain at point P is completely defined by the (3 × 3) real symmetric matrix

$$[\varepsilon_{ij}] = \begin{bmatrix} \varepsilon_x & \varepsilon_{xy} & \varepsilon_{xz} \\ \varepsilon_{yx} & \varepsilon_y & \varepsilon_{yz} \\ \varepsilon_{zx} & \varepsilon_{zy} & \varepsilon_z \end{bmatrix}_{(3\times3)} . \tag{2.1}$$

$[\varepsilon_{ij}]$ is real and symmetric (i.e., $\varepsilon_{ij} = \varepsilon_{ij}$).

$[\varepsilon_{ij}]$ is a second rank (or second order) tensor called the strain tensor.

In (2.1), $\varepsilon_{xy} = \frac{1}{2}\gamma_{xy}; \varepsilon_{xz} = \frac{1}{2}\gamma_{xz}; \varepsilon_{yz} = \frac{1}{2}\gamma_{yz}$.

The 1/2 factor has been introduced for pure mathematical considerations in order to force $[\varepsilon_{ij}]$ to become a second rank (or second order) tensor, thus obeying the equations of transformation in physics that are characteristic of a second-rank tensor. γ is often referred to as engineering shear strain, while ε is referred to as mathematical shear strain. Both are unitless (dimensionless).

γ_{xy} is often referred to as the engineering shear strain, while ε_{xy} is called the mathematical shear strain.

2.2 Strain Transformation Equations

We notice that $[\varepsilon_{ij}]$ in (2.1) has subscripts x, y, and z, which implies that such a matrix is relevant to an xyz coordinate system. If we rotate the coordinate system, we will obtain $[\varepsilon'_{ij}]$, completely defining the state of strain at the same point P in the new primed coordinate system.

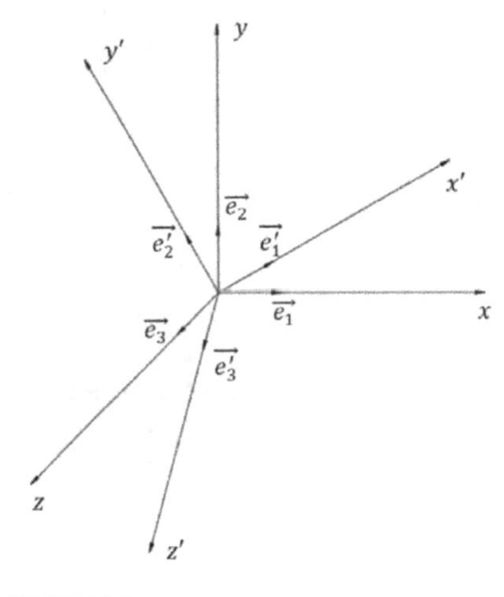

FIGURE 2.2

$[\varepsilon_{ij}]$ and $[\varepsilon'_{ij}]$ are related by the following relationship:

$$[\varepsilon'_{ij}] = [M][\varepsilon_{ij}][M]^T, \tag{2.2}$$

where $[M]$ is the same (3×3) orthonormal transformation matrix we encountered in chapter 1.

$$[M] = \begin{bmatrix} \vec{e}'_1 \cdot \vec{e}_1 & \vec{e}'_1 \cdot \vec{e}_2 & \vec{e}'_1 \cdot \vec{e}_3 \\ \vec{e}'_2 \cdot \vec{e}_1 & \vec{e}'_2 \cdot \vec{e}_2 & \vec{e}'_2 \cdot \vec{e}_3 \\ \vec{e}'_3 \cdot \vec{e}_1 & \vec{e}'_3 \cdot \vec{e}_2 & \vec{e}'_3 \cdot \vec{e}_3 \end{bmatrix}_{(3\times 3)} \tag{2.3}$$

Equations (2.2) are called the strain transformation equations. Notice that they are similar to the stress transformation equations (1.26).

For the 2D problem, we also can write:

$$\begin{aligned} \varepsilon_{x'(\theta)} &= \frac{\varepsilon_x + \varepsilon_y}{2} + \frac{\varepsilon_x - \varepsilon_y}{2}\cos 2\theta + \varepsilon_{xy}\sin 2\theta \\ \varepsilon_{y'(\theta)} &= \frac{\varepsilon_x + \varepsilon_y}{2} - \frac{\varepsilon_x - \varepsilon_y}{2}\cos 2\theta - \varepsilon_{xy}\sin 2\theta \\ \varepsilon_{x'y'(\theta)} &= \varepsilon_{xy}\cos 2\theta - \frac{\varepsilon_x - \varepsilon_y}{2}\sin 2\theta. \end{aligned} \tag{2.4}$$

Notice that (2.4) are identical in mathematical form to (1.17) in chapter 1 if we replace σ_x with ε_x, σ_y with ε_y, and τ_{xy} with ε_{xy} (and not γ_{xy}).

$$\begin{aligned} \varepsilon_{max} &= \frac{\varepsilon_x + \varepsilon_y}{2} + \frac{1}{2}\sqrt{(\varepsilon_x - \varepsilon_y)^2 + 4\varepsilon_{xy}^2} \\ \varepsilon_{min} &= \frac{\varepsilon_x + \varepsilon_y}{2} - \frac{1}{2}\sqrt{(\varepsilon_x - \varepsilon_y)^2 + 4\varepsilon_{xy}^2} \end{aligned} \tag{2.5}$$

and

$$\tan 2\theta = \frac{2\varepsilon_{xy}}{\varepsilon_x - \varepsilon_y} \tag{2.6}$$

Equations (2.5) give us the principal strains, while equation (2.6) gives us the principal directions.

Notice that again equations (2.5) and (2.6) are similar to equations (1.20) in chapter 1.

EXAMPLE 2.1

If the strains are $\varepsilon_x = -900\mu, \varepsilon_y = -300\mu$, and $\varepsilon_{xy} = 900\mu$, what are the principal strains, and in which directions do they occur?

SOLUTION The principal strains are

$$\varepsilon_{max} = \frac{\varepsilon_x + \varepsilon_y}{2} + \frac{1}{2}\sqrt{(\varepsilon_x - \varepsilon_y)^2 + 4\varepsilon_{xy}^2}$$

$$\varepsilon_{min} = \frac{\varepsilon_x + \varepsilon_y}{2} - \frac{1}{2}\sqrt{(\varepsilon_x - \varepsilon_y)^2 + 4\varepsilon_{xy}^2}$$

$$\varepsilon_x = -900\mu; \varepsilon_y = -300\mu; \varepsilon_{xy} = \frac{1}{2}\gamma_{xy} = 450\mu.$$

Therefore,

$$\varepsilon_{max} = \frac{-900 - 300}{2} + \frac{1}{2}\sqrt{(-900 + 300)^2 + (4)(450)^2}$$

$$\varepsilon_{min} = \frac{-900 - 300}{2} - \frac{1}{2}\sqrt{(-900 + 300)^2 + (4)(450)^2}$$

$$\Rightarrow \qquad \varepsilon_{max} = -59\mu; \ \varepsilon_{min} = -1141\mu.$$

Notice that

$$\varepsilon_{max} + \varepsilon_{min} = \varepsilon_x + \varepsilon_y = -1200\mu \qquad \text{(strain invariant)}.$$

The principal directions can be determined using

$$\tan 2\theta = \frac{2\varepsilon_{xy}}{\varepsilon_x - \varepsilon_y} = \frac{(2)(450)}{-900 - (-300)} = -1.5.$$

Therefore,

$$2\theta = -56.31° \Rightarrow \theta = -28.15°$$

or

$$2\theta = 123.69° \Rightarrow \theta = 61.85°.$$

Notice that $61.85° - (-28.15°) = 90°$. In order to determine which angle corresponds to ε_{max} and which corresponds to ε_{min}, we use the expression for $\varepsilon_{x'}(\theta)$.

$$\varepsilon_{x'}(\theta) = \frac{\varepsilon_x + \varepsilon_y}{2} + \frac{\varepsilon_x - \varepsilon_y}{2}\cos 2\theta + \varepsilon_{xy}\sin 2\theta$$

$$\Rightarrow \qquad \varepsilon_{x'}(-28.15°). = \frac{-900 - 300}{2} + \frac{-900 - (-300)}{2}\cos(-56.31°) + (450)$$

$$\sin(-56.31°) = -1141\mu$$

Thus $\theta = -28.15°$ corresponds to ε_{min}. Therefore, the principal strains and their corresponding directions are

$$\varepsilon_{max} = -59\mu \leftrightarrow \theta = 61.85°$$

$$\varepsilon_{min} = -1141\mu \leftrightarrow \theta = -28.15°.$$

EXAMPLE 2.2

The strain rosette shown in the figure below has been used to determine the following strains at a point on the surface of a crane hook:

$$\varepsilon_1 = 420\mu \quad \varepsilon_2 = -45\mu \quad \varepsilon_4 = 165\mu.$$

a) What should the reading of gage three be?
b) Determine the principal strains.
c) Determine the maximum in-plane shearing angle γ_{max}.

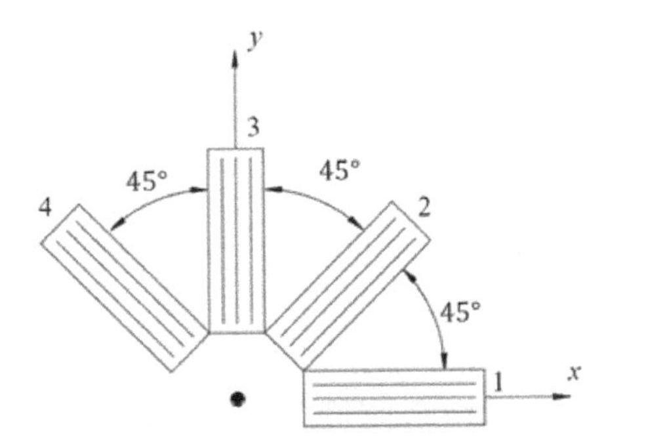

FIGURE 2.3A Strain rosette

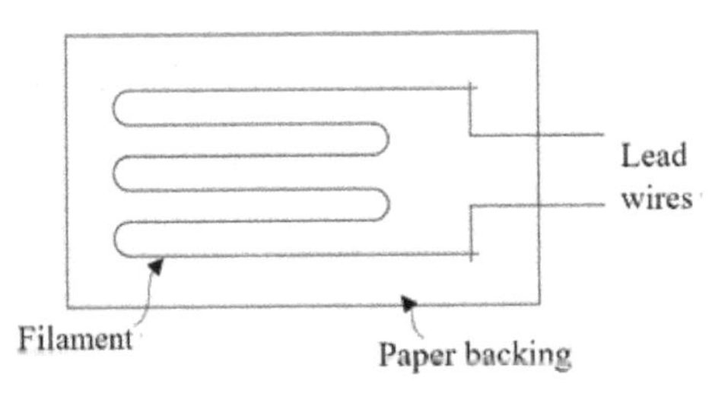

FIGURE 2.3B Strain gage

SOLUTION We said in chapter 1 that the state of stress at a point in a loaded body (or structure) is completely defined by the (3×3) real symmetric matrix $[\sigma_{ij}]$, which means that we need to establish the six independent components in matrix $[\sigma_{ij}]$. Have you ever wondered how these six components can be measured? The reality is that these components are usually very difficult to measure. Instead, we measure strains. In a 2D problem, and in order to establish the (2×2) real symmetric matrix $[\sigma_{ij}]$, we must find three independent components (ε_x, ε_y, and ε_{xy}). Therefore, we need to come up with three equations in order to solve for the three unknowns. Thus, we obtain three readings at three different orientations, using a device called strain rosette. Once $[\varepsilon_{ij}]$ is established, $[\sigma_{ij}]$ can be computed using Hooke's generalized laws. This is not uncommon in physics. For instance, it is difficult to measure a force directly. Instead, we measure the effect of the force. In order to measure weight W, we attach such a weight to a calibrated linear spring (with known spring constant k). By measuring the amount of elongation of the spring δ, we can compute the weight $W = k\delta$.

We will use

$$\varepsilon_{x'}(\theta) = \frac{\varepsilon_x + \varepsilon_y}{2} + \frac{\varepsilon_x - \varepsilon_y}{2}\cos 2\theta + \varepsilon_{xy}\sin 2\theta$$

in order to generate three equations for the three unknowns ε_x, ε_y, and ε_{xy}.

$$\theta = 0^\circ \quad \Rightarrow \quad \varepsilon_1 = \varepsilon_x = 420\mu$$

$$\theta = 45^\circ \quad \Rightarrow \quad \varepsilon_2 = \varepsilon_{x'(45^\circ)} = \frac{\varepsilon_x + \varepsilon_y}{2} + \frac{\varepsilon_x - \varepsilon_y}{2}\cos 90^\circ + \varepsilon_{xy}\sin 90^\circ$$

$$\Rightarrow \quad \varepsilon_2 = \varepsilon_{x'(45^\circ)} = \frac{\varepsilon_x + \varepsilon_y}{2} + \varepsilon_{xy}$$

$$\Rightarrow \quad \frac{\varepsilon_x + \varepsilon_y}{2} + \varepsilon_{xy} = -45\mu$$

$$\theta = 135^\circ \quad \Rightarrow \quad \varepsilon_4 = \varepsilon_{x'(135^\circ)} = \frac{\varepsilon_x + \varepsilon_y}{2} + \frac{\varepsilon_x - \varepsilon_y}{2}\cos 270^\circ + \varepsilon_{xy}\sin 270^\circ$$

$$\Rightarrow \quad \frac{\varepsilon_x + \varepsilon_y}{2} - \varepsilon_{xy} = 165\mu$$

Solving the above three equations simultaneously, we obtain:

$$\varepsilon_x = 420\mu; \quad \varepsilon_y = -300\mu; \quad \varepsilon_{xy} - 105\mu.$$

a) ε_3 should be $\varepsilon_y = -300\mu$.
b) The principal strains are

$$\varepsilon_{\max}^{\min} = \frac{\varepsilon_x + \varepsilon_y}{2} \mp \frac{1}{2}\sqrt{(\varepsilon_x - \varepsilon_y)^2 + 4\varepsilon_{xy}^2}.$$

Therefore,

$$\varepsilon_{\max} = (60 + 375)\mu = 435\mu;$$

$$\varepsilon_{\min} = (60 - 375)\mu = -315\mu.$$

Notice that, as predicted:

$$\varepsilon_{\max} + \varepsilon_{\min} = \varepsilon_x + \varepsilon_y = 120\mu \text{ (Strain invariant)}$$

c) $(\varepsilon_{xy})_{\max} = \frac{1}{2}\sqrt{(\varepsilon_x - \varepsilon_y)^2 + 4\varepsilon_{xy}^2} = 375\mu$

⇒ The maximum in-plane shearing angle:

$$\gamma_{\max} = 2(\varepsilon_{xy})_{\max} = 750\mu$$

2.3 Principal Strains and Principal Directions in 3D

The principal strains are the eigenvalues of

$$\left[\varepsilon_{ij}\right] = \begin{bmatrix} \varepsilon_x & \varepsilon_{xy} & \varepsilon_{xz} \\ \varepsilon_{yx} & \varepsilon_y & \varepsilon_{yz} \\ \varepsilon_{zx} & \varepsilon_{zy} & \varepsilon_z \end{bmatrix}_{(3\times3)}.$$

The principal directions are the corresponding eigenvectors.

In order to determine the eigenvalues of $[\varepsilon_{ij}]$, we set

$$\begin{vmatrix} (\varepsilon_x - \varepsilon) & \varepsilon_{xy} & \varepsilon_{xz} \\ \varepsilon_{yx} & (\varepsilon_y - \varepsilon) & \varepsilon_{yz} \\ \varepsilon_{zx} & \varepsilon_{zy} & (\varepsilon_z - \varepsilon) \end{vmatrix} = 0, \tag{2.7}$$

$$\Rightarrow \qquad \varepsilon^3 - J_1\varepsilon^2 + J_2\varepsilon - J_3 = 0 \tag{2.8}$$

where

$$\begin{gathered} J_1 = \varepsilon_x + \varepsilon_y + \varepsilon_z = \mathrm{Tr}[\varepsilon_{ij}] \\ J_2 = \varepsilon_x\varepsilon_y + \varepsilon_x\varepsilon_z + \varepsilon_y\varepsilon_z - \varepsilon_{xy}^2 - \varepsilon_{xz}^2 - \varepsilon_{yz}^2 \\ J_3 = \det[\varepsilon_{ij}]. \end{gathered} \tag{2.9}$$

J_1, J_2, and J_3 are the strain invariants, and (2.8) is the cubic characteristic equation for strain. Upon solving it, we obtain the three principal strains.

EXAMPLE 2.3

At a point in a stressed body, the strains, related to a Cartesian coordinate system *xyz*, are defined by the following (3×3) matrix:

$$\left[\varepsilon_{ij}\right] = \begin{bmatrix} \varepsilon_x & \varepsilon_{xy} & \varepsilon_{xz} \\ \varepsilon_{yx} & \varepsilon_y & \varepsilon_{yz} \\ \varepsilon_{zx} & \varepsilon_{zy} & \varepsilon_z \end{bmatrix} = \begin{bmatrix} 4 & 1 & 0 \\ 1 & 0 & -2 \\ 0 & -2 & 6 \end{bmatrix} \times 10^{-6}.$$

Determine the principal strains $\varepsilon 1$, $\varepsilon 2$, and $\varepsilon 3$. Determine also the principal directions.

SOLUTION The characteristic equation for strain can be determined by setting (apart from $\mu = 10^{-6}$):

$$\begin{vmatrix} (4-\varepsilon) & 1 & 0 \\ 1 & (0-\varepsilon) & -2 \\ 0 & -2 & (6-\varepsilon) \end{vmatrix} = 0.$$

Alternatively, we can compute the stain invariants:

$$J_1 = \varepsilon_x + \varepsilon_y + \varepsilon_z = 10\mu$$

$$J_2 = \varepsilon_x\varepsilon_y + \varepsilon_x\varepsilon_z + \varepsilon_y\varepsilon_z - \varepsilon_{xy}^2 - \varepsilon_{xz}^2 - \varepsilon_{yz}^2 = 19(\mu)^2$$

$$J_3 = \det[\varepsilon_{ij}] = -22(\mu)^3.$$

Therefore, the characteristic equation (apart from $\mu = 10^{-6}$) is:

$$\varepsilon^3 - 10\varepsilon^2 + 19\varepsilon + 22 = 0.$$

The roots of the above cubic equation are: 6.64, 4.16 and −0.80.

Thus, the principal strains are:

$$\varepsilon_1 = 6.64\mu$$
$$\varepsilon_2 = 4.16\mu$$
$$\varepsilon_3 = -0.80\mu.$$

Notice that

$$\varepsilon_1 + \varepsilon_2 + \varepsilon_3 = J_1$$

$$\varepsilon_1\varepsilon_2 + \varepsilon_1\varepsilon_3 + \varepsilon_2\varepsilon_3 = J_2$$

$$\varepsilon_1\varepsilon_2\varepsilon_3 = J_3.$$

A normalized eigenvector corresponding to the eigenvalue $\varepsilon_1 = 6.64\mu$ is:

$$\begin{pmatrix} 0.116 \\ 0.303 \\ -0.946 \end{pmatrix}.$$

A normalized eigenvector corresponding to the eigenvalue $\varepsilon_2 = 4.16\mu$ is:

$$\begin{pmatrix} 0.973 \\ 0.156 \\ 0.169 \end{pmatrix}.$$

A normalized eigenvector corresponding to the eigenvalue $\varepsilon_3 = -0.80\mu$ is:

$$\begin{pmatrix} 0.198 \\ -0.946 \\ -0.277 \end{pmatrix}.$$

$$\varepsilon_1 = 6.64\mu \quad \leftrightarrow \begin{pmatrix} 0.116 \\ 0.303 \\ -0.946 \end{pmatrix}$$

$$\varepsilon_2 = 4.16\mu \quad \leftrightarrow \begin{pmatrix} 0.973 \\ 0.156 \\ 0.169 \end{pmatrix}$$

$$\varepsilon_3 = -0.80\mu \quad \leftrightarrow \begin{pmatrix} 0.198 \\ -0.946 \\ -0.277 \end{pmatrix}$$

Notice also that the above vectors are three-unit vectors mutually perpendicular to each other.

2.4 The Five Elastic Constants

Hooke's generalized laws for a homogeneous isotropic material behaving in the linearly elastic range, which we referred to in chapter 1, are:

$$\begin{aligned} \varepsilon_x &= \frac{\sigma_x}{E} - \frac{\nu}{E}(\sigma_y + \sigma_z) \quad ; \quad \gamma_{xy} = \frac{\tau_{xy}}{G} \\ \varepsilon_y &= \frac{\sigma_y}{E} - \frac{\nu}{E}(\sigma_x + \sigma_z) \quad ; \quad \gamma_{xz} = \frac{\tau_{xz}}{G} \\ \varepsilon_z &= \frac{\sigma_z}{E} - \frac{\nu}{E}(\sigma_x + \sigma_y) \quad ; \quad \gamma_{yz} = \frac{\tau_{yz}}{G}. \end{aligned} \tag{2.10}$$

We can notice that three constants E, ν, and G were used in these relationships. These three constants are not independent. Indeed, it can be shown that:

$$G = \frac{E}{2(1+\nu)}. \tag{2.11}$$

Let us invert the above six linear relationships in (2.10) (i.e., let us express stress in terms of strain rather than strain in terms of stress).

From (2.10), we can write:

$$\varepsilon_x + \varepsilon_y + \varepsilon_z = \frac{\sigma_x + \sigma_y + \sigma_z}{E}(1 - 2\nu). \tag{2.12}$$

Let $\varepsilon_x + \varepsilon_y + \varepsilon_z = e$ (dilatation coefficient).

Therefore,

$$\sigma_x + \sigma_y + \sigma_z = \frac{Ee}{1-2\nu}.$$

The first equation in (2.10) can be written as:

$$\sigma_x - \nu(\sigma_y + \sigma_z) = E\varepsilon_x$$

$$\Rightarrow \quad \sigma_x = E\varepsilon_x + \nu(\sigma_y + \sigma_z)$$

$$= E\varepsilon_x + \nu(\sigma_x + \sigma_y + \sigma_z - \sigma_x)$$

$$= E\varepsilon_x + \nu(\sigma_x + \sigma_y + \sigma_z) - \nu\sigma_x$$

$$\Rightarrow \quad \sigma_x(1+\nu) = E\varepsilon_x + \frac{\nu Ee}{1-2\nu}$$

$$\Rightarrow \quad \sigma_x = \frac{E\varepsilon_x}{1+\nu} + \frac{E\nu}{(1+\nu)(1-2\nu)}e.$$

However, $\frac{E}{2(1+\nu)} = G$.

Also, $\frac{E\nu}{(1+\nu)(1-2\nu)}$ is another elastic constant called λ.

Therefore, $\sigma_x = 2G\varepsilon_x + \lambda e$, G and λ are called Lamé* constants.

Similar expressions can also be obtained for σ_y and σ_z. Finally, we end up with the following six linear relationships:

$$\sigma_x = 2G\varepsilon_x + \lambda e \quad ; \quad \tau_{xy} = G\gamma_{xy}$$

$$\sigma_y = 2G\varepsilon_y + \lambda e \quad ; \quad \tau_{xz} = G\gamma_{xz}$$

$$\sigma_z = 2G\varepsilon_z + \lambda e \quad ; \quad \tau_{yz} = G\gamma_{yz}.$$

The above six relationships are also called Hooke's generalized laws.

---

* After a Frech mathematician Lamé who contributed to applied mechanics and theory of elasticity. Lamé taught at École Polytechnique in Paris.

In summary,

$$\varepsilon_x = \frac{\sigma_x}{E} - \frac{\nu}{E}(\sigma_y + \sigma_z);\ \gamma_{xy} = \frac{\tau_{xy}}{G}$$

$$\varepsilon_y = \frac{\sigma_y}{E} - \frac{\nu}{E}(\sigma_x + \sigma_z);\ \gamma_{xz} = \frac{\tau_{xz}}{G}$$

$$\varepsilon_z = \frac{\sigma_z}{E} - \frac{\nu}{E}(\sigma_x + \sigma_y);\ \gamma_{yz} = \frac{\tau_{yz}}{G}$$

$$\Updownarrow$$

$$\sigma_x = 2G\varepsilon_x + \lambda e \quad ; \quad \tau_{xy} = G\gamma_{xy}$$

$$\sigma_y = 2G\varepsilon_y + \lambda e \quad ; \quad \tau_{xz} = G\gamma_{xz}$$

$$\sigma_z = 2G\varepsilon_z + \lambda e \quad ; \quad \tau_{yz} = G\gamma_{yz}.$$

So far, we defined four elastic constants: E, ν, G, and λ. We will now define a fifth elastic constant. In (2.10), if we assume $\sigma_x = \sigma_y = \sigma_z = -p$ (hydrostatic pressure), we conclude that:

$$e = \frac{-3P(1-2\nu)}{E}$$

$$\Rightarrow \quad \frac{P}{-e} = \frac{E}{3(1-2\nu)}.$$

E and ν are constants. Therefore, $\frac{E}{3(1-2\nu)}$ is another elastic constant called bulk modules of elasticity K:

$$K = \frac{E}{3(1-2\nu)}. \tag{2.13}$$

$[\sigma_{ij}]$ is a (3×3) matrix that has nine elements. $[\varepsilon_{ij}]$ is also a (3×3) matrix that has nine elements. From pure mathematical considerations, if we want to write down the most general linear relationship between the stress and strain tensors, 81 elastic constants $(9 \times 9 = 81)$ will be needed. However, the symmetry of both $[\sigma_{ij}]$ and $[\varepsilon_{ij}]$ will automatically reducc these 81 elastic constants to 36, since actually, we have only six independent elements in $[\sigma_{ij}]$ and another six independent elements in $[\varepsilon_{ij}]$. It can be shown that for a homogeneous isotropic material behaving in the linearly elastic range only two independent elastic constants are needed to write down the equations of elasticity. We encountered five elastic constants E, ν, G, λ, and K. All these constants have the dimension of stress, except ν which is dimensionless. Only two of these five elastic constants are independent. The remaining three constants can be written in terms of these two independent ones. Engineers prefer choosing E and ν to be the independent constants. We call them engineering elastic constants. In soil mechanics, K and ν are preferred. In theory of elasticity, G and λ (Lamé constants) are usually chosen.

EXAMPLE 2.4

Express bulk modules of elasticity K in terms of Lamé constants G and λ.

SOLUTION

$$G = \frac{E}{2(1+\nu)};\ \lambda = \frac{E\nu}{(1+\nu)(1-2\nu)};\ K = \frac{E}{3(1-2\nu)}$$

$$\Rightarrow \quad \frac{G}{\lambda} = \frac{E}{2(1+\nu)}\frac{(1+\nu)(1-2\nu)}{E\nu} = \frac{1}{2\nu} - 1$$

$$\Rightarrow \quad \nu = \frac{\lambda}{2(G+\lambda)}$$

Therefore,

$$K = \frac{E}{3(1-2\nu)} = \frac{2G(1+\nu)}{3(1-2\nu)} = \frac{2G\left[1+\dfrac{\lambda}{2(G+\lambda)}\right]}{3\left[1-\dfrac{2\lambda}{2(G+\lambda)}\right]}$$

$$\Rightarrow \quad K = \frac{2}{3}G + \lambda$$

2.5 Interpretation of the Dilatation Coefficient e

In the uniaxial state of stress when we considered a prismatic bar loaded axially with a load *P*, we defined $\varepsilon = \frac{\Delta l}{l_0}$ $\Rightarrow$ the initial length l_0 becomes, after deformation, $l_0 + \Delta l = l_0 + \varepsilon l_0 = l_0(1+\varepsilon)$.

Now, consider a rectangular box of dimensions x_0, y_0, and z_0 before deformation (**figure 2.4**).

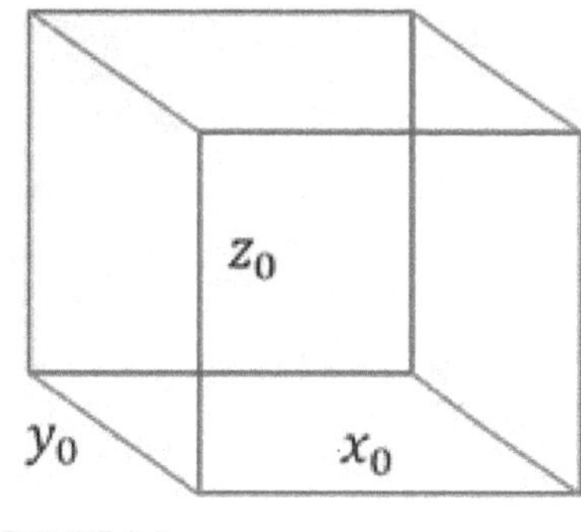

FIGURE 2.4

After deformation, x_0 becomes $x_0(1+\varepsilon_x)$, y_0 becomes $y_0(1+\varepsilon_y)$, and z_0 becomes $z_0(1+\varepsilon_z)$. Therefore, the initial volume $V_0 = x_0y_0z_0$ becomes, after deformation,

$$V_0 + \Delta V = x_0y_0z_0\left(1+\varepsilon_x\right)\left(1+\varepsilon_y\right)\left(1+\varepsilon_z\right) = x_0y_0z_0(1+\varepsilon_x+\varepsilon_y+\varepsilon_z+\varepsilon_x\varepsilon_y+$$
$$\varepsilon_x\varepsilon_z+\varepsilon_y\varepsilon_z+\varepsilon_x\varepsilon_y\varepsilon_z).$$

Since ε_x, ε_y, and ε_z are very small (of the order of 10^{-3} or 10^{-4}), we can ignore higher order terms.

Let:

$$e = \varepsilon_x + \varepsilon_y + \varepsilon_z. \tag{2.14}$$

We conclude that:

$$e = \frac{\Delta V}{V_0}. \tag{2.15}$$

e is related to the volumetric change and is called the dilatation coefficient. Notice that e is dimensionless (unitless).

2.6 Strain Energy

Let us revisit the simplest type of loading in structural engineering when we have a prismatic bar loaded axially with a load *P*. This is a uniaxial state of stress. We saw earlier that, as long as the material is still behaving in the linearly elastic range, such a prismatic bar behaves like a linear spring with spring constant k given by:

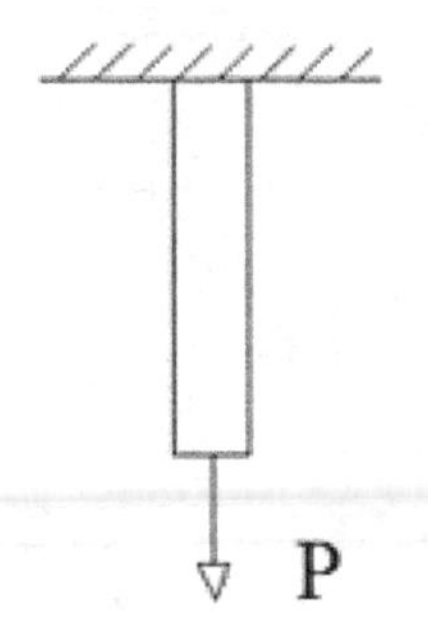

FIGURE 2.5

$$k = \frac{AE}{l}. \tag{2.16}$$

We also found the amount of deformation δ to be given by:

$$\delta = \frac{P}{k} = \frac{P}{\frac{AE}{l}}.$$

We learned in an elementary course in physics that the potential energy in the spring, or the strain energy U in the bar, is given by:

$$U = \frac{1}{2}k\delta^2 = \frac{1}{2}\left(\frac{AE}{l}\right)\left(\frac{P}{\frac{AE}{l}}\right)^2 = \frac{P^2 l}{2AE}. \tag{2.17}$$

Notice that the strain energy has the dimension of (force)(length). It is measured in joules in the SI system or $lb_f \cdot ft$ in the technical English system. Dividing the strain energy U by the volume *V* of the bar, we define the strain energy density:

$$u = \frac{U}{V} = \frac{P^2 l}{2AEAl} = \frac{P^2}{2EA^2} = \frac{\left(\frac{P}{A}\right)^2}{2E} = \frac{\sigma^2}{2E} = \frac{1}{2}\sigma\frac{\sigma}{E} = \frac{1}{2}\sigma\varepsilon. \tag{2.18}$$

It is interesting to observe that the strain energy density has the same dimension as stress:

$$\frac{\text{Joule}}{m^3} = \frac{Nm}{m^3} = \frac{N}{m^2} = Pa.$$

Also, notice that $u = \frac{1}{2}\sigma\varepsilon$ measures the area of the shaded triangle under the curve $\sigma = \sigma_{(\varepsilon)}$ shown in the figure below:

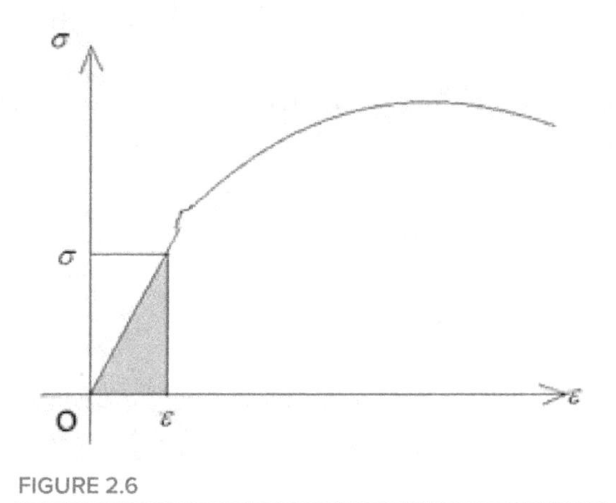

FIGURE 2.6

In the most general case when, instead of dealing with a uniaxial state of stress, the state of stress is defined by the matrix $[\sigma_{ij}] = \begin{bmatrix} \sigma_x & \tau_{xy} & \tau_{xz} \\ \tau_{yx} & \sigma_y & \tau_{yz} \\ \tau_{zx} & \tau_{zy} & \sigma_z \end{bmatrix}_{(3\times3)}$, and the state of strain is defined by the matrix $[\varepsilon_{ij}] = \begin{bmatrix} \varepsilon_x & \varepsilon_{xy} & \varepsilon_{xz} \\ \varepsilon_{yx} & \varepsilon_y & \varepsilon_{yz} \\ \varepsilon_{zx} & \varepsilon_{zy} & \varepsilon_z \end{bmatrix}_{(3\times3)}$. It can be shown that the strain energy density u is given by:

$$u = \frac{1}{2}(\sigma_x\varepsilon_x + \sigma_y\varepsilon_y + \sigma_z\varepsilon_z + \tau_{xy}\gamma_{xy} + \tau_{xz}\gamma_{xz} + \tau_{yz}\gamma_{yz}) \quad (2.19)$$

The above expression for u is the most general one. However, this is valid only when the material is behaving in the linearly elastic range. Notice also that u, like stress and strain, is a point function.

It is convenient sometimes to express u in terms of stress only by eliminating strain from (2.19). Using Hooke's generalized laws, we can eliminate strain. The expression for u becomes:

$$u = \frac{1}{2E}(\sigma_x^2 + \sigma_y^2 + \sigma_z^2) - \frac{\nu}{E}(\sigma_x\sigma_y + \sigma_x\sigma_z + \sigma_y\sigma_z) + \frac{1}{2G}(\tau_{xy}^2 + \tau_{xz}^2 + \tau_{yz}^2). \quad (2.20)$$

Alternatively, we can eliminate stress in (2.19) and, therefore, write:

$$u = \frac{1}{2}[\lambda e^2 + 2G(\varepsilon_x^2 + \varepsilon_y^2 + \varepsilon_z^2) + G(\gamma_{xy}^2 + \gamma_{xz}^2 + \gamma_{yz}^2)]. \tag{2.21}$$

The area under the curve up to the yield stress (proportionality limit) is called the modulus of resilience.

$$\text{modulus of resilience} = \frac{1}{2}\sigma_{\text{yield}}\varepsilon_{\text{yield}} = \frac{\sigma_{\text{yield}}^2}{2E} \tag{2.22}$$

Modulus of resilience has the dimension of stress.

2.7 Computation of the Total Strain Energy *U*

It can be easily shown that the total strain energy *U* for simple cases of loading (the ones encountered in an elementary course of Mechanics of Materials) can be evaluated using the formulas listed below:

Axial Loading

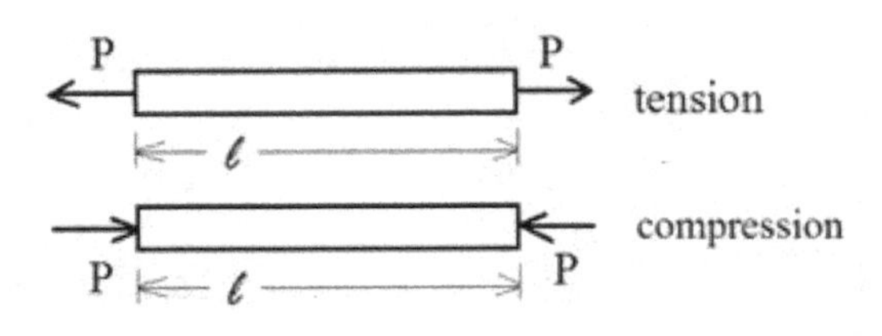

FIGURE 2.7

$$U = \frac{P^2 l}{2AE}$$

Torsion of a Circular Rod

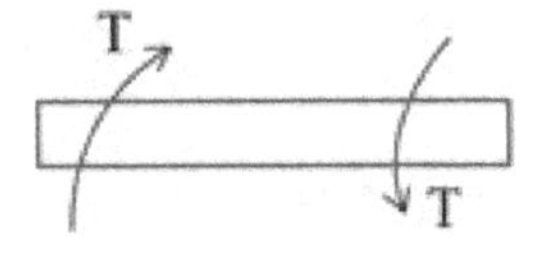

FIGURE 2.8

$$U = \frac{T^2 l}{2GJ},$$

where G is the modulus of rigidity (shear modulus of elasticity), and J is the area polar moment of inertia of the circular cross section.

Bending of a Beam

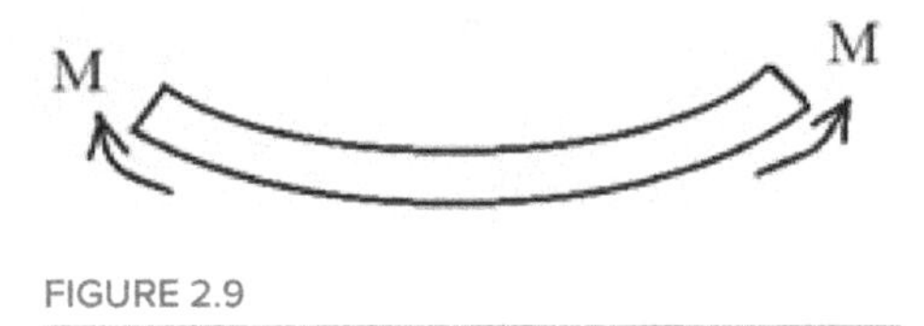

FIGURE 2.9

$$U = \int \frac{M_{(x)}^2 dx}{2EI}$$

Where $M_{(x)}$ is the bending moment, E is Young's modulus of elasticity, and I is the area moment of inertia of the cross section.

For more complicated structures (e.g., plates, shells, 3D solid objects, etc.) and loadings, *U* can be evaluated using the following integral:

$$U = \int_V u_{(x,y,z)} dV.$$

Notice that the above integral is a triple integral, and often, evaluating it is not simple.

EXAMPLE 2.5

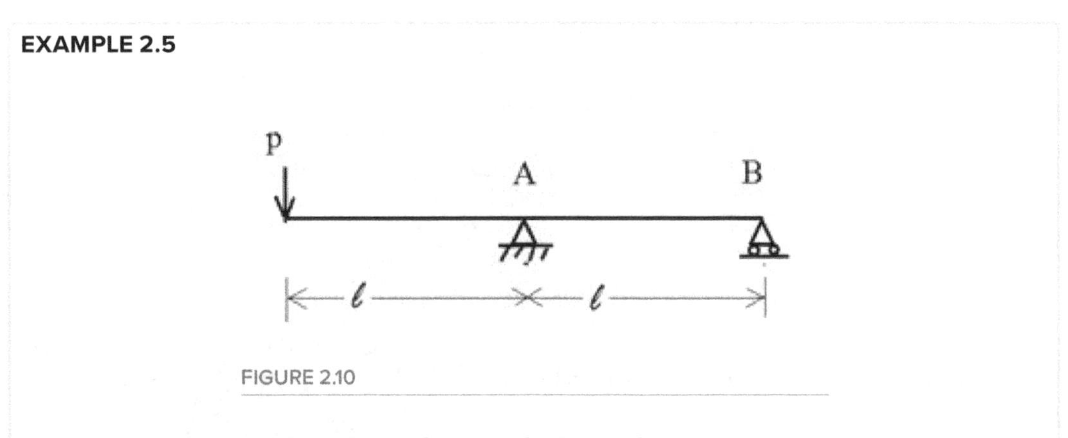

FIGURE 2.10

For the statically determinate beam shown in the figure above, compute the strain energy U. Assume that the total strain energy is due to bending only. Assume EI to be constant throughout.

SOLUTION

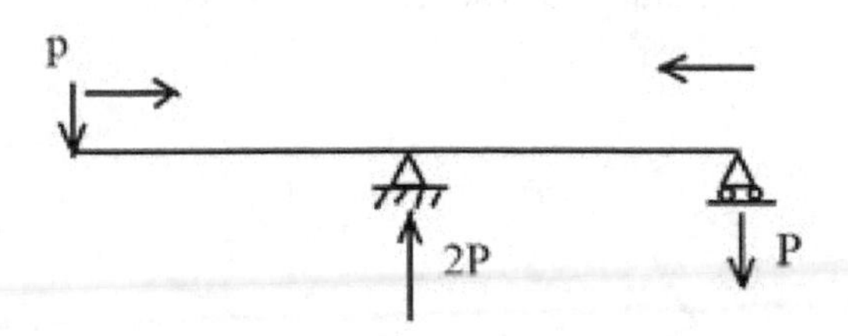

FIGURE 2.11

Using elementary statics, the reactions at the pin A and the roller B can be evaluated.

$$U = \int \frac{M_{(x)}^2 dx}{2EI} = \int_0^1 \frac{(-Px)^2 dx}{2EI} + \int_0^1 \frac{(-Px)^2 dx}{2EI} = \frac{P^2 l^3}{3EI}$$

Notice that U has the dimension of energy (joule in the SI system):

$$\frac{N^2 m^3}{\frac{N}{m^2} m^4} = Nm = Joule$$

EXAMPLE 2.6

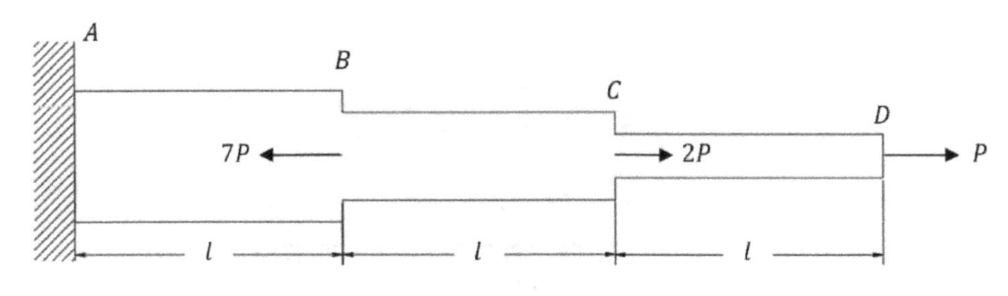

FIGURE 2.12

Determine the strain energy U in the stepped prismatic bar subject to axial loading shown in the figure above. The cross section area in regions AB, BC, and CD are 3A, 2A, and A, respectively.
Assume E to be constant throughout.

SOLUTION

$$U = \frac{P^2 l}{2AE} + \frac{(3P)^2 l}{2(2A)E} + \frac{(4P)^2 l}{2(3A)E} = \frac{65P^2 l}{12AE}$$

2.8 Components of the Stress Tensor

Often, it is useful and convenient to decompose $[\sigma_{ij}]$ into two components:

$$[\sigma_{ij}] = \begin{bmatrix} \sigma_x & \tau_{xy} & \tau_{xz} \\ \tau_{yx} & \sigma_y & \tau_{yz} \\ \tau_{zx} & \tau_{zy} & \sigma_z \end{bmatrix} = \begin{bmatrix} \bar{\sigma} & 0 & 0 \\ 0 & \bar{\sigma} & 0 \\ 0 & 0 & \bar{\sigma} \end{bmatrix} + \begin{bmatrix} (\sigma_x - \bar{\sigma}) & \tau_{xy} & \tau_{xz} \\ \tau_{yx} & (\sigma_y - \bar{\sigma}) & \tau_{yz} \\ \tau_{zx} & \tau_{zy} & (\sigma_z - \bar{\sigma}) \end{bmatrix},$$

↓ Dilatational component ↓ Distortional component

where $\bar{\sigma} = \frac{\sigma_x + \sigma_y + \sigma_z}{3} = \frac{1}{3}\mathrm{Tr}[\sigma_{ij}] = \frac{1}{3}I_1$.

The first component $\begin{bmatrix} \bar{\sigma} & 0 & 0 \\ 0 & \bar{\sigma} & 0 \\ 0 & 0 & \bar{\sigma} \end{bmatrix}$ is called the dilatational or spherical component. It is responsible for changing (i.e., increasing or decreasing) the volume.

The second component $\begin{bmatrix} (\sigma_x - \bar{\sigma}) & \tau_{xy} & \tau_{xz} \\ \tau_{yx} & (\sigma_x - \bar{\sigma}) & \tau_{yz} \\ \tau_{zx} & \tau_{zy} & (\sigma_x - \bar{\sigma}) \end{bmatrix}$ is called the deviatoric or distortional component. It is responsible for distorting the solid (changing the shape of the body).

EXAMPLE 2.7

The same prismatic bar (same I, A, and E) is subjected to an axial loading P_1 in fig.(a), to an axial loading P_2 in fig.(b), and to an axial loading $(P_1 + P_2)$ in fig.(c).

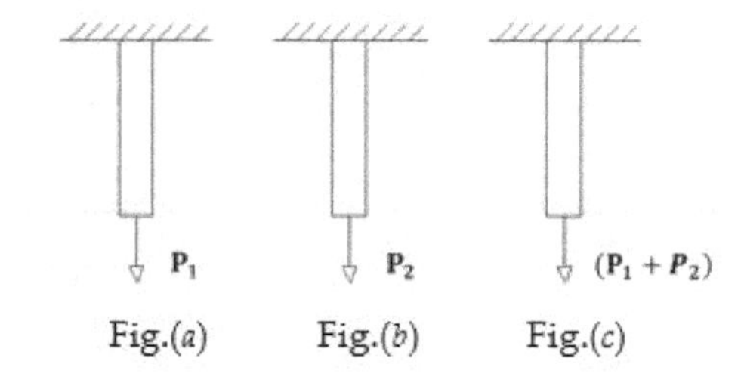

FIGURE 2.13

Will the axial elongation of the bar in fig.(c) be equal to the sum of the two axial elongations of the bar in fig.(a) and fig.(b)?

SOLUTION The axial elongation of the bar in fig.(c) is

$$\delta = \frac{(P_1 + P_2)}{AE} l = \frac{P_1 l}{AE} + \frac{P_2 l}{AE},$$

which is equal to the sum of the two axial elongations in fig.(a) and fig.(b). The principle of superposition holds.

On the other hand, the strain energy in the bar in fig.(c) is:

$$U = \frac{(P_1 + P_2)^2}{2AE} l \neq \frac{P_1^2 l}{2AE} + \frac{P_2^2 l}{2AE},$$

which means the strain energy stored in fig.(c) is not equal to the sum of the strain energies stored in fig.(a) and fig.(b). The principle of superposition does not hold.

2.9 Components of Strain Energy

The dilatational (or volumetric) strain energy density is

$$u_{dilatational} = \frac{1}{2E}\left(\bar{\sigma}^2 + \bar{\sigma}^2 + \bar{\sigma}^2\right) - \frac{\nu}{E}\left(\bar{\sigma}^2 + \bar{\sigma}^2 + \bar{\sigma}^2\right) = \frac{3\bar{\sigma}^2}{2E} - \frac{3\nu\bar{\sigma}^2}{E}$$

$$= \frac{3\bar{\sigma}^2}{2E}(1 - 2\nu) = \frac{\bar{\sigma}^2}{2K}.$$

Therefore,

$$u_{dilatational} = \frac{1}{18K}(\sigma_x + \sigma_y + \sigma_z)^2 = \frac{I_1^2}{18K} = \frac{Tr^2[\sigma_{ij}]}{18K},$$

where $I_1 = \sigma_x + \sigma_y + \sigma_z$ is the first stress invariant, and $K = \frac{E}{3(1-2\nu)}$ is the bulk modulus of elasticity.

Similarly, it can be shown that the distortional (or deviatoric) strain energy density is

$$u_{distortional} = \frac{3}{4G}\tau_{oct}^2,$$

where

$$\tau_{oct} = \frac{1}{3}\sqrt{\left(\sigma_x - \sigma_y\right)^2 + \left(\sigma_x - \sigma_z\right)^2 + \left(\sigma_y - \sigma_z\right)^2 + 6\left(\tau_{xy}^2 + \tau_{xz}^2 + \tau_{yz}^2\right)}$$

is the octahedral shear stress, and $G = \frac{E}{2(1+\nu)}$ is the shear modules of elasticity.

Notice that both the dilatational strain energy density and the distortional strain energy density, as expected, will have the dimension of stress. The unit in the SI system will be: $\frac{\mathrm{J}}{\mathrm{m}^3} = \frac{\mathrm{N}}{\mathrm{m}^2} = \mathrm{Pa}$.

2.10 What Did We Learn in Chapter 2?

- Like stress, strain is a point function. It is defined at a point and can vary from one point to the other.
- To completely define the state of strain at a point of a body, a (3×3) real symmetric matrix is needed. Strain is a second rank (or second order) tensor.
- $[\sigma_{ij}]$ and $[\varepsilon_{ij}]$ are second-rank tensors. The formulas encountered in chapter 2 are very similar to the ones in chapter 1. These formulas are characteristic of a second-rank tensor in physics.
- Stress and strain are related to each other. Stress causes strain, and strain causes stress.

Problems

2.1. If the strains at a point are $\varepsilon_x = 250\,\mu$, $\varepsilon_y = 850\,\mu$, and $\gamma_{xy} = -850\,\mu$, what are the principal strains? In what direction do they occur?

2.2. A 45° strain rosette is used to measure strain at a critical point on the surface of a loaded beam. The readings are $\varepsilon_a = -150\,\mu$, $\varepsilon_b = 50\,\mu$, $\varepsilon_c - 150\,\mu$ for $\theta = 0°$, $\theta_b = 45°$, and $\theta_c = 90°$. Calculate the principal strains and their directions.

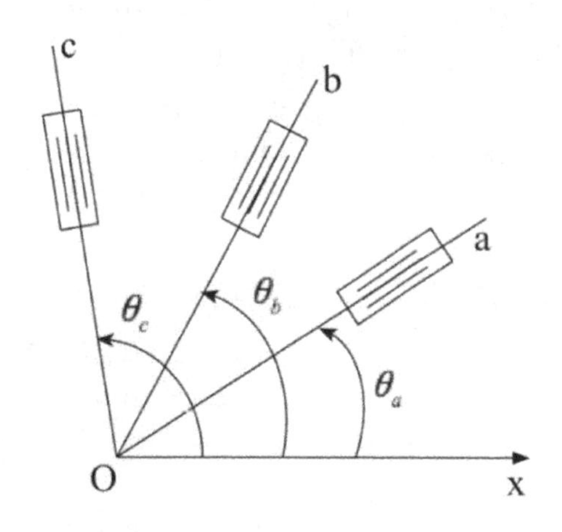

FIGURE 2.14

2.3. The principal strains at a point are $\varepsilon_{max} = 500\,\mu$ and $\varepsilon_{min} = 300\,\mu$. Determine (a) $(\gamma_{xy})_{max}$ and the direction along which it occurs and (b) the strains in the direction at $\theta = 30^\circ$ from the principal axes.

2.4. For a given material,

$$\begin{aligned} E &= 29 \times 10^6\ psi \\ G &- 12 \times 10^6\ psi \end{aligned}.$$

If the state of strain at a point within this material is defined by

$$[\varepsilon_{ij}] = \begin{bmatrix} \varepsilon_x & \varepsilon_{xy} & \varepsilon_{xz} \\ \varepsilon_{yx} & \varepsilon_y & \varepsilon_{yz} \\ \varepsilon_{zx} & \varepsilon_{zy} & \varepsilon_z \end{bmatrix} = \begin{bmatrix} 0.003 & 0.002 & 0 \\ 0.002 & 0.004 & 0.005 \\ 0 & 0.005 & 0 \end{bmatrix},$$

determine the corresponding stress tensor $[\sigma_{ij}]$.

Assume that the material is homogeneous, isotropic, and linearly elastic.

2.5. For a homogeneous, isotropic, and linearly elastic material with

$$\begin{aligned} G &= 12 \times 10^6\ psi \\ E &= 30 \times 10^6\ psi \end{aligned},$$

determine the strain tensor $[\varepsilon_{ij}]$ for a state of stress given by:

$$[\sigma_{ij}] = \begin{bmatrix} 25 & -5 & 10 \\ -5 & 0 & 15 \\ 10 & 15 & 20 \end{bmatrix} \times 10^3\ psi.$$

2.6. At a point in a stressed body, the strain tensor, related to the coordinate set xyz, is given by

$$\left[\varepsilon_{ij}\right] = \begin{bmatrix} \varepsilon_x & \varepsilon_{xy} & \varepsilon_{xz} \\ \varepsilon_{yx} & \varepsilon_y & \varepsilon_{yz} \\ \varepsilon_{zx} & \varepsilon_{zy} & \varepsilon_z \end{bmatrix} = \begin{bmatrix} 100 & 200 & 100 \\ 200 & -100 & 400 \\ 100 & 400 & -300 \end{bmatrix} \mu.$$

Determine (a) the strain invariants; (b) the normal strain in the x' direction, obtained by rotating the coordinate system about the z-axis counterclockwise at an angle $\theta = 30^\circ$ from the x-axis; (c) the principal strains ε_1, ε_2, and ε_3; and (d) the maximum shear strain.

2.7. The state of strain at a point in a structural member is defined by the following (3×3) real symmetric matrix

$$[\varepsilon_{ij}] = \begin{bmatrix} \varepsilon_x & \varepsilon_{xy} & \varepsilon_{xz} \\ \varepsilon_{yx} & \varepsilon_y & \varepsilon_{yz} \\ \varepsilon_{zx} & \varepsilon_{zy} & \varepsilon_z \end{bmatrix} = \begin{bmatrix} 400 & 500 & 800 \\ 500 & 200 & 700 \\ 800 & 700 & 100 \end{bmatrix} \mu.$$

Determine the magnitudes and directions of the principal strains.

2.8. Express the elastic constant G in terms of Young's modulus of elasticity E and bulk modulus of elasticity K.

2.9. Express Poisson's ratio v in terms of E and K.

2.10. The modulus of rigidity for steel is $G = 80\ GPa$. Its bulk modulus of elasticity is $K = 163\ GPa$. Compute its Young's modulus of elasticity E.

2.11. Compute the total strain energy in the beam shown in the figure below. Assume that the total strain energy is due to bending only. Assume EI to be constant throughout.

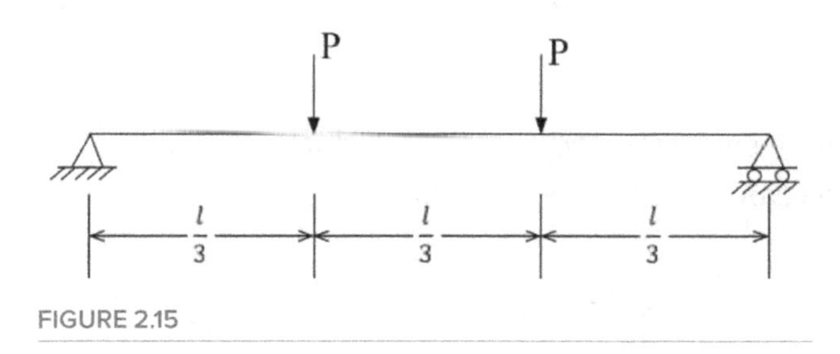

FIGURE 2.15

2.12. Compute the total strain energy in the beam shown in the figure below. Assume that the total strain energy is due to bending only. Assume EI to be constant throughout.

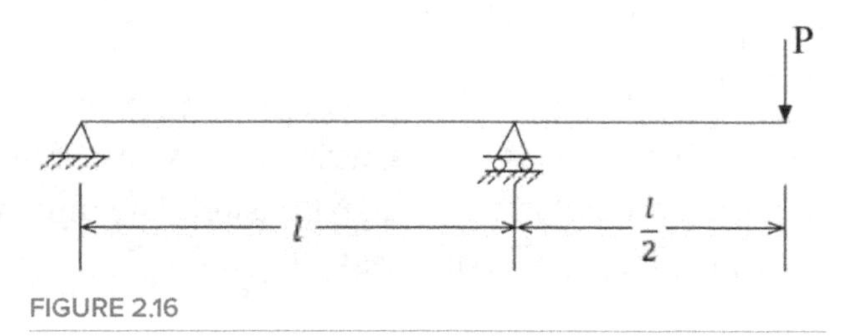

FIGURE 2.16

2.13. Compute the total strain energy in the beam shown in the figure below. Assume that the total strain energy is due to bending only. Assume EI to be constant throughout.

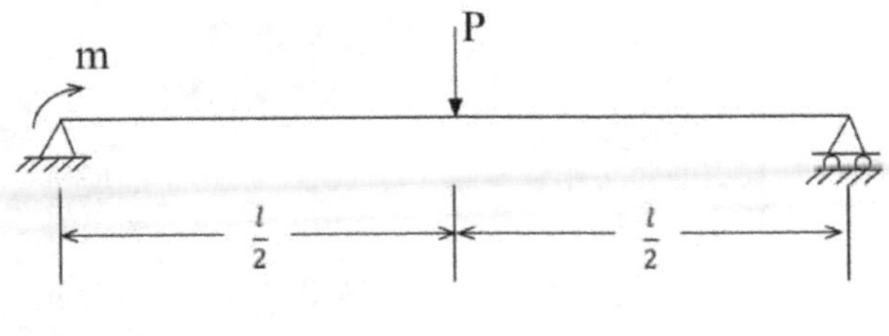

FIGURE 2.17

2.14. For the beam and loading shown in the figure below, determine the strain energy due to bending only. Assume EI to be constant throughout.

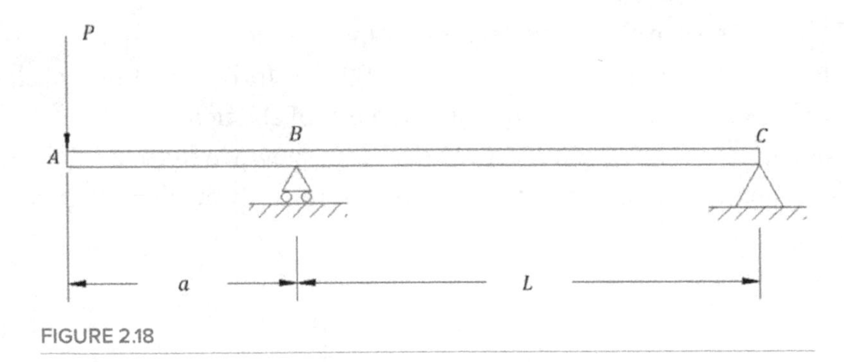

FIGURE 2.18

2.15. For a homogeneous isotropic material which is behaving in the linearly elastic range, we can write Hooke's generalized laws:

$$\varepsilon_x = \frac{\sigma_x}{E} - \frac{\nu}{E}(\sigma_y + \sigma_z) + \alpha\Delta T \quad ; \quad \gamma_{xy} = \frac{\tau_{xy}}{G}$$

$$\varepsilon_y = \frac{\sigma_y}{E} - \frac{\nu}{E}(\sigma_x + \sigma_z) + \alpha\Delta T \quad ; \quad \gamma_{xz} = \frac{\tau_{xz}}{G}$$

$$\varepsilon_z = \frac{\sigma_z}{E} - \frac{\nu}{E}(\sigma_x + \sigma_y) + \alpha\Delta T \quad ; \quad \gamma_{yz} = \frac{\tau_{yz}}{G}.$$

(Thermal effects were included.)

Invert the above six equations; that is, write down stresses in terms of strains. (α is the linear coefficient of thermal expansion. The unit is $/°C$ per degree Celsius. For this reason, $\alpha\,\Delta T$ is unitless.)

2.16. Consider a simply supported rectangular beam of depth h, width b, and length l subjected to a uniformly distributed load of intensity w (force/length). Show that the maximum strain energy density u_{max} can be written as:

$$u_{max} = \frac{45}{8} u_{average} = \frac{45}{8} \frac{U}{V}$$

in which U is the total strain energy in the beam, and V is its volume.

2.17. Calculate the strain energy per unit volume in changing the volume and in changing the shape of the material at any point on the surface of a steel shaft 100 mm in diameter subjected to torques of 25 $kN \times m$ and bending moments of 25 $kN \times m$ at its ends. Use $E = 200$ GPa and $v = 0.25$.

2.18. The state of stress at a point in a loaded member is represented in the figure below. Express the dilatational strain energy density and the distortional strain energy density in terms of the given stress σ and τ at the point and the material properties E and v.

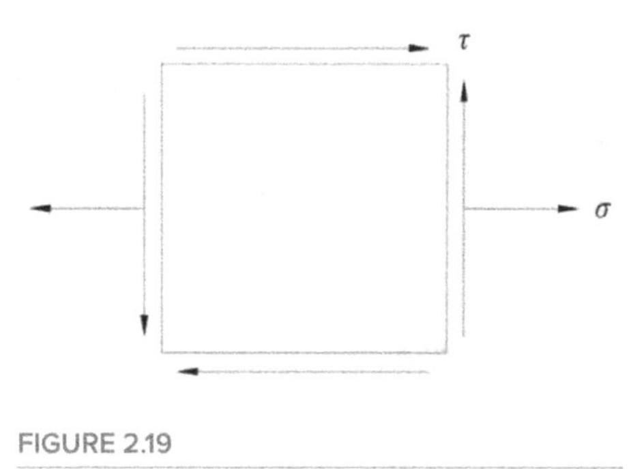

FIGURE 2.19

2.19. The state of stress at a point in a loaded structure is defined by the following (3 × 3) real symmetric matrix:

$$[\sigma_{ij}] = \begin{bmatrix} 25 & 10 & -15 \\ 10 & 0 & 10 \\ -15 & 10 & 5 \end{bmatrix} (MPa)$$

Decompose this array into a set of dilatational (spherical) stresses and a set of deviator (distortional) stresses. Determine the values of the principal deviator stresses.

2.20. At a point in a stressed isotropic homogeneous body, the strains, related to a Cartesian coordinate system xyz, are given by the following tensor:

$$[\varepsilon_{ij}] = \begin{bmatrix} \varepsilon_x & \varepsilon_{xy} & \varepsilon_{xz} \\ \varepsilon_{yx} & \varepsilon_y & \varepsilon_{yz} \\ \varepsilon_{zx} & \varepsilon_{zy} & \varepsilon_z \end{bmatrix} = \begin{bmatrix} 4 & 1 & 0 \\ 1 & 0 & -2 \\ 0 & -2 & 6 \end{bmatrix} \times 10^{-6}.$$

a) Determine the principal strains ε_1, ε_2, and ε_3.
b) Determine the stress tensor $[\sigma_{ij}]$ at that point.
c) Determine the principal stresses σ_1, σ_2, and σ_3.
Assume that $E = 30 \times 10^6$ *psi* and $\nu = 0.3$.

2.21. A solid bronze sphere ($E = 110$ GPa, $\nu = \frac{1}{3}$, $r = 175$mm) is subjected to hydrostatic pressure p so that its volume is reduced by 0.45%. Determine:

a) the pressure p
b) the strain energy U stored in the sphere
(Note: the volume of a sphere is $V = \frac{4}{3}\pi r^3$.)

Further Reading

Beer, Ferdinand P., E. Russell Johnston, Jr., John T. DeWolf, and David. F. Mazurek. *Mechanics of Materials.* 7th ed. New York City: McGraw-Hill, 2015.

Budynas, Richard G. *Advanced Strength and Applied Stress Analysis.* New York City: McGraw-Hill, 1977.

Curtis, H. D. *Fundamentals of Aircraft Structural Analysis.* New York City: McGraw-Hill, 1997.

Donaldson, Bruce K. *Analysis of Aircraft Structures—An Introduction.* New York City: McGraw-Hill, 1993.

Roylance, David. *Mechanics of Materials.* Hoboken: Wiley, 1996.

Ugural, Ansel. C. *Mechanical Design: An Integrated Approach.* New York City: McGraw-Hill, 2004.

Ugural, Ansel C., and Saul K. Fenster. *Advanced Mechanics of Materials and Applied Elasticity.* 5th ed. Upper Saddle River: Prentice Hall, 2012.

CHAPTER 3

Theory of Elasticity

3.1 Introduction

The first course in mechanics of deformable bodies that college students take after studying statics is Strength of Materials. The term is a translation from the French of "Résistance des Matériaux." Strength of Materials is sometimes called Introduction to Mechanics of Deformable Bodies or Technical Theory. It is simple and much preferred by engineers, since it does not require advanced mathematics. However, the technical theory has many limitations and restrictions. It only covers simple structures and loadings, such as Euler-Bernoulli beam theory pertaining to straight beams having a span much larger than any of the other two dimensions of the cross section. Typically, in Strength of Materials we do not cover Timoshenko beam theory pertaining to stubby beams having a short span. Also, we do not cover in such an elementary course curved beams or more complex structures, such as plates and shells. In addition to that, the Strength of Materials course's approach cannot explain phenomena such as stress concentration. The elementary theory cannot predict the high values of stress in holes and notches, which are likely starting points of material failure. The stress in these regions can be analyzed using the theory of elasticity. Such theory can also be used to study plates, shells, and more complex structures. It is more general than the technical theory. However, it requires much more advanced mathematics. This chapter serves as an introduction to the theory of elasticity and, specifically, linear elasticity. Students who develop interest in it can later take an entire advanced course on the topic.

3.2 Elasticity 3D Problem

We saw in chapter 1 that the state of stress at point P in a body is completely defined by the (3×3) real symmetric matrix:

$$[\sigma_{ij}] = \begin{bmatrix} \sigma_x & \tau_{xy} & \tau_{xz} \\ \tau_{yx} & \sigma_y & \tau_{yz} \\ \tau_{zx} & \tau_{zy} & \sigma_z \end{bmatrix}.$$

In the above stress tensor, there are six quantities that need to be determined. These are σ_x, σ_y, σ_z, τ_{xy}, τ_{xz}, and τ_{yz}.

We also saw in chapter 2, and since the material is not rigid, that the state of strain at the same point P in the body is completely defined by the (3×3) real symmetric matrix:

$$[\varepsilon_{ij}] = \begin{bmatrix} \varepsilon_x & \varepsilon_{xy} & \varepsilon_{xz} \\ \varepsilon_{yx} & \varepsilon_y & \varepsilon_{yz} \\ \varepsilon_{zx} & \varepsilon_{zy} & \varepsilon_z \end{bmatrix}.$$

In the above strain tensor, there are six quantities that need to be determined. These are ε_x, ε_y, ε_z, ε_{xy}, ε_{xz}, and ε_{yz}.

Stress and strain are point functions. They usually vary from one specific point to an adjacent one.

We can also define three functions

$$u = u(x,y,z)$$

$$v = v(x,y,z)$$

$$w = w(x,y,z),$$

describing the displacement field that gives the displacement at every point of the body. u, v, and w determine the displacement of point P in the x, y, and z directions, respectively.

Therefore, at every point P in the body, we are interested in determining 15 quantities (15 unknowns): six stress components, six strain components, and three displacement components.

In order to solve for these 15 unknowns, we need 15 equations. These will be: three equilibrium equations, three kinematic relations, six stress–strain relationships.
The equilibrium equations are:

$$\frac{\partial \sigma_x}{\partial x} + \frac{\partial \tau_{yx}}{\partial y} + \frac{\partial \tau_{zx}}{\partial z} + F_x = 0$$

$$\frac{\partial \tau_{xy}}{\partial x} + \frac{\partial \sigma_y}{\partial y} + \frac{\partial \tau_{zy}}{\partial z} + F_y = 0$$

$$\frac{\partial \tau_{xz}}{\partial x} + \frac{\partial \tau_{yz}}{\partial y} + \frac{\partial \sigma_z}{\partial z} + F_z = 0.$$

The above three equilibrium equations are derived from Newton's first law:

$$\sum \vec{F} = \vec{0} \Leftrightarrow \begin{cases} \sum F_x = 0 \\ \sum F_y = 0 \\ \sum F_z = 0 \end{cases}.$$

They are simply Newton's equilibrium equations expressed in terms of stresses rather than forces.

Derivation of the Equilibrium Equations in the State of Plane Stress

Consider the following free body diagram (FBD) for an elementary differential element:

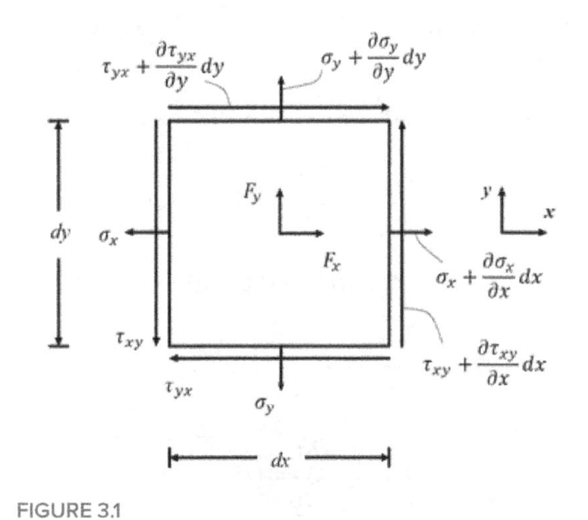

FIGURE 3.1

In the above FBD, F_x and F_y are body forces (dimension: $\frac{\text{Force}}{\text{Volume}}$; units: *N/m3, kips/in3*, etc.).

Also, notice that stresses (and not forces) are the ones shown in the above FBD. Newton's first law states that the sum of forces must be zero. Therefore, when applying it, stress must be converted into a force by multiplying it by the appropriate cross sectional area.

$$\sum \vec{F} = \vec{0} \Rightarrow \sum F_x = 0 \text{ and} \sum F_y = 0$$

$$\sum F_x = 0 \Rightarrow$$

$$\left(\sigma_x + \frac{\partial \sigma_x}{\partial x} dx\right) dydz - \sigma_x dydz + \left(\tau_{yx} + \frac{\partial \tau_{yx}}{\partial y} dy\right) dxdz - \tau_{yx} dxdz + F_x dxdydz = 0 \Rightarrow$$

$$\frac{\partial \sigma_x}{\partial x} dxdydz + \frac{\partial \tau_{yx}}{\partial y} dxdydz + F_x dxdydz = 0$$

Dividing the above equation by dxdydz, we obtain:

$$\frac{\partial \sigma_x}{\partial x} + \frac{\partial \tau_{yx}}{\partial y} + F_x = 0$$

$$\sum F_y = 0 \Rightarrow$$

$$\left(\sigma_y + \frac{\partial \sigma_y}{\partial y} dy\right) dxdz - \sigma_y dxdz + \left(\tau_{xy} + \frac{\partial \tau_{xy}}{\partial x} dx\right) dydz - \tau_{xy} dydz + F_y dxdydz = 0 \Rightarrow$$

$$\frac{\partial \sigma_y}{\partial y} dxdydz + \frac{\partial \tau_{xy}}{\partial x} dxdydz + F_y dxdydz = 0.$$

Dividing the above equation by dxdydz, we obtain:

$$\frac{\partial \tau_{xy}}{\partial x} + \frac{\partial \sigma_y}{\partial y} + F_y = 0.$$

Therefore, the equilibrium equations in the state of plane stress can be written as:

$$\frac{\partial \sigma_x}{\partial x} + \frac{\partial \tau_{yx}}{\partial y} + F_x = 0$$

$$\frac{\partial \tau_{xy}}{\partial x} + \frac{\partial \sigma_y}{\partial y} + F_y = 0.$$

It is very clear to see how these two equilibrium equations in the state of plane stress can be generalized to the following three equations in the 3D case:

$$\frac{\partial \sigma_x}{\partial x} + \frac{\partial \tau_{yx}}{\partial y} + \frac{\partial \tau_{zx}}{\partial z} + F_x = 0$$

$$\frac{\partial \tau_{xy}}{\partial x} + \frac{\partial \sigma_y}{\partial y} + \frac{\partial \tau_{zy}}{\partial z} + F_y = 0$$

$$\frac{\partial \tau_{xz}}{\partial x} + \frac{\partial \tau_{yz}}{\partial y} + \frac{\partial \sigma_z}{\partial z} + F_z = 0.$$

The above equations are Newton's first law in the x, y, and z directions, respectively. Also, notice that each term in them has the dimension of $\frac{\text{force}}{\text{volume}}$ $\left(\frac{N}{m^3}, \frac{lb_f}{ft^3}, \text{etc.}\right)$.

Strain–displacement relations of continuum mechanics are as follows:

$$\varepsilon_x = \frac{\partial u}{\partial x} \qquad \varepsilon_y = \frac{\partial v}{\partial y} \qquad \varepsilon_z = \frac{\partial w}{\partial z}$$

$$\gamma_{xy} = 2\varepsilon_{xy} = \frac{\partial u}{\partial y} + \frac{\partial v}{\partial x} \qquad \gamma_{xz} = 2\varepsilon_{xz} = \frac{\partial u}{\partial z} + \frac{\partial w}{\partial x} \qquad \gamma_{yz} = 2\varepsilon_{yz} = \frac{\partial v}{\partial z} + \frac{\partial w}{\partial y}.$$

The above six relations are called the kinematic* relations. They describe the geometry of strain.

* They are called "Kinematic" since no stresses (or forces) are involved in them. In Dynamics, kinematics is the study of the geometry of motion (relationship among position vector $\vec{r}$, velocity vector $\vec{v}$, and acceleration vector $\vec{a}$ without any reference to what causes the motion (no forces involved)). In Fluid Mechanics, kinematic viscosity ν has the unit of $\frac{m^2}{s}$ (no mass or force involved) while dynamic viscosity μ has the unit of $\frac{Ns}{m^2} = \frac{kg}{ms}$ (mass or force involved).

Stress–Strain Relationships

Assuming that the material is homogeneous, isotropic, and behaving in the linearly elastic range, we can use Hooke's generalized laws:

$$\varepsilon_x = \frac{\sigma_x}{E} - \frac{\nu}{E}(\sigma_y + \sigma_z) \qquad \gamma_{xy} = \frac{\tau_{xy}}{G}$$

$$\varepsilon_y = \frac{\sigma_y}{E} - \frac{\nu}{E}(\sigma_x + \sigma_z) \qquad \gamma_{xz} = \frac{\tau_{xz}}{G}$$

$$\varepsilon_z = \frac{\sigma_z}{E} - \frac{\nu}{E}(\sigma_x + \sigma_y) \qquad \gamma_{yz} = \frac{\tau_{yz}}{G}.$$

The above six relations relate stress to strain.

Thus, a 3D elasticity problem boils down to solving 15 equations (three equilibrium equations, six kinematic relations, and six stress–strain relationships) simultaneously for the 15 unknowns (six stress components, six strain components, and three displacement components).

The compatibility equations are as follows:

$$\varepsilon_x = \frac{\partial u}{\partial x} \Rightarrow \frac{\partial^2 \varepsilon_x}{\partial y^2} = \frac{\partial^2}{\partial y^2}\left(\frac{\partial u}{\partial x}\right) = \frac{\partial^3 u}{\partial y^2\, \partial x}$$

$$\varepsilon_y = \frac{\partial v}{\partial y} \Rightarrow \frac{\partial^2 \varepsilon_y}{\partial x^2} = \frac{\partial^2}{\partial x^2}\left(\frac{\partial v}{\partial y}\right) = \frac{\partial^3 v}{\partial x^2\, \partial y}.$$

Therefore,

$$\frac{\partial^2 \varepsilon_x}{\partial y^2} + \frac{\partial^2 \varepsilon_y}{\partial x^2} = \frac{\partial^3 u}{\partial y^2\, \partial x} + \frac{\partial^3 v}{\partial x^2\, \partial y} = \frac{\partial^2}{\partial x\, \partial y}\left(\frac{\partial u}{\partial y} + \frac{\partial v}{\partial x}\right) = \frac{\partial^2 \gamma_{xy}}{\partial x\, \partial y}.$$

We conclude that:

$$\frac{\partial^2 \varepsilon_x}{\partial y^2} + \frac{\partial^2 \varepsilon_y}{\partial x^2} = \frac{\partial^2 \gamma_{xy}}{\partial x\, \partial y}.$$

The above equation is called a compatibility equation. Similarly, we can derive five more equations in order to obtain the following six compatibility equations:

$$\frac{\partial^2 \varepsilon_x}{\partial y^2} + \frac{\partial^2 \varepsilon_y}{\partial x^2} = \frac{\partial^2 \gamma_{xy}}{\partial x \partial y} \qquad 2\frac{\partial^2 \varepsilon_x}{\partial y \partial z} = \frac{\partial}{\partial x}\left(-\frac{\partial \gamma_{yz}}{\partial x} + \frac{\partial \gamma_{xz}}{\partial y} + \frac{\partial \gamma_{xy}}{\partial z}\right)$$

$$\frac{\partial^2 \varepsilon_y}{\partial z^2} + \frac{\partial^2 \varepsilon_z}{\partial y^2} = \frac{\partial^2 \gamma_{yz}}{\partial y \partial z} \qquad 2\frac{\partial^2 \varepsilon_y}{\partial z \partial x} = \frac{\partial}{\partial y}\left(\frac{\partial \gamma_{yz}}{\partial x} - \frac{\partial \gamma_{xz}}{\partial y} + \frac{\partial \gamma_{xy}}{\partial z}\right)$$

$$\frac{\partial^2 \varepsilon_z}{\partial x^2} + \frac{\partial^2 \varepsilon_x}{\partial z^2} = \frac{\partial^2 \gamma_{xz}}{\partial z \partial x} \qquad 2\frac{\partial^2 \varepsilon_z}{\partial x \partial y} = \frac{\partial}{\partial z}\left(\frac{\partial \gamma_{yz}}{\partial x} + \frac{\partial \gamma_{xz}}{\partial y} - \frac{\partial \gamma_{xy}}{\partial z}\right).$$

The six kinematic relations may be replaced by the above six compatibility equations. The physical interpretation of the compatibility equations is that the body must be pieced together. The mathematical interpretation is that $u = u_{(x,y,z)}$, $v = v_{(x,y,z)}$, and $w = w_{(x,y,z)}$ are single-valued and continuous functions.

Thus, we have 15 equations (three equilibrium equations, six kinematic relations, and six stress–strain relationships) in order to solve for the 15 unknowns. Alternatively, these 15 equations can be replaced by three equilibrium equations, six compatibility equations, and six stress–strain relationships.

Indicial Notation

Indicial notation can be used to simplify the writing of elasticity equations. i, j, and k are indices that can take the values of 1, 2, and 3. The index (or subscript) 1 replaces x, 2 replaces y, and 3 replaces z. A comma in a term denotes a partial derivative. A repeating index in a term implies summation. Using such rules, the 15 linear elasticity equations for a homogeneous isotropic material referred to in this section can be written in a more compact indicial notation:

$$\sigma_{ij,j} + F_i = 0 \text{ (the 3 equilibrium equations)}$$

$$\varepsilon_{ij} = \frac{1}{2}\left(u_{i,j} + u_{j,i}\right) \text{ (the 6 kinematic equations)}$$

$$\varepsilon_{ij} = \frac{1+\nu}{E}\sigma_{ij} - \frac{\nu}{E}\sigma_{kk}\delta_{ij} \text{ (the stress–strain relationship),}$$

where δ_{ij} is "Kronecker delta" defined by:

$$\delta_{ij} = \begin{cases} 1 \text{ if } i = j \\ 0 \text{ if } i \neq j \end{cases}.$$

For example, in order to see how $\sigma_{ij,j} + F_i = 0$, indeed, generates the three equilibrium equations:

$$\frac{\partial \sigma_x}{\partial x} + \frac{\partial \tau_{yx}}{\partial y} + \frac{\partial \tau_{zx}}{\partial z} + F_x = 0$$

$$\frac{\partial \tau_{xy}}{\partial x} + \frac{\partial \sigma_y}{\partial y} + \frac{\partial \tau_{zy}}{\partial z} + F_y = 0$$

$$\frac{\partial \tau_{xz}}{\partial x} + \frac{\partial \tau_{yz}}{\partial y} + \frac{\partial \sigma_z}{\partial z} + F_z = 0.$$

In $\sigma_{ij,j} + F_i = 0$, for $i = 1$:

$$\sigma_{1j,j} + F_1 = 0$$

$$\Rightarrow \sigma_{11,1} + \sigma_{12,2} + \sigma_{13,3} + F_1 = 0$$

$$\Rightarrow \frac{\partial \sigma_x}{\partial x} + \frac{\partial \tau_{yx}}{\partial y} + \frac{\partial \tau_{zx}}{\partial z} + F_x = 0.$$

The remaining two equilibrium equations can be obtained by letting $i = 2$ and then $i = 3$.

The reader can easily verify how the remaining 12 equations can be generated. Indicial notation is used to make the equations in theory of elasticity more compact and elegant. It is also used in other branches of physics and engineering, such as Einstein theory. Indicial notation will not be used in this textbook, since we will not encounter tensors of rank (or order) higher than two. Matrix algebra and vector algebra will be adequate. In topics where tensors of high order are encountered, usage of indicial notation will become necessary.

3.3 Elasticity 2D Problem

As stated in the previous section, a 3D elasticity problem requires solving 15 equations with 15 unknowns. This is a formidable task not easy to accomplish. Fortunately, many practical elasticity problems can be reduced into 2D ones. A state of plane stress is one in which we suppress the third row and third column in the (3×3) $[\sigma_{ij}]$matrix, thus letting $\sigma_z = \tau_{xz} = \tau_{yz} = 0$. On the other hand, a state of plane strain is one in which we suppress the third row and third column in the (3×3) $[\varepsilon_{ij}]$ matrix, thus letting $\varepsilon_z = \varepsilon_{xz} = \varepsilon_{yz} = 0$.

For a plane state (plane stress or plane strain), the equilibrium and compatibility equations can be enormously simplified.

3.3.1 Compatibility Equation for the State of Plane Stress

The following compatibility equation

$$\frac{\partial^2 \varepsilon_x}{\partial y^2} + \frac{\partial^2 \varepsilon_y}{\partial x^2} = \frac{\partial^2 \gamma_{xy}}{\partial x \, \partial y} \tag{3.1}$$

can be expressed in a more convenient form for a state of plane stress. Hooke's generalized laws can be written for such a state:

$$\varepsilon_x = \frac{\sigma_x}{E} - \frac{\nu}{E}\sigma_y$$

$$\varepsilon_y = \frac{\sigma_y}{E} - \frac{\nu}{E}\sigma_x$$

$$\gamma_{xy} = \frac{\tau_{xy}}{G} = 2(1+\nu)\frac{\tau_{xy}}{E}.$$

Inserting these in equations (3.1), we obtain:

$$\frac{\partial^2}{\partial y^2}(\sigma_x - \nu\sigma_y) + \frac{\partial^2}{\partial x^2}(\sigma_y - \nu\sigma_x) = 2(1+\nu)\frac{\partial^2 \tau_{xy}}{\partial x \, \partial y}.$$

However, the equilibrium equations for a state of plane stress are:

$$\frac{\partial \sigma_x}{\partial x} + \frac{\partial \tau_{xy}}{\partial y} + F_x = 0$$

$$\frac{\partial \tau_{xy}}{\partial x} + \frac{\partial \sigma_y}{\partial y} + F_y = 0,$$

which can be written as:

$$\frac{\partial^2 \sigma_x}{\partial x^2} + \frac{\partial^2 \tau_{xy}}{\partial x \, \partial y} + \frac{\partial F_x}{\partial x} = 0$$

$$\frac{\partial^2 \tau_{xy}}{\partial x \, \partial y} + \frac{\partial^2 \sigma_y}{\partial y^2} + \frac{\partial F_y}{\partial y} = 0.$$

Adding the above equations member to member, we conclude that:

$$2\frac{\partial^2 \tau_{xy}}{\partial x \partial y} = -\frac{\partial^2 \sigma_x}{\partial x^2} - \frac{\partial^2 \sigma_y}{\partial y^2} - \frac{\partial F_x}{\partial x} - \frac{\partial F_y}{\partial y}.$$

Inserting this into the previous compatibility equation and after manipulation, we obtain:

$$\left(\frac{\partial^2}{\partial x^2} + \frac{\partial^2}{\partial y^2}\right)(\sigma_x + \sigma_y) = -(1+\nu)\left(\frac{\partial F_x}{\partial x} + \frac{\partial F_y}{\partial y}\right). \tag{3.2}$$

3.3.2 Compatibility Equation for the State of Plane Strain

Similarly, it can be shown that for a state of plane strain, the compatibility equation can be written as:

$$\left(\frac{\partial^2}{\partial x^2} + \frac{\partial^2}{\partial y^2}\right)(\sigma_x + \sigma_y) = -\left(\frac{1}{1-\nu}\right)\left(\frac{\partial F_x}{\partial x} + \frac{\partial F_y}{\partial y}\right). \tag{3.3}$$

3.3.3 The Biharmonic Equation

When ignoring body forces (which is often the case), the compatibility equation for a state of plane stress or a state of plane strain can be written as:

$$\left(\frac{\partial^2}{\partial x^2} + \frac{\partial^2}{\partial y^2}\right)(\sigma_x + \sigma_y) = 0.$$

G. B. Airy[1] introduced a stress function ϕ (called Airy stress function) such that:

$$\sigma_x = \frac{\partial^2 \phi}{\partial y^2};\ \sigma_y = \frac{\partial^2 \phi}{\partial x^2};\ \tau_{xy} = -\frac{\partial^2 \phi}{\partial x \partial y}. \tag{3.4}$$

Notice that defining ϕ as in (3.4) will force the equilibrium equations to be satisfied:

$$\frac{\partial \sigma_x}{\partial x} + \frac{\partial \tau_{xy}}{\partial y} = \frac{\partial}{\partial x}\left(\frac{\partial^2 \phi}{\partial y^2}\right) + \frac{\partial}{\partial y}\left(-\frac{\partial^2 \phi}{\partial x \partial y}\right) = 0$$

---

1 Sir George Biddell Airy (1801–1892) was an English mathematician and astronomer. He also contributed to solid mechanics and the theory of elasticity.

$$\frac{\partial \tau_{xy}}{\partial x} + \frac{\partial \sigma_y}{\partial y} = \frac{\partial}{\partial x}\left(-\frac{\partial^2 \phi}{\partial x \partial y}\right) + \frac{\partial}{\partial y}\left(\frac{\partial^2 \phi}{\partial x^2}\right) = 0.$$

Using (3.4), the compatibility equation becomes:

$$\left(\frac{\partial^2}{\partial x^2} + \frac{\partial^2}{\partial y^2}\right)\left(\frac{\partial^2 \phi}{\partial x^2} + \frac{\partial^2 \phi}{\partial y^2}\right) = 0$$

$$or\, \nabla^2(\nabla^2 \phi) = 0$$

$$or\, \nabla^4 \phi = 0. \tag{3.5}$$

$\frac{\partial^2}{\partial x^2} + \frac{\partial^2}{\partial y^2}$ is the two-dimensional Laplacian operator, and (3.5) is called the biharmonic equation. In mathematics, the second order PDE $\nabla^2 \Psi = 0$ is called Laplace equation. A function $\Psi_{(x,y)}$ satisfying Laplace equation is called a harmonic function. (3.5) is a fourth order PDE, and the Laplacian of the Laplacian of ϕ is zero. For this reason, it is called the biharmonic equation.

Thus, the 15 equations and 15 unknowns in the 3D elasticity problem have been reduced, for a state of plane stress or a state of plane strain and ignoring body forces, into a single fourth-order partial differential equation (the biharmonic equation) satisfying given boundary conditions. The problem is known in mathematics as a BVP (boundary value problem).

3.4 Basic Relations in Polar Coordinates

In the previous sections, Cartesian (rectangular) coordinates were used. However, geometry of the problem dictates what type of coordinates we need to use. Often, we must use polar coordinates for 2D problems in elasticity.

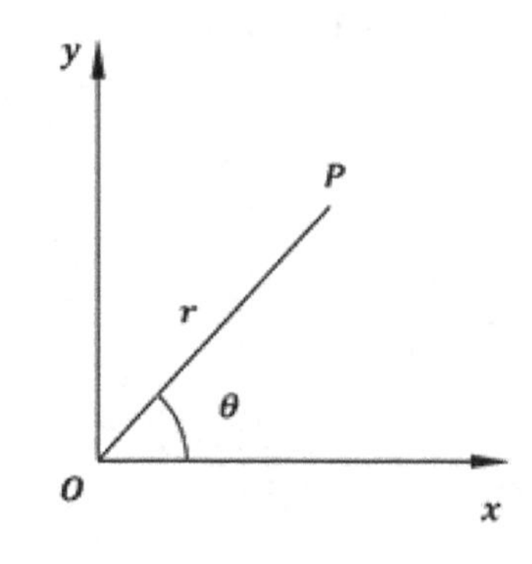

FIGURE 3.2

The equations of transformation that take us from polar coordinates to Cartesian coordinates are:

$$x = r\cos\theta$$
$$y = r\sin\theta.$$

The above relations can be inverted as:

$$r = \sqrt{x^2 + y^2}$$
$$\theta = \tan^{-1}\left(\frac{y}{x}\right),$$

which are the equations of transformation that take us from Cartesian coordinates to polar coordinates.

Below are basic relations in polar coordinates:

The equations of equilibrium are:

$$\frac{\partial \sigma_r}{\partial r} + \frac{1}{r}\frac{\partial \tau_{r\theta}}{\partial \theta} + \frac{\sigma_r - \sigma_\theta}{r} + F_r = 0$$
$$\frac{1}{r}\frac{\partial \sigma_\theta}{\partial \theta} + \frac{\partial \tau_{r\theta}}{\partial r} + \frac{2\tau_{r\theta}}{r} + F_\theta = 0.$$

In the absence of body forces, the above equations are satisfied by an Airy stress function $\phi(r, \theta)$ for which:

$$\sigma_r = \frac{1}{r}\frac{\partial \phi}{\partial r} + \frac{1}{r^2}\frac{\partial^2 \phi}{\partial \theta^2}$$
$$\sigma_\theta = \frac{\partial^2 \phi}{\partial r^2}$$
$$\tau_{r\theta} = \frac{1}{r^2}\frac{\partial \phi}{\partial \theta} - \frac{1}{r}\frac{\partial^2 \phi}{\partial r\,\partial \theta} = -\frac{\partial}{\partial r}\left(\frac{1}{r}\frac{\partial \phi}{\partial \theta}\right).$$

The strain–displacement relations are:

$$\varepsilon_r = \frac{\partial u}{\partial r}$$
$$\varepsilon_\theta = \frac{1}{r}\frac{\partial v}{\partial \theta} + \frac{u}{r}$$

$$\gamma_{r\theta} = \frac{\partial v}{\partial r} + \frac{1}{r}\frac{\partial u}{\partial \theta} - \frac{v}{r}$$

Hooke's Laws

Equations of Hooke's laws are presented below.

- Plane stress:

$$\varepsilon_r = \frac{1}{E}(\sigma_r - \nu\sigma_\theta)$$

$$\varepsilon_\theta = \frac{1}{E}(\sigma_\theta - \nu\sigma_r)$$

$$\gamma_{r\theta} = \frac{1}{G}\tau_{r\theta}$$

- Plane strain:

$$\varepsilon_r = \frac{1+\nu}{E}\left[(1-\nu)\sigma_r - \nu\sigma_\theta\right]$$

$$\varepsilon_\theta = \frac{1+\nu}{E}\left[(1-\nu)\sigma_\theta - \nu\sigma_r\right]$$

$$\gamma_{r\theta} = \frac{1}{G}\tau_{r\theta}$$

- Compatibility equation:

$$\frac{\partial^2 \varepsilon_\theta}{\partial r^2} + \frac{1}{r^2}\frac{\partial^2 \varepsilon_r}{\partial \theta^2} + \frac{2}{r}\frac{\partial \varepsilon_\theta}{\partial r} - \frac{1}{r}\frac{\partial \varepsilon_r}{\partial r} = \frac{1}{r}\frac{\partial^2 \gamma_{r\theta}}{\partial r\,\partial \theta} + \frac{1}{r^2}\frac{\partial \gamma_{r\theta}}{\partial \theta}$$

- Laplacian operator:

$$\nabla^2 \equiv \frac{\partial^2}{\partial r^2} + \frac{1}{r}\frac{\partial}{\partial r} + \frac{1}{r^2}\frac{\partial^2}{\partial \theta^2}$$

- The Biharmonic equation:

$$\nabla^4\phi = \nabla^2(\nabla^2\phi) = \left(\frac{\partial^2}{\partial r^2} + \frac{1}{r}\frac{\partial}{\partial r} + \frac{1}{r^2}\frac{\partial^2}{\partial \theta^2}\right)\left(\frac{\partial^2\phi}{\partial r^2} + \frac{1}{r}\frac{\partial\phi}{\partial r} + \frac{1}{r^2}\frac{\partial^2\phi}{\partial \theta^2}\right) = 0$$

3.5 Practice Problems

Problem 3.5-1

Determine whether the following state of plane stress within an elastic solid is admissible (A is a nonzero constant). Ignore body forces. $\sigma_x = 2Ax^2$; $\sigma_y = 2A(4x^2 + y^2)$; $\tau_{xy} = -4Axy$.

Solution

First, let us check the equilibrium equations. In the absence of body forces, the equilibrium equations for a state of plane stress are:

$$\frac{\partial \sigma_x}{\partial x} + \frac{\partial \tau_{xy}}{\partial y} = 0$$

$$\frac{\partial \tau_{xy}}{\partial x} + \frac{\partial \sigma_y}{\partial y} = 0.$$

We can easily see that:

$$4Ax - 4Ax = 0 \checkmark$$

$$-4Ay + 4Ay = 0 \checkmark.$$

Therefore, the equilibrium equations are satisfied.

Next, let us check the compatibility equation. In the absence of body forces, the compatibility equation is:

$$\left(\frac{\partial^2}{\partial x^2} + \frac{\partial^2}{\partial y^2}\right)(\sigma_x + \sigma_y) = 0$$

$$\left(\frac{\partial^2}{\partial x^2} + \frac{\partial^2}{\partial y^2}\right)(\sigma_x + \sigma_y) = \left(\frac{\partial^2}{\partial x^2} + \frac{\partial^2}{\partial y^2}\right)(10Ax^2 + 2Ay^2)$$

$$= 24A$$

$$\neq 0.$$

Therefore, the compatibility equation is not satisfied. We conclude that the given state of plane stress is not admissible.

Problem 3.5-2

The state of plane stress in the thin square plate shown in the figure below with Young's modulus of elasticity E and Poisson's ratio ν is defined by:

$$\sigma_x = 0; \qquad \sigma_y = 0; \qquad \tau_{xy} = \tau_o,$$

where τ_o has the unit of stress. Use elasticity theory to find the components of displacement at point A if $u = v = \frac{\partial v}{\partial x} = 0$ at point O.

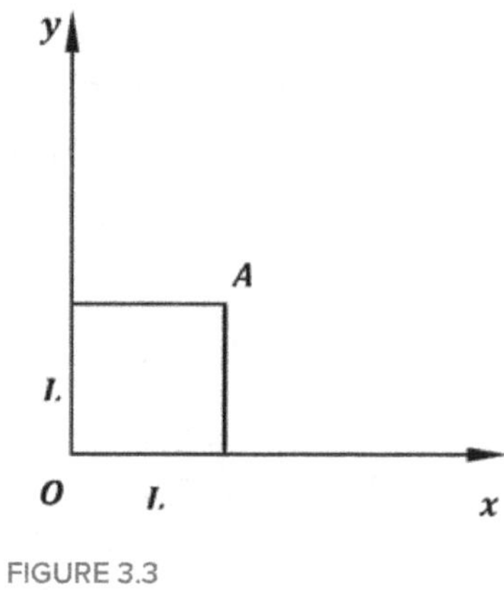

FIGURE 3.3

Solution

First, notice that the equilibrium equations in the absence of body forces

$$\frac{\partial \sigma_x}{\partial x} + \frac{\partial \tau_{xy}}{\partial y} = 0$$

$$\frac{\partial \tau_{xy}}{\partial x} + \frac{\partial \sigma_y}{\partial y} = 0$$

are satisfied.

The compatibility equation:

$$\frac{\partial^2 \sigma_x}{\partial y^2} + \frac{\partial^2 \sigma_y}{\partial x^2} - \nu\left(\frac{\partial^2 \sigma_x}{\partial x^2} + \frac{\partial^2 \sigma_y}{\partial y^2}\right) \quad 2(1+\nu)\frac{\partial^2 \tau_{xy}}{\partial x \partial y} = 0$$

is also satisfied.

Therefore, both the equilibrium equations and the compatibility equation are satisfied.

The strategy to work out such a problem is first to determine strain from stress (using Hooke's Generalized Laws). Then, we can determine displacement from strain (using the kinematic relations).

$$\varepsilon_x = \frac{\sigma_x}{E} - \frac{\nu}{E}\sigma_y = 0$$

$$\varepsilon_y = \frac{\sigma_y}{E} - \frac{\nu}{E}\sigma_x = 0$$

$$\gamma_{xy} = \frac{\tau_{xy}}{G} = 2(1+\nu)\frac{\tau_o}{E}$$

$$\varepsilon_x = 0 \Rightarrow \frac{\partial u}{\partial x} = 0 \Rightarrow u = f(y)$$

$$\varepsilon_y = 0 \Rightarrow \frac{\partial v}{\partial y} = 0 \Rightarrow v = g(x)$$

$$\gamma_{xy} = \frac{\partial u}{\partial y} + \frac{\partial v}{\partial x} = 2(1+\nu)\frac{\tau_o}{E}$$

$$\Rightarrow \frac{df}{dy} + \frac{dg}{dx} = 2(1+\nu)\frac{\tau_0}{E}$$

$$\Rightarrow \frac{dg}{dx} = 2(1+\nu)\frac{\tau_o}{E} - \frac{df}{dy}$$

The left-hand side is a function of x only, while the right-hand side is a function of y only. This can be true iff both sides are equal to a constant C (independent of both x and y).

$$\frac{dg}{dx} = C \Rightarrow g = Cx + D$$

$$\frac{df}{dy} = 2(1+\nu)\frac{\tau_o}{E} - C \Rightarrow f = 2(1+\nu)\frac{\tau_o}{E}y - Cy + F$$

Therefore,

$$u = 2(1+\nu)\frac{\tau_o}{E}y - Cy + F$$

$$v = Cx + D$$

$$\frac{\partial v}{\partial x} = C.$$

At point O (x = 0 and y = 0):

$$u = 0 \Rightarrow F = 0$$

$$v = 0 \Rightarrow D = 0$$

$$\frac{\partial v}{\partial x} = 0 \Rightarrow C = 0.$$

We conclude that at point A (x – L, y = L):

$$u = 2(1 + \nu)\frac{\tau_o}{E}L$$

$$v = 0$$

Notice that everything we write down should be dimensionally homogeneous. u has the dimension of length. In the SI system, the unit of u will be: $\frac{N/m^2}{N/m^2}m = m.$

Problem 3.5-3

Show that, in the absence of body forces, the equilibrium equations for the case of plane stress can be written as:

$$\frac{\partial^2 u}{\partial x^2} + \frac{\partial^2 u}{\partial y^2} + \frac{1+\nu}{1-\nu}\frac{\partial}{\partial x}\left(\frac{\partial u}{\partial x} + \frac{\partial v}{\partial y}\right) = 0$$

$$\frac{\partial^2 v}{\partial y^2} + \frac{\partial^2 v}{\partial x^2} + \frac{1+v}{1-\nu}\frac{\partial}{\partial y}\left(\frac{\partial v}{\partial y} + \frac{\partial u}{\partial x}\right) = 0.$$

Solution

Newton's equilibrium equations (Newton's first law) are:

$$\Sigma\vec{F} = \vec{0} \Rightarrow \begin{cases} \Sigma F_x = 0 \\ \Sigma F_y = 0 \end{cases}$$

The above are the equilibrium equations written in terms of forces.

In the absence of body forces, the equilibrium equations for the case of plane stress become:

$$\frac{\partial \sigma_x}{\partial x} + \frac{\partial \tau_{xy}}{\partial y} = 0 \text{ and } \frac{\partial \tau_{xy}}{\partial x} + \frac{\partial \sigma_y}{\partial y} = 0.$$

The above are the same equilibrium equations but now written in terms of stresses. Hooke's laws are:

$$\varepsilon_x = \frac{\sigma_x}{E} - \frac{\nu}{E}\sigma_y$$

$$\varepsilon_y = \frac{\sigma_y}{E} - \frac{\nu}{E}\sigma_x$$

$$\gamma_{xy} = \frac{\tau_{xy}}{G}$$

Therefore,

$$\sigma_x = \frac{E}{1-\nu^2}(\varepsilon_x + \nu\varepsilon_y)$$

$$\sigma_y = \frac{E}{1-\nu^2}(\varepsilon_y + \nu\varepsilon_x)$$

$$\tau_{xy} = \frac{E}{2(1+\nu)}\gamma_{xy}$$

⇒ The equilibrium equations become:

$$\frac{\partial}{\partial x}\left[\frac{E}{1-\nu^2}(\varepsilon_x + \nu\varepsilon_y)\right] + \frac{\partial}{\partial y}\left[\frac{E}{2(1+\nu)}\gamma_{xy}\right] = 0$$

$$\frac{\partial}{\partial x}\left[\frac{E}{2(1+\nu)}\gamma_{xy}\right] + \frac{\partial}{\partial y}\left[\frac{E}{1-\nu^2}(\varepsilon_y + \nu\varepsilon_x)\right] = 0.$$

The above equilibrium equations are written in terms of strains.
Let us manipulate the first equation:

$$\frac{E}{(1-\nu)(1+\nu)}\left(\frac{\partial \varepsilon_x}{\partial x} + \nu\frac{\partial \varepsilon_y}{\partial x}\right) + \frac{E}{2(1+\nu)}\frac{\partial \gamma_{xy}}{\partial y} = 0$$

$$\Rightarrow \frac{1}{(1-\nu)}\left(\frac{\partial \varepsilon_x}{\partial x}+\nu\frac{\partial \varepsilon_y}{\partial x}\right)+\frac{1}{2}\frac{\partial \gamma_{xy}}{\partial y}=0$$

$$\Rightarrow \frac{2}{(1-\nu)}\left(\frac{\partial \varepsilon_x}{\partial x}+\nu\frac{\partial \varepsilon_y}{\partial x}\right)+\frac{\partial \gamma_{xy}}{\partial y}=0.$$

However,

$$\varepsilon_x=\frac{\partial u}{\partial x};\ \varepsilon_y=\frac{\partial v}{\partial y};\gamma_{xy}=\frac{\partial u}{\partial y}+\frac{\partial v}{\partial x}$$

$$\Rightarrow \frac{1-\nu+1+\nu}{(1-\nu)}\left(\frac{\partial^2 u}{\partial x^2}+\nu\frac{\partial^2 v}{\partial x\partial y}\right)+\frac{\partial}{\partial y}\left(\frac{\partial u}{\partial y}+\frac{\partial v}{\partial x}\right)=0$$

$$\Rightarrow \left(1+\frac{1+\nu}{1-\nu}\right)\left(\frac{\partial^2 u}{\partial x^2}+\nu\frac{\partial^2 v}{\partial x\partial y}\right)+\frac{\partial^2 u}{\partial y^2}+\frac{\partial^2 v}{\partial x\partial y}=0$$

$$\Rightarrow \frac{\partial^2 u}{\partial x^2}+\nu\frac{\partial^2 v}{\partial x\partial y}+\frac{1+\nu}{1-\nu}\frac{\partial^2 u}{\partial x^2}+\nu\frac{1+\nu}{1-\nu}\frac{\partial^2 v}{\partial x\partial y}+\frac{\partial^2 u}{\partial y^2}+\frac{\partial^2 v}{\partial x\partial y}=0$$

$$\Rightarrow \frac{\partial^2 u}{\partial x^2}+\frac{\partial^2 u}{\partial y^2}+\frac{1+\nu}{1-\nu}\frac{\partial^2 u}{\partial x^2}+\frac{1+\nu}{1-\nu}\frac{\partial^2 v}{\partial x\partial y}=0$$

$$\Rightarrow \frac{\partial^2 u}{\partial x^2}+\frac{\partial^2 u}{\partial y^2}+\frac{1+\nu}{1-\nu}\frac{\partial}{\partial x}\left(\frac{\partial u}{\partial x}+\frac{\partial v}{\partial y}\right)=0.$$

Similarly, the second equation can be manipulated. Finally, we obtain the following equilibrium equations:

$$\frac{\partial^2 u}{\partial x^2}+\frac{\partial^2 u}{\partial y^2}+\frac{1+\nu}{1-\nu}\frac{\partial}{\partial x}\left(\frac{\partial u}{\partial x}+\frac{\partial v}{\partial y}\right)=0$$

$$\frac{\partial^2 v}{\partial y^2}+\frac{\partial^2 v}{\partial x^2}+\frac{1+\nu}{1-\nu}\frac{\partial}{\partial y}\left(\frac{\partial v}{\partial y}+\frac{\partial u}{\partial x}\right)=0,$$

and the above equilibrium equations are now written in terms of displacements.

In summary, the following are the equilibrium equations for a state of plane stress (neglecting body forces):

$$\sum \vec{F} = \vec{0}$$

$$\Downarrow$$

$$\sum F_x = 0$$

$$\sum F_y = 0$$

$$\Downarrow$$

$$\frac{\partial \sigma_x}{\partial x} + \frac{\partial \tau_{yx}}{\partial y} = 0$$

$$\frac{\partial \tau_{xy}}{\partial x} + \frac{\partial \sigma_y}{\partial y} = 0$$

$$\Downarrow$$

$$\frac{\partial}{\partial x}\left[\frac{E}{1-\nu^2}(\varepsilon_x + \nu\varepsilon_y)\right] + \frac{\partial}{\partial y}\left[\frac{E}{2(1+\nu)}\gamma_{xy}\right] = 0$$

$$\frac{\partial}{\partial x}\left[\frac{E}{2(1+\nu)}\gamma_{xy}\right] + \frac{\partial}{\partial y}\left[\frac{E}{1-\nu^2}(\varepsilon_y + \nu\varepsilon_x)\right] = 0$$

$$\Downarrow$$

$$\frac{\partial^2 u}{\partial x^2} + \frac{\partial^2 u}{\partial y^2} + \frac{1+\nu}{1-\nu}\frac{\partial}{\partial x}\left(\frac{\partial u}{\partial x} + \frac{\partial v}{\partial y}\right) = 0$$

$$\frac{\partial^2 v}{\partial y^2} + \frac{\partial^2 v}{\partial x^2} + \frac{1+\nu}{1-\nu}\frac{\partial}{\partial y}\left(\frac{\partial v}{\partial y} + \frac{\partial u}{\partial x}\right) = 0$$

written in terms of forces, stresses, strains, and displacements respectively.

Problem 3.5-4

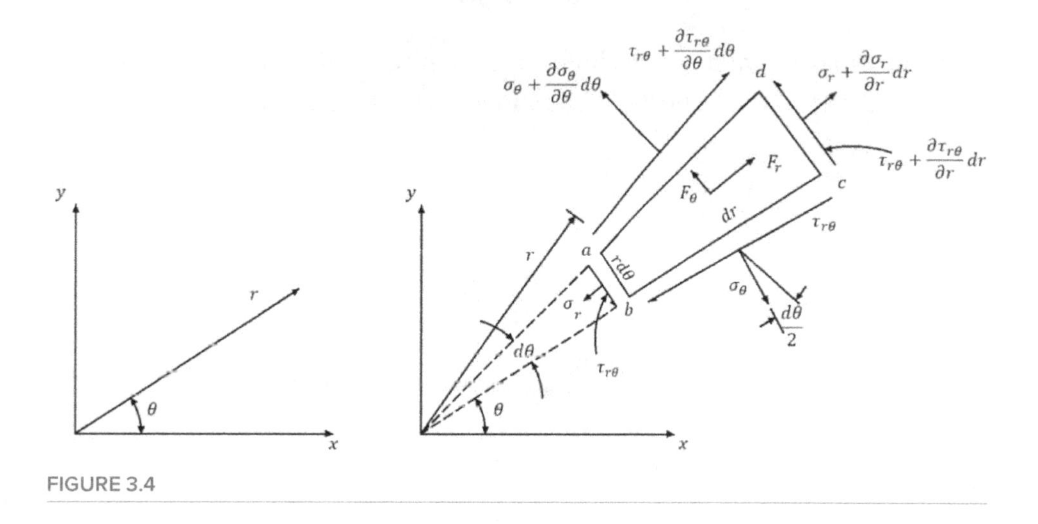

FIGURE 3.4

Show that the equations of equilibrium in polar coordinates take the following form:

$$\frac{\partial \sigma_r}{\partial r} + \frac{1}{r}\frac{\partial \tau_{r\theta}}{\partial \theta} + \frac{\sigma_r - \sigma_\theta}{r} + F_r = 0$$

$$\frac{1}{r}\frac{\partial \sigma_\theta}{\partial \theta} + \frac{\partial \tau_{r\theta}}{\partial r} + \frac{2\tau_{r\theta}}{r} + F_\theta = 0.$$

Solution

When we derived the equations of equilibrium in Cartesian (rectangular) coordinates, we considered an elementary differential element that lay between x and $x + dx$, y and $y + dy$, as shown in the figure below.

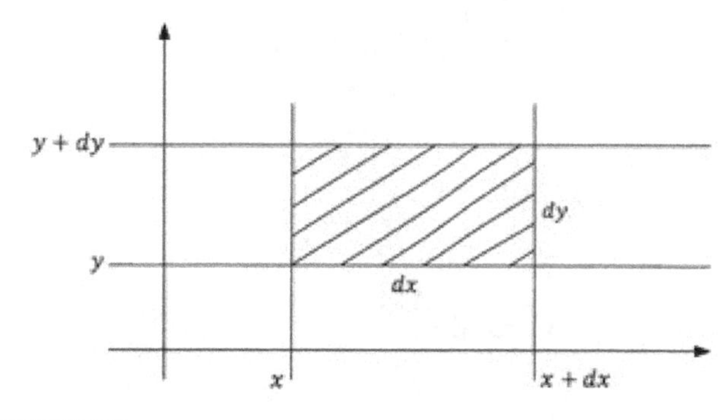

FIGURE 3.5

dA for such elementary differential element (a rectangle) is:

$$dA = dxdy.$$

In polar coordinates, we must consider an elementary differential element that lies between r and r + dr and θ and θ + dθ, as shown in the figure below.

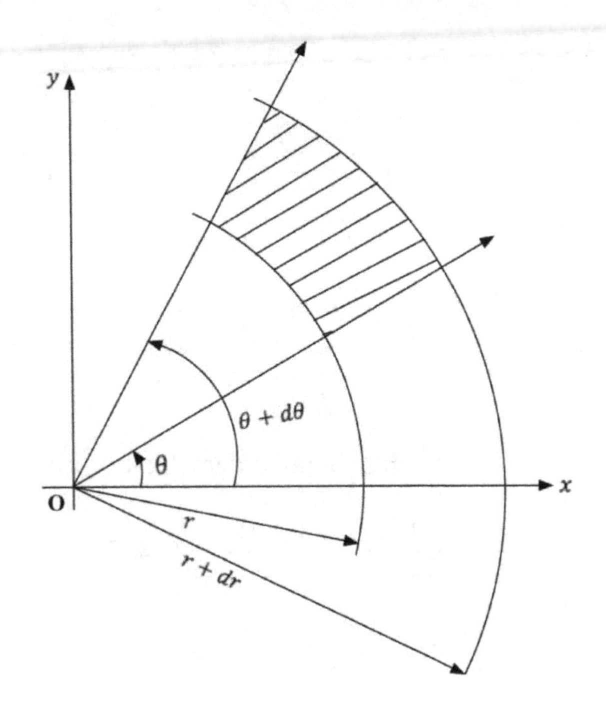

FIGURE 3.6

In polar coordinates,

$$\begin{aligned} dA &= \frac{1}{2}(r + dr)^2 d\theta - \frac{1}{2}r^2 d\theta \\ &= \frac{1}{2}\left[(r + dr)^2 - r^2\right]d\theta \\ &= \frac{1}{2}(r + dr - r)(r + dr + r)d\theta. \\ &= rdrd\theta + \frac{1}{2}(dr)^2 d\theta \\ &\approx rdrd\theta \end{aligned}$$

Now, consider $\sum F_r = 0$ in the free body diagram shown in the figure:

$$\left(\sigma_r + \frac{\partial \sigma_r}{\partial r} dr\right)(r + dr)d\theta dz - \sigma_r r d\theta dz + \left(\tau_{r\theta} + \frac{\partial \tau_{r\theta}}{\partial \theta} d\theta\right) drdz\cos\left(\frac{d\theta}{2}\right) - \tau_{r\theta} drdz\cos\left(\frac{d\theta}{2}\right)$$
$$-\left(\sigma_\theta + \frac{\partial \sigma_\theta}{\partial \theta} d\theta\right) drdz\sin\left(\frac{d\theta}{2}\right) - \sigma_\theta drdz\sin\left(\frac{d\theta}{2}\right) + F_r(rdrd\theta)dz = 0.$$

But
$$\cos\left(\frac{d\theta}{2}\right) \approx 1 \text{ and } \sin\left(\frac{d\theta}{2}\right) \approx \frac{d\theta}{2}.$$

Therefore,

$$\sigma_r rd\theta dz + \sigma_r drd\theta dz + \frac{\partial \sigma_r}{\partial r} rdrd\theta dz + \frac{\partial \sigma_r}{\partial r}(dr)^2 d\theta dz - \sigma_r rd\theta dz + \tau_{r\theta} drdz + \frac{\partial \tau_{r\theta}}{\partial \theta} d\theta drdz$$
$$-\tau_{r\theta} drdz - \sigma_\theta drdz\frac{d\theta}{2} - \frac{\partial \sigma_\theta}{\partial \theta} d\theta drdz\frac{d\theta}{2} - \sigma_\theta drdz\frac{d\theta}{2} + F_r(rdrd\theta)dz = 0.$$

Simplifying the above relation, we obtain:

$$\sigma_r rd\theta dz + \frac{\partial \sigma_r}{\partial r} rdrd\theta dz + \frac{\partial \sigma_r}{\partial r}(dr)^2 d\theta dz + \frac{\partial \tau_{r\theta}}{\partial \theta} d\theta drdz - \sigma_\theta drdzd\theta$$
$$-\frac{\partial \sigma_\theta}{\partial \theta} drdz\frac{(d\theta)^2}{2} + F_r rdrdzd\theta = 0.$$

Ignoring the higher order terms such as $(dr)^2 d\theta dz$:

$$\sigma_r rd\theta dz + \frac{\partial \sigma_r}{\partial r} rdrd\theta dz + \frac{\partial \tau_{r\theta}}{\partial \theta} d\theta drdz - \sigma_\theta drdzd\theta + F_r rdrdzd\theta = 0.$$

Dividing the above relation by $drd\theta dz$, we conclude that:

$$\frac{\partial \sigma_r}{\partial r} + \frac{1}{r}\frac{\partial \tau_{r\theta}}{\partial \theta} + \frac{\sigma_r - \sigma_\theta}{r} + F_r = 0.$$

Similarly, considering $\sum F_\theta = 0$ in the free body diagram, we can obtain:

$$\frac{1}{r}\frac{\partial \sigma_\theta}{\partial \theta} + \frac{\partial \tau_{r\theta}}{\partial r} + \frac{2\tau_{r\theta}}{r} + F_\theta = 0.$$

3.6 Stresses around a Circular Hole

A large thin plate is subjected to uniform tensile stress σ_0 at its ends, as shown in the figure below:

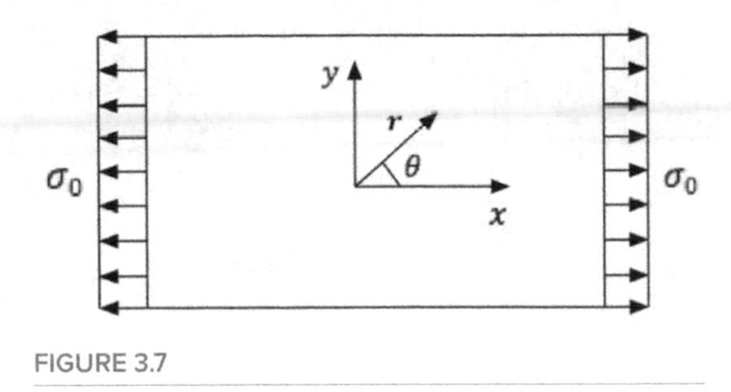

FIGURE 3.7

Our objective is to determine the stress distribution within the plate.

Method (i)

$$\sigma_x = \sigma_0;\ \sigma_y = \tau_{xy} = 0$$

$$\begin{pmatrix} \sigma_{x'} & \tau_{x'y'} \\ \tau_{y'x'} & \sigma_{y'} \end{pmatrix} = \begin{pmatrix} \cos\theta & \sin\theta \\ -\sin\theta & \cos\theta \end{pmatrix} \begin{pmatrix} \sigma_x & \tau_{xy} \\ \tau_{yx} & \sigma_y \end{pmatrix} \begin{pmatrix} \cos\theta & -\sin\theta \\ \sin\theta & \cos\theta \end{pmatrix}$$

Therefore,

$$\sigma_{x'}(\theta) = \frac{\sigma_x + \sigma_y}{2} + \frac{\sigma_x - \sigma_y}{2}\cos 2\theta + \tau_{xy}\sin 2\theta$$

$$\sigma_{y'}(\theta) = \frac{\sigma_x + \sigma_y}{2} - \frac{\sigma_x - \sigma_y}{2}\cos 2\theta - \tau_{xy}\sin 2\theta$$

$$\tau_{x'y'}(\theta) = \tau_{xy}\cos 2\theta - \frac{1}{2}(\sigma_x - \sigma_y)\sin 2\theta$$

$$\sigma_{x'}(\theta) = \sigma_r(\theta);\ \sigma_{y'}(\theta) = \sigma_\theta(\theta);\ \tau_{x'y'}(\theta) = \tau_{r\theta}(\theta)$$

$\Rightarrow$

$$\sigma_r(\theta) = \frac{\sigma_0}{2}(1 + \cos 2\theta)$$

$$\sigma_\theta(\theta) = \frac{\sigma_0}{2}(1 - \cos 2\theta)$$

$$\tau_{r\theta}(\theta) = -\frac{1}{2}\sigma_0 \sin 2\theta$$

$$\sigma_{r\ max} = \sigma_0 \quad (\text{for } \theta = 0 \text{ or } \theta = \pi)$$

$$\sigma_{\theta\ max} = \sigma_0 \quad \left(\text{for } \theta = \frac{\pi}{2} \text{ or } \theta = \frac{3\pi}{2}\right)$$

$$\left|\tau_{r\theta}\right|_{max} = \frac{1}{2}\sigma_0 \quad \left(\text{for } \theta = \frac{\pi}{4}, \frac{3\pi}{4}, \frac{5\pi}{4}, \frac{7\pi}{4}\right).$$

Method (ii)

Airy's stress function,

$$\phi = \frac{\sigma_0 y^2}{2},$$

satisfies the biharmonic equation,

$$\nabla^4\phi = \nabla^2(\nabla^2\phi) = 0.$$

In terms of polar coordinates, the stress function can be written as

$$\phi = \frac{\sigma_0}{2} r^2 \sin^2\theta = \frac{\sigma_0}{4} r^2 (1 - \cos 2\theta)$$

$\Rightarrow$

$$\sigma_r(\theta) = \frac{\sigma_0}{2}(1 + \cos 2\theta)$$

$$\sigma_\theta(\theta) = \frac{\sigma_0}{2}(1 - \cos 2\theta)$$

$$\tau_{r\theta}(\theta) = -\frac{1}{2}\sigma_0 \sin 2\theta,$$

which are the same results obtained in method (i).

The elementary theory, or mechanics of materials approach, cannot predict the high values of stress in configurations such as holes and notches, which are likely starting points of material failure. The stress in these regions can be analyzed by applying the theory of elasticity. Experimental techniques and, in particular, photoelastic methods can also be used for the analysis.

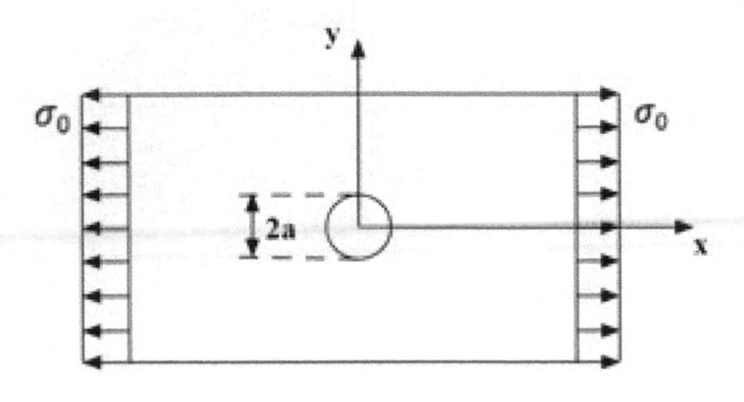

FIGURE 3.8

A large, thin plate containing a small circular hole of radius a is subjected to simple tension. Let us determine the stress distribution within the plate.

Airy's stress function, ϕ (r, θ), must satisfy the biharmonic equation:

$$\nabla^4\phi = \nabla^2(\nabla^2\phi) = 0.$$

The boundary conditions for this problem are:
$\sigma_r = \tau_{r\theta} = 0$ (for r = a) and when $r \to \infty$

$$\begin{cases} \sigma_r = \dfrac{\sigma_o}{2}(1+\cos 2\theta) \\ \sigma_\theta = \dfrac{\sigma_o}{2}(1-\cos 2\theta) \\ \tau_{r\theta} = -\dfrac{\sigma_o}{2}\sin 2\theta \end{cases}.$$

The partial differential equation,

$$\nabla^4\phi = \nabla^2(\nabla^2\phi) = 0,$$

can be written in more details as:

$$\left(\frac{\partial^2}{\partial r^2} + \frac{1}{r}\frac{\partial}{\partial r} + \frac{1}{r^2}\frac{\partial^2}{\partial \theta^2}\right)\left(\frac{\partial^2\phi}{\partial r^2} + \frac{1}{r}\frac{\partial\phi}{\partial r} + \frac{1}{r^2}\frac{\partial^2\phi}{\partial \theta^2}\right) = 0$$

$$\frac{\partial^4\phi}{\partial r^4}+\frac{2}{r}\frac{\partial^3\phi}{\partial r^3}-\frac{1}{r^2}\frac{\partial^2\phi}{\partial r^2}+\frac{1}{r^3}\frac{\partial\phi}{\partial r}+\frac{1}{r^4}\frac{\partial^4\phi}{\partial\theta^4}-\frac{2}{r^3}\frac{\partial^3\phi}{\partial\theta^2\partial r}+\frac{4}{r^4}\frac{\partial^2\phi}{\partial\theta^2}+\frac{2}{r^2}\frac{\partial^4\phi}{\partial\theta^2\partial r^2}=0.$$

Assume a stress function of the form:

$$\phi(r,\theta)=f_1(r)+f_2(r)\cos 2\theta$$

$$\Rightarrow \begin{cases} \dfrac{d^4f_1}{dr^4}+\dfrac{2}{r}\dfrac{d^3f_1}{dr^3}-\dfrac{1}{r^2}\dfrac{d^2f_1}{dr^2}+\dfrac{1}{r^3}\dfrac{df_1}{dr}=0 & (*) \\ \dfrac{d^4f_2}{dr^4}+\dfrac{2}{r}\dfrac{d^3f_2}{dr^3}-\dfrac{9}{r^2}\dfrac{d^2f_2}{dr^2}+\dfrac{9}{r^3}\dfrac{df_2}{dr}=0 & (**) \end{cases}$$

Thus, the fourth-order PDE has been reduced to two separate fourth-order linear ordinary differential equations.

$$\frac{d^4f_1}{dr^4}+\frac{2}{r}\frac{d^3f_1}{dr^3}-\frac{1}{r^2}\frac{d^2f_1}{dr^2}+\frac{1}{r^3}\frac{df_1}{dr}=0 \qquad (*)$$

The above is a fourth-order homogeneous linear ordinary differential equation with variable coefficients. It is of the Euler type.

Let $t=\ln r \Rightarrow$

$$\frac{df_1}{dr}=\frac{1}{r}\frac{df_1}{dt}$$

$$\frac{d^2f_1}{dr^2}=\frac{1}{r^2}\frac{d^2f_1}{dt^2}-\frac{1}{r^2}\frac{df_1}{dt}$$

$$\frac{d^3f_1}{dr^3}=\frac{1}{r^3}\frac{d^3f_1}{dt^3}-\frac{3}{r^3}\frac{d^2f_1}{dt^2}+\frac{2}{r^3}\frac{df_1}{dt}$$

$$\frac{d^4f_1}{dr^4}=\frac{1}{r^4}\frac{d^4f_1}{dt^4}-\frac{6}{r^4}\frac{d^3f_1}{dt^3}+\frac{11}{r^4}\frac{d^2f_1}{dt^2}-\frac{6}{r^4}\frac{df_1}{dt}.$$

Therefore, the equation (*) becomes:

$$\frac{1}{r^4}\frac{d^4f_1}{dt^4}-\frac{4}{r^4}\frac{d^3f_1}{dt^3}+\frac{4}{r^4}\frac{d^2f_1}{dt^2}=0$$

$$\Rightarrow \frac{d^4f_1}{dt^4}-4\frac{d^3f_1}{dt^3}+4\frac{d^2f_1}{dt^2}=0.$$

The above equation is a fourth-order homogeneous linear ordinary differential equation with constant coefficients.

The corresponding characteristic equation is:

$$\lambda^4 - 4\lambda^3 + 4\lambda^2 = 0$$

$$\Rightarrow \lambda^2(\lambda - 2)^2 = 0$$

$$\Rightarrow \lambda = 0 \text{ (double root) and } \lambda = 2 \text{ (double root)}$$

$$\Rightarrow f_1(t) = c_1 + c_2 t + (c_3 + c_4 t)e^{2t}$$

$$\Rightarrow f_1(r) = c_1 + c_2 \ln r + (c_3 + c_4 \ln r)r^2$$

$$\frac{d^4 f_2}{dr^4} + \frac{2}{r}\frac{d^3 f_2}{dr^3} - \frac{9}{r^2}\frac{d^2 f_2}{dr^2} + \frac{9}{r^3}\frac{df_2}{dr} = 0. \qquad (**)$$

Let $t = \ln r \Rightarrow$

The equation (**) becomes:

$$\frac{1}{r^4}\frac{d^4 f_2}{dt^4} - \frac{4}{r^4}\frac{d^3 f_2}{dt^3} - \frac{4}{r^4}\frac{d^2 f_2}{dt^2} + \frac{16}{r^4}\frac{df_2}{dt} = 0$$

$$\Rightarrow \frac{d^4 f_2}{dt^4} - 4\frac{d^3 f_2}{dt^3} - 4\frac{d^2 f_2}{dt^2} + 16\frac{df_2}{dt} = 0.$$

The above equation is also a fourth-order homogeneous linear ordinary differential equation with constant coefficients.

The corresponding characteristic equation is:

$$\lambda^4 - 4\lambda^3 - 4\lambda^2 + 16\lambda = 0$$

$$\Rightarrow \lambda(\lambda - 2)(\lambda + 2)(\lambda - 4) = 0$$

$$\Rightarrow \text{Either } \lambda = 0 \text{ or } \lambda = -2 \text{ or } \lambda = 2 \text{ or } \lambda = 4$$

$$\Rightarrow f_2(t) = c_5 + c_6 e^{-2t} + c_7 e^{2t} + c_8 e^{4t}$$

$$\Rightarrow f_2(r) = c_5 + \frac{c_6}{r^2} + c_7 r^2 + c_8 r^4.$$

Therefore,

$$\phi(r,\theta) = \left(c_1 + c_2 \ln r + c_3 r^2 + c_4 r^2 \ln r\right) + \left(c_5 + \frac{c_6}{r^2} + c_7 r^2 + c_8 r^4\right)\cos 2\theta.$$

Now, using

$$\sigma_r = \frac{1}{r}\frac{\partial\phi}{\partial r} + \frac{1}{r^2}\frac{\partial^2\phi}{\partial\theta^2}$$

$$\sigma_\theta = \frac{\partial^2\phi}{\partial r^2}$$

$$\tau_{r\theta} = \frac{1}{r^2}\frac{\partial\phi}{\partial\theta} - \frac{1}{r}\frac{\partial^2\phi}{\partial r\,\partial\theta}$$

we obtain:

$$\sigma_r = \frac{c_2}{r^2} + 2c_3 + c_4(1+2\ln r) - \left(2c_7 + \frac{4}{r^2}c_5 + \frac{6}{r^4}c_6\right)\cos 2\theta$$

$$\sigma_\theta = 2c_3 - \frac{c_2}{r^2} + c_4(3+2\ln r) + \left(2c_7 + 12c_8r^2 + \frac{6}{r^4}c_6\right)\cos 2\theta$$

$$\tau_{r\theta} = 2\sin 2\theta\left(c_7 - \frac{c_5}{r^2} - \frac{3}{r^4}c_6 + 3c_8r^2\right)$$

$$r \to \infty$$

$$\Rightarrow \begin{cases} \sigma_r = \dfrac{\sigma_o}{2}(1+\cos 2\theta) \\ \sigma_\theta = \dfrac{\sigma_o}{2}(1-\cos 2\theta) \\ \tau_{r\theta} = -\dfrac{\sigma_o}{2}\sin 2\theta \end{cases}$$

$$\Rightarrow c_4 = 0,\ c_8 = 0, c_3 = \frac{\sigma_o}{4}, c_7 = -\frac{\sigma_o}{4}$$

$$\sigma_r = \tau_{r\theta} = 0 \text{ (for } r = a)$$

$$\Rightarrow c_2 = -\frac{\sigma_o}{2}a^2$$

$$c_5 = \frac{\sigma_o}{2}a^2$$

$$c_6 = -\frac{\sigma_o}{4}a^4.$$

Finally, we obtain the stress distribution in an infinite plate containing a circular hole:

$$\begin{cases} \sigma_r = \dfrac{\sigma_0}{2}\left[\left(1-\dfrac{a^2}{r^2}\right)+\left(1+\dfrac{3a^4}{r^4}-\dfrac{4a^2}{r^2}\right)\cos 2\theta\right] \\ \sigma_\theta = \dfrac{\sigma_0}{2}\left[\left(1+\dfrac{a^2}{r^2}\right)-\left(1+\dfrac{3a^4}{r^4}\right)\cos 2\theta\right] \\ \tau_{r\theta} = -\dfrac{\sigma_0}{2}\left(1-\dfrac{3a^4}{r^4}+\dfrac{2a^2}{r^2}\right)\sin 2\theta \end{cases}.$$

The stress function, $\phi(r,\theta)$, is:

$$\phi(r,\theta) = \left(\frac{\sigma_0}{4}r^2 - \frac{a^2\sigma_0}{2}\ln r + c\right) + \left(\frac{a^2\sigma_0}{2} - \frac{\sigma_0 r^2}{4} - \frac{\sigma_0 a^4}{4r^2}\right)\cos 2\theta.$$

The above formulas describe the stress distribution in a plate of infinite dimensions, which contains a circular hole of radius a when it is subjected to a uniaxial stress σ_0. The deformation is assumed to occur in a plane state of stress.

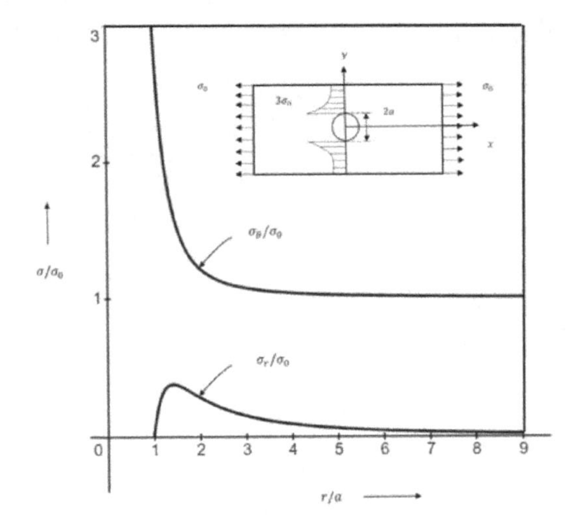

The variation of σ_r as a function of r and of σ_θ as a function of r.

$\left(\theta = \frac{\pi}{2}\right)$

Note that,

$$(\sigma_\theta)_{max} = 3\sigma_0 \ at \ r = a$$

and $\sigma_\theta \approx \sigma_0 \ at \ r = 9a$

$$(\sigma_r)_{max} = \frac{3}{8}\sigma_0 \ at \ r = \sqrt{2}a$$

FIGURE 3.9

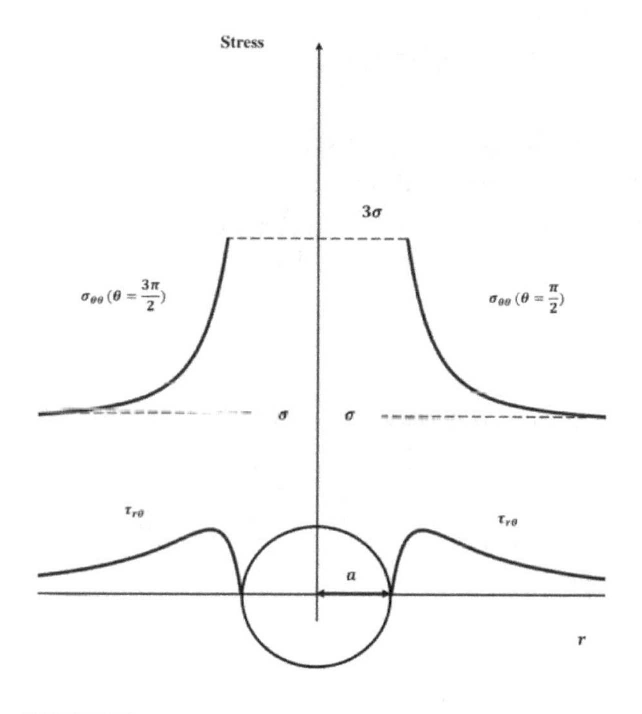

Distribution of stress around a circular hole in an infinite plate, subject to a uniform stress, σ (Plane Stress)

FIGURE 3.10

It is usual to specify the high local stresses owing to geometrical irregularities in terms of a stress concentration factor: the ratio of the distributed stress (the high, localized stress) to the uniform stress in the remainder of the body (or the average or nominal stress).

In the absence of the hole,

$$(\sigma_\theta)_{max} = \sigma_0 \; for \; \theta = \frac{\pi}{2} \; or \; -\frac{\pi}{2}.$$

In the presence of the hole,

$$(\sigma_\theta)_{max} = 3\sigma_0 \; for \; \theta = \frac{\pi}{2} \; or \; -\frac{\pi}{2} \; and \; when \; r = a.$$

Thus, the stress concentration factor

$$K = \frac{3\sigma_0}{\sigma_0} = 3.$$

It is interesting to notice that when $r = 9a$, we have

$$\sigma_\theta \approx 1.006\sigma_0 \text{ and } \sigma_r \approx 0.018\sigma_0, \text{ for } \theta = \frac{\pi}{2};$$

therefore, simple tension prevails at a distance of approximately nine radii. We say that the hole has a local effect upon the stress distribution.

For a plate with finite dimensions containing a centrally located hole and subjected to a uniaxial stress σ_0, the stress concentration factor K_t depends on the ratio of $\frac{d}{w}$, as shown in the figure below.

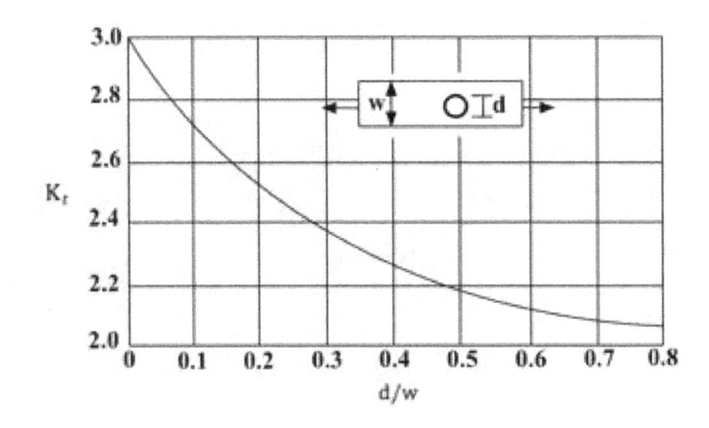

$$K_t = \frac{\sigma_{max}}{\sigma_{nom}}$$

FIGURE 3.11

Stress concentration factor K_t as a function of d / w. Notice that K_t $(d / w = 0)$ is 3.0 (infinite plate).

The average or nominal stress is defined to be the uniform stress in the remainder of the body.

3.7 Stresses around an Elliptical Hole

If, instead of a plate with a circular hole, we have an infinite plate subjected to a uniaxial tensile stress that contains an elliptical hole with semi-major axis length a and semi-minor axis length b, the problem becomes mathematically more challenging.

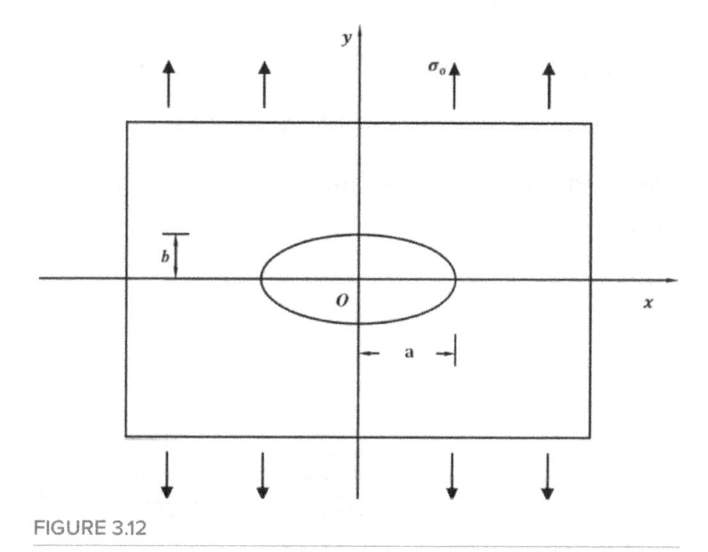

FIGURE 3.12

Polar coordinates cannot be used now, since circular symmetry has been destroyed. Instead, elliptical coordinates can be used. Elliptical coordinates are a special case of curvilinear coordinates. When using Cartesian rectangular coordinates in order to identify the position of point $P(x_o, y_o)$ in the xy plane, such a point can be looked upon as the intersection of two straight lines in the plane, a vertical line $x = x_o$, and a horizontal one $y = y_o$. When using polar coordinates to determine the position of point $P(r_o, \theta_o)$ in the plane, such a point can be looked upon as the intersection of a circle $r = r_o$ and a straight line $\theta = \theta_o$. In elliptical coordinates, a point can be looked upon as the intersection of an ellipse and a hyperbola.

In 1913, a British engineer named Sir Charles Edward Inglis* approached this problem and concluded that the stress concentration factor is given by $1 + 2\frac{a}{b}$.

Notice that for a circular hole (special case $a = b$), we obtain a stress concentration factor equal to three in agreement with the results obtained in the previous section. However, the theory of linear elasticity predicts a stress concentration factor much higher than three when $a > b$. Inglis's work permits cracklike geometries to be treated by making the minor axis of the ellipse small.

Linear elasticity theory is inadequate to handle stresses around cracks. This is studied using fracture mechanics.

* A British civil engineer (1875–1952) who contributed to structural mechanics and vibration analysis.

Problems

3.1. Determine whether the following Airy stress function

$$\phi = ax^3 + bx^2y + cxy^2 + dy^3$$

satisfies the conditions of compatibility for a state of plane stress.

If so, establish

$$[\sigma_{ij}] = \begin{bmatrix} \sigma_x & \tau_{xy} \\ \tau_{yx} & \sigma_y \end{bmatrix}$$

that results from ϕ.

Here, *a, b, c,* and *d* are constants. Neglect body forces.

3.2. Determine whether the following stress distribution is a valid solution for a state of plane stress

$$\sigma_x = -ax^2y; \sigma_y = -\frac{1}{3}ay^3; \tau_{xy} = axy^2,$$

where a is a non-zero constant. You can disregard body forces.

3.3. Given the following stress field within a body

$$\sigma_x = a\left[y^2 + b(x^2 - y^2)\right]$$

$$\sigma_y = a\left[x^2 + b(y^2 - x^2)\right]$$

$$\sigma_z = ab(x^2 + y^2)$$

$$\tau_{xy} = -2abxy$$

$$\tau_{yz} = 0$$

$$\tau_{xz} = 0,$$

where a and b are non-zero constants, determine whether such a stress distribution represents a solution for a plane strain problem. Body forces can be disregarded.

3.4. Given zero body forces, determine whether the following stress distribution can exist for a body in equilibrium:

$$\sigma_x = -2c_1 xy$$
$$\sigma_y = c_2 z^2$$
$$\sigma_z = 0$$
$$\tau_{xy} = c_1(c_2 - y^2) + c_3 xz$$
$$\tau_{xz} = -c_3 y$$
$$\tau_{yz} = 0,$$

where c_1, c_2, and c_3 are non-zero constants.

3.5. For what body forces will the following stress field describe a state of equilibrium?

$$\sigma_x = -2x^2 + 3y^2 - 5z; \qquad \tau_{xy} = z + 4xy - 7$$
$$\sigma_y = -2y^2; \qquad \tau_{xz} = -3x + y + 1$$
$$\sigma_z = 3x + y + 3z - 5; \qquad \tau_{yz} = 0$$

3.6. An Airy stress function $\phi_{(x,y)} = cx^3 y$ is suggested for a state of plane stress. Establish:

$$[\sigma_{ij}] = \begin{bmatrix} \sigma_x & \tau_{xy} \\ \tau_{yx} & \sigma_y \end{bmatrix}.$$

3.7. For a thin plate with no body forces, a biaxial state of stress exists, where

$$\sigma_x = ay^3 + bx^2 y - cx$$
$$\sigma_y = dy^3 - e$$
$$\tau_{xy} = fxy^2 + gx^2 y - h$$

and where a, b, c, d, e, f, g, and h are constants. What are the constraints on the constants such that the stress field satisfies both equilibrium and compatibility?

3.8. Assume an Airy stress function

$$\phi_{(r,\theta)} = cPr\theta sin\theta.$$

Establish the corresponding (2×2) real symmetric stress matrix

$$[\sigma_{ij}] = \begin{vmatrix} \sigma_r & \tau_{r\theta} \\ \tau_{\theta r} & \sigma_\theta \end{vmatrix}.$$

3.9. For a rectangular curved beam in pure bending, polar coordinates are used. Neglecting body forces, the following Airy stress function has been suggested:

$$\phi_{(r,\theta)} = A + Blnr + Cr^2 + Dr^2lnr,$$

where *A*, *B*, *C*, and *D* are constants.

Can $\phi_{(r,\theta)}$ be an Airy stress function?

If so, establish:

$$[\sigma_{ij}] = \begin{vmatrix} \sigma_r & \tau_{r\theta} \\ \tau_{\theta r} & \sigma_\theta \end{vmatrix}.$$

3.10. In order to determine the state of stress in a semi-infinite plate due to a normal load, the following stress function was suggested:

$$\phi(r,\theta) = A\theta + Br^2\theta + Cr\theta sin\theta + Dr\theta \cos\theta,$$

where *A*, *B*, *C*, and *D* are constants.

(a) Neglecting body forces, does the above stress function satisfy the conditions of compatibility for a two-dimensional problem?

(b) Determine the stress matrix:

$$[\sigma_{ij}] = \begin{vmatrix} \sigma_r & \tau_{r\theta} \\ \tau_{\theta r} & \sigma_\theta \end{vmatrix}.$$

3.11. Assume the moment *M* acts in the plane and at the vertex of the wedge-cantilever shown in the figure below. Neglecting body forces, assume an Airy stress function

$$\phi_{(r,\theta)} = -\frac{M(\sin 2\theta - 2\theta \cos 2\alpha)}{2(\sin 2\alpha - 2\alpha \cos 2\alpha)}.$$

Determine $[\sigma_{ij}] = \begin{bmatrix} \sigma_r & \tau_{r\theta} \\ \tau_{\theta r} & \sigma_\theta \end{bmatrix}$.

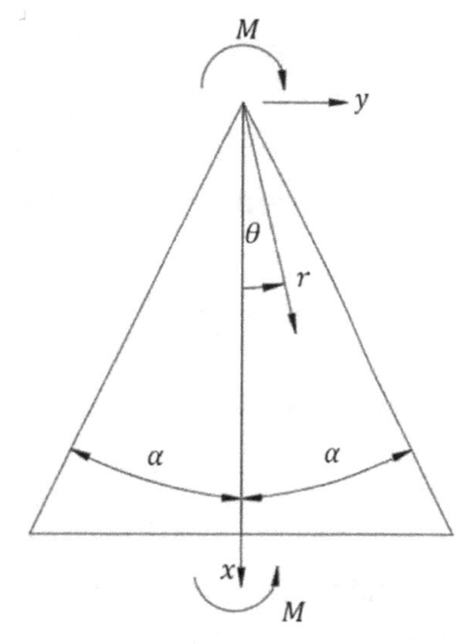

FIGURE 3.13

3.12. For the axially loaded bar shown in the figure below, the displacement field is:

$$u = \frac{Px}{AE}$$

$$v = -\nu \frac{Py}{AE}$$

$$w = -\nu \frac{Pz}{AE}.$$

(E and v are Young's modulus of elasticity and Poisson's ratio respectively.)

Establish the stress matrix $[\sigma_{ij}] = \begin{bmatrix} \sigma_x & \tau_{xy} & \tau_{xz} \\ \tau_{yx} & \sigma_y & \tau_{yz} \\ \tau_{zx} & \tau_{zy} & \sigma_z \end{bmatrix}$.

Assume that the material is homogenous, isotropic, and behaving in the linearly elastic range.

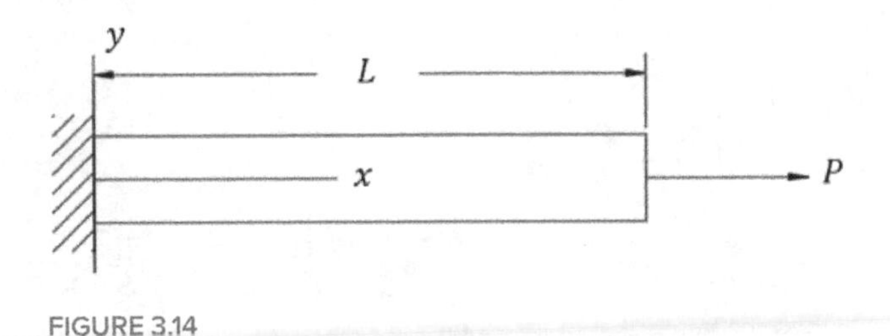

FIGURE 3.14

3.13. For a cantilever beam loaded by a shear force at the free end, the following state of plane stress is proposed:

$$\sigma_x = 2Ay(L - x)$$

$$\sigma_y = 0$$

$$\tau_{xy} = A(y^2 - c^2),$$

where A is a constant. Find the displacement u and v at point B of the beam if $u = v = \frac{\partial v}{\partial x} = 0$ at $x = y = 0$. The Cartesian coordinates of point B are $(L, c, 0)$. (Express your answer in terms of P, E, L, c, ν, and t.)

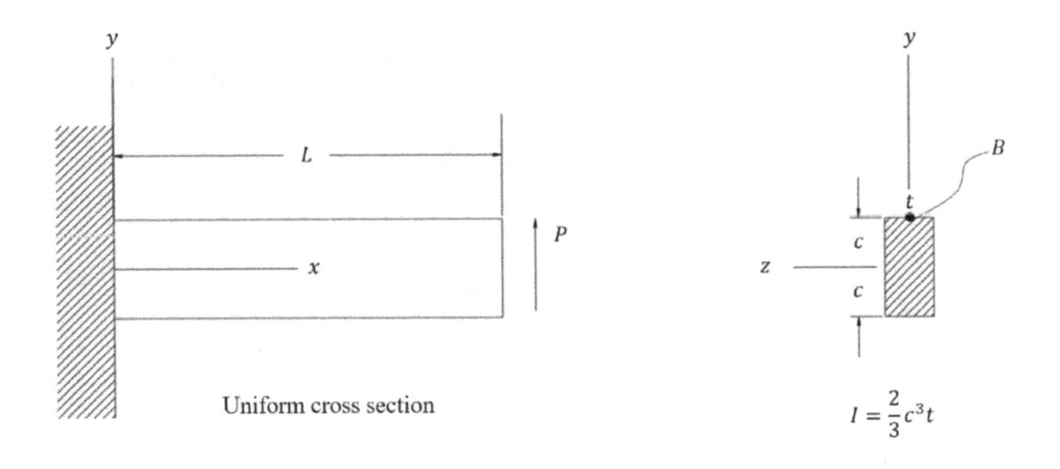

FIGURE 3.15

3.14. The state of plane stress within an elastic uniformly loaded cantilever beam (shown in the figure below—notice the orientation of the xy-coordinate system) is defined by the (2×2) real symmetric matrix

$$[\sigma_{ij}] = \begin{bmatrix} \sigma_x & \tau_{xy} \\ \tau_{xy} & \sigma_y \end{bmatrix},$$

where

$$\sigma_x = -\frac{p}{10I}(5x^2 + 2h^2)y + \frac{p}{3I}y^3$$

$$\sigma_y = -\frac{p}{6I}(2h^3 - 3h^2y + y^3)$$

$$\tau_{xy} = -\frac{px}{2I}(h^2 - y^2).$$

Here, $I = \frac{2th^3}{3}$, and the body forces can be neglected. Given $p = 10\frac{kN}{m}$, $L = 2m$, $h = 100\ mm$, $t = 40\ mm$, $\nu = 0.3$, and $E = 200\,GPa$, compute the axial strain ε_x at point Q.

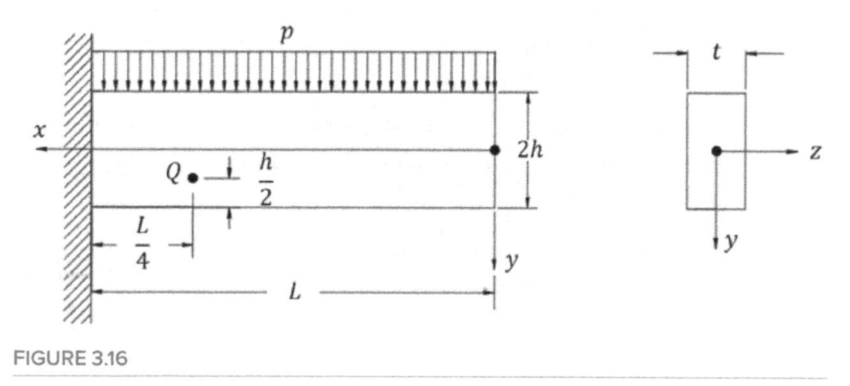

FIGURE 3.16

3.15. The state of plane stress in the thin rectangular region shown in the figure below is given by:

$$[\sigma_{ij}] = \begin{bmatrix} \sigma_x & \tau_{xy} \\ \tau_{yx} & \sigma_y \end{bmatrix} = \begin{bmatrix} \frac{3}{2}\frac{p}{tc^3}y^2 & 0 \\ 0 & -\frac{3}{2}\frac{p}{tc^3}x^2 \end{bmatrix}.$$

Determine the components of displacement of point A if $u = v = \frac{\partial v}{\partial x} = 0$ at the origin O.

Young's modulus of elasticity for the material is E, and its Poisson ratio is ν.

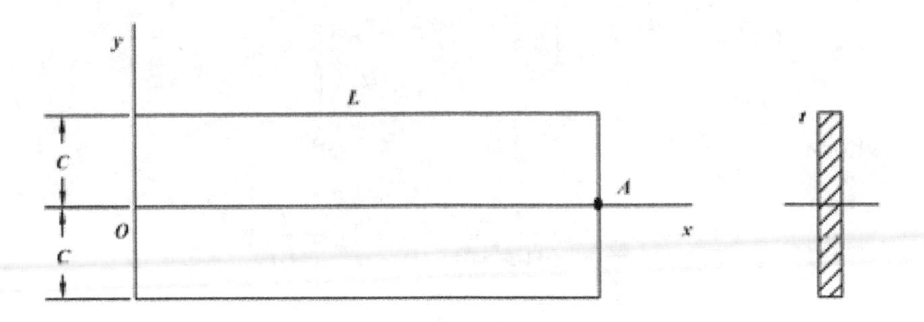

FIGURE 3.17

3.16. We propose in this problem to determine, by solving the biharmonic equation, the stress distribution in an infinite plate that is uniformly stressed. The plate has a hole of radius a located in the middle as shown below. S has the dimension of stress.

i. Assume a suitable Airy stress function ϕ, and use it to solve the biharmonic equation $\nabla^4\phi = 0$. Your solution will obviously include arbitrary constants of integration.
ii. Establish the boundary conditions that correspond to this problem.
iii. Use the boundary conditions to determine the constants of integration.
iv. Finally, determine $[\sigma_{ij}] = \begin{bmatrix} \sigma_r & \tau_{r\theta} \\ \tau_{\theta r} & \sigma_\theta \end{bmatrix}$.

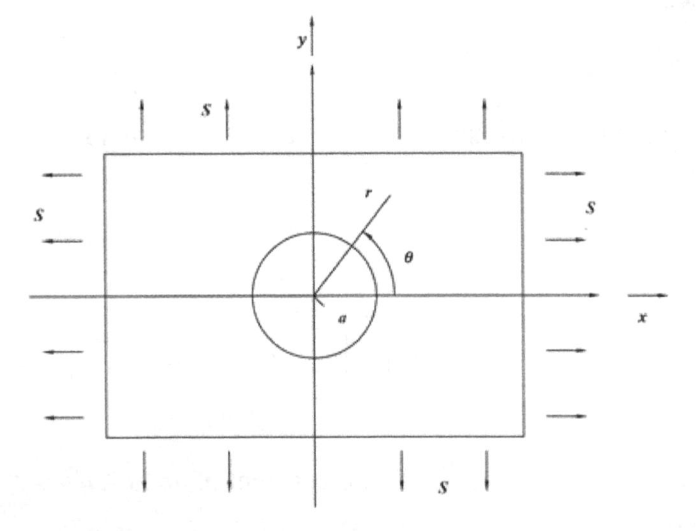

FIGURE 3.18

3.17. The strain–displacement relationship can be written in the concise "pseudovector-matrix" form:

$$\{\varepsilon\} = [\boldsymbol{L}]\{\delta\},$$

where $\{\varepsilon\}$ is the strain pseudovector, and $\{\delta\}$ is the displacement vector. $\{\varepsilon\}$ is a (6×1) pseudovector in the 3D case:

$$\{\varepsilon\} = \begin{Bmatrix} \varepsilon_x \\ \varepsilon_y \\ \varepsilon_z \\ \gamma_{xy} \\ \gamma_{yz} \\ \gamma_{xz} \end{Bmatrix}.$$

$\{\delta\}$ is a (3×1) pseudovector in the 3D case:

$$\{\delta\} = \begin{Bmatrix} \boldsymbol{u} \\ \boldsymbol{v} \\ \boldsymbol{w} \end{Bmatrix}.$$

Write down $[\boldsymbol{L}]_{(6\times3)}$ in the 3D case.

Write down the equilibrium equations, in the absence of body forces, in pseudovector-matrix form in terms of $[\boldsymbol{L}]_{(6\times3)}$ and the (6×1) stress pseudovector $\{\sigma\}$ defined as:

$$\{\sigma\} = \begin{Bmatrix} \sigma_x \\ \sigma_y \\ \sigma_z \\ \tau_{xy} \\ \tau_{yz} \\ \tau_{xz} \end{Bmatrix}.$$

Further Reading

Budynas, Richard G. *Advanced Strength and Applied Stress Analysis.* New York City: McGraw-Hill, 1977.

Curtis, H. D. *Fundamentals of Aircraft Structural Analysis.* New York City: McGraw-Hill, 1997.

Roylance, David. *Mechanics of Materials.* Hoboken: Wiley, 1996.

Saada, Adel S. *Elasticity Theory and Applications.* 2nd ed. Krieger Publishing Company, 1993.

Ugural, Ansel. C. *Mechanical Design: An Integrated Approach.* New York City: McGraw-Hill, 2004.

Ugural, Ansel C., and Saul K. Fenster. *Advanced Mechanics of Materials and Applied Elasticity.* 5th ed. Upper Saddle River: Prentice Hall, 2012.

CHAPTER 4

Failure by Yielding Theories

4.1 Introduction

Consider a prismatic bar, as shown in **figure 4.1**, loaded axially with a load *P*. This is the simplest type of loading in structural engineering. It corresponds to a uniaxial state of stress. We defined in chapter 1, the engineering (or conventional) axial (or normal) stress.

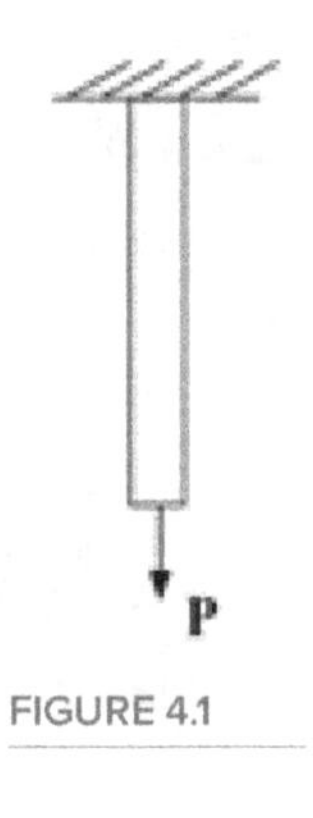

FIGURE 4.1

$$\sigma = \frac{P}{A}$$

We also found out that, since the material is not rigid, there will be deformation in the bar. A typical graph depicting the relationship between σ (engineering axial stress) and ε (engineering axial strain) for a ductile material (such as steel) subject to a uniaxial tensile stress is shown in **figure 4.2.**

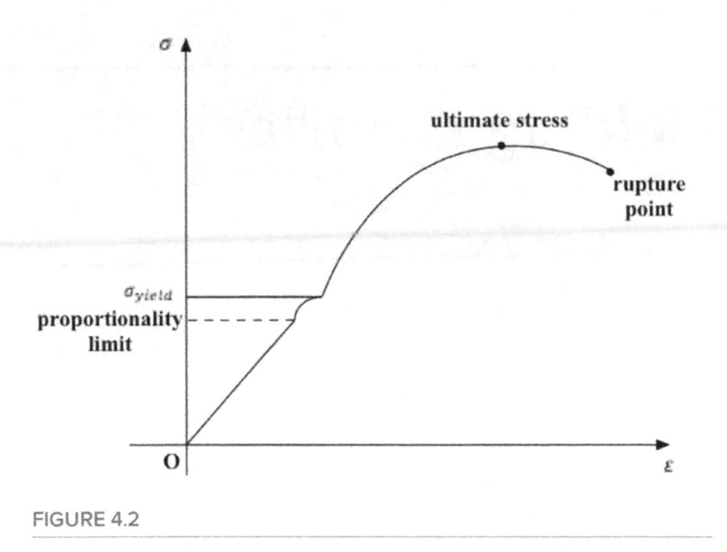

FIGURE 4.2

σ_{yield} is a mechanical property of the material. It is important in design theories. We prefer to stay in the linearly elastic range, and we do not want to surpass σ_{yield}. When σ becomes larger than σ_{yield}, we say that failure by yielding occurs. The above argument is logical and straightforward. However, it only pertains to a uniaxial state of stress for which:

$$[\sigma_{ij}] = \begin{bmatrix} \sigma & 0 & 0 \\ 0 & 0 & 0 \\ 0 & 0 & 0 \end{bmatrix}_{(3\times3)}.$$

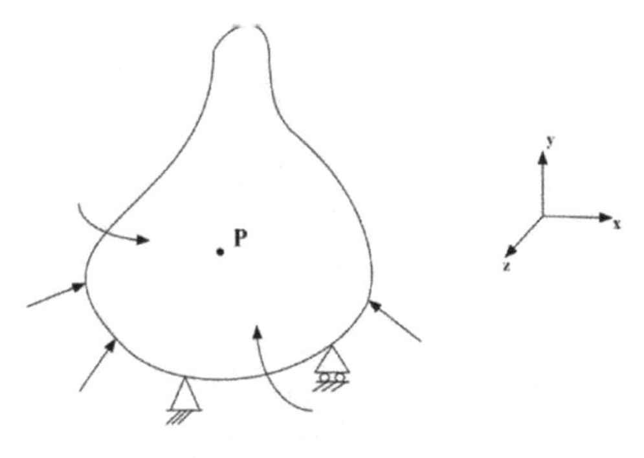

FIGURE 4.3

In the most general case, when a body (a structure) is subject to certain loading (a system of forces) as shown in **figure 4.3**, the state of stress at point *P* (stress is a point function) is defined by a fully populated matrix:

$$[\sigma_{ij}] = \begin{bmatrix} \sigma_x & \tau_{xy} & \tau_{xz} \\ \tau_{yx} & \sigma_y & \tau_{yz} \\ \tau_{zx} & \tau_{zy} & \sigma_z \end{bmatrix}_{(3\times3)}.$$

A natural and challenging question that comes up is the following: When does yielding occur in case the stress matrix is fully populated? This is not easy to answer. In the literature there are several theories that attempt to address such a question. These different theories often lead to different answers. When different theories try to answer the same question or when several formulas attempt to interpret the same phenomenon, the validity and accuracy of these theories are certainly questionable.

4.2 Failure by Yielding Theories

1. Maximum principal stress theory (Rankine[1]):

A material fails by yielding when the maximum principal stress exceeds the tensile yield strength or when the minimum principal stress exceeds the compressive yield strength.

2. Maximum shear stress theory (Tresca[2]):

Yielding will start when the maximum shear stress in the material equals the maximum shear stress at yielding in a simple tension test:

$$|\sigma_1 - \sigma_3| = \sigma_{yield}.$$

3. Maximum principal strain theory:

A material fails by yielding when the maximum principal strain exceeds the tensile yield strain $\left(\varepsilon'_{yield}\right)$ or when the minimum principal strain exceeds the compressive yield strain $\left(\varepsilon''_{yield}\right)$

---

1 William John Macquorn Rankine was a Scottish mathematician, physicist, and engineer. He was born in 1820 in Edinburgh and died in 1872 in Glasgow. Rankine is famous for proposing the Rankine scale of temperature, an absolute temperature scale related to the Fahrenheit scale.

2 Henri Tresca was a prominent French mechanical engineer born in 1814. He died in 1885. He was a pioneer in the field of plasticity.

$$|\sigma_1 - \nu(\sigma_2 + \sigma_3)| = (\sigma'_{yield})$$
$$|\sigma_3 - \nu(\sigma_1 + \sigma_2)| = (\sigma''_{yield}).$$

4. Maximum distortion energy theory (von Mises[3]):

Failure occurs when, at any point in the body, the distortion energy per unit volume in a state of combined stress becomes equal to that associated with yielding in a simple tension test

$$\sqrt{\frac{1}{2}\left[(\sigma_1 - \sigma_2)^2 + (\sigma_1 - \sigma_3)^2 + (\sigma_2 - \sigma_3)^2\right]} = \sigma_{yield.}$$

5. The octahedral shear stress theory:

It predicts failure by yielding when the octahedral shearing stress at a point reaches a particular value:

$$\tau_{oct} = \frac{\sqrt{2}}{3}\sigma_{yield.}$$

The above theories are the most widely used, but there are other theories encountered in the literature. Theories 4 and 5 are equivalent and lead to precisely the same results.

4.3 "Derivation" of the Octahedral Shear Stress Theory Criterion and the Maximum Distortion Energy Theory Criterion

Below is the logic behind these two equivalent and most popular criteria. We derived in chapter 1 an expression for the octahedral shear stress τ_{oct}.

$$\tau_{oct} = \frac{1}{3}\sqrt{(\sigma_1 - \sigma_2)^2 + (\sigma_1 - \sigma_3)^2 + (\sigma_2 - \sigma_3)^2} \qquad (4.1)$$

---

3 Richard Edler von Mises was a brilliant mathematician and scientist. Born in 1883 in Austria-Hungary (in Lemberg which, nowadays, is in Ukraine), he died in Massachusetts in 1953. He contributed to solid and fluid mechanics. He moved to Turkey before World War II and became the chair of pure and applied mathematics at the University of Istanbul before accepting a position at Harvard University in 1939. Richard's brother Ludwig von Mises was a famous economist who won a Nobel Prize in economics.

τ_{oct} is the shear stress acting on the octahedral plane, one that makes equal angles with the three principal axes.

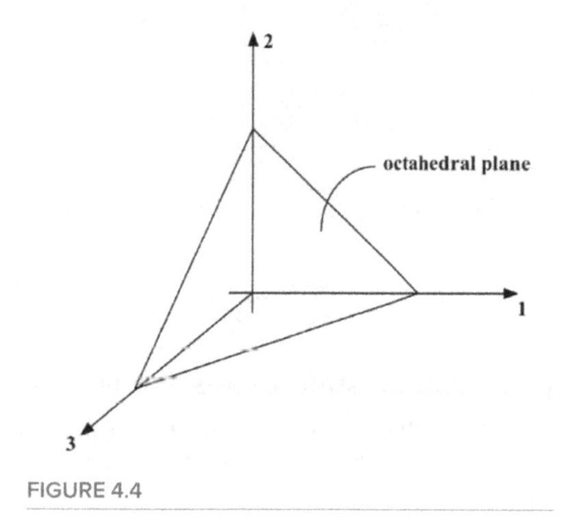

FIGURE 4.4

In a simple axial tensile test

$$\sigma_1 = \sigma_{yield}$$

$$\sigma_2 = \sigma_3 = 0.$$

Therefore,

$$\tau_{oct} = \frac{\sqrt{2}}{3}\sigma_{yield}. \qquad (4.2)$$

Comparing (4.1) to (4.2), we conclude that the octahedral shear stress theory criterion is:

$$\sqrt{\frac{1}{2}\left[(\sigma_1 - \sigma_2)^2 + (\sigma_1 - \sigma_3)^2 + (\sigma_2 - \sigma_3)^2\right]} = \sigma_{yield.}$$

On the other hand, we saw in chapter 2 that the strain energy density (strain energy per unit volume) at a point in a stressed body is given by:

$$u = \frac{1}{2}(\sigma_x\varepsilon_x + \sigma_y\varepsilon_y + \sigma_z\varepsilon_z + \tau_{xy}\gamma_{xy} + \tau_{xz}\gamma_{xz} + \tau_{yz}\gamma_{yz}).$$

In the absence of shear stresses, the above expression becomes:

$$u = \frac{1}{2}(\sigma_x \varepsilon_x + \sigma_y \varepsilon_y + \sigma_z \varepsilon_z)$$

$$= \frac{1}{2}\sigma_x\left[\frac{\sigma_x}{E} - \frac{\nu}{E}(\sigma_y + \sigma_z)\right] + \frac{1}{2}\sigma_y\left[\frac{\sigma_y}{E} - \frac{\nu}{E}(\sigma_x + \sigma_z)\right] + \frac{1}{2}\sigma_z\left[\frac{\sigma_z}{E} - \frac{\nu}{E}(\sigma_x + \sigma_y)\right].$$

$$= \frac{1}{2E}\left(\sigma_x^2 - \nu\sigma_x\sigma_y - \nu\sigma_x\sigma_z + \sigma_y^2 - \nu\sigma_x\sigma_y - \nu\sigma_y\sigma_z + \sigma_z^2 - \nu\sigma_x\sigma_z - \nu\sigma_y\sigma_z\right)$$

Therefore, the strain energy density at a point in the absence of shear stresses is:

$$u = \frac{1}{2E}\left[\sigma_x^2 + \sigma_y^2 + \sigma_z^2 - 2\nu(\sigma_x\sigma_y + \sigma_x\sigma_z + \sigma_y\sigma_z)\right]. \tag{4.3}$$

We also showed in chapter 2 that any state of stress can be decomposed into two components: a dilatational component and a distortional component:

$$[\sigma_{ij}] = \begin{bmatrix} \sigma_x & \tau_{xy} & \tau_{xz} \\ \tau_{yx} & \sigma_y & \tau_{yz} \\ \tau_{zx} & \tau_{zy} & \sigma_z \end{bmatrix}$$

$$= \begin{bmatrix} \bar{\sigma} & 0 & 0 \\ 0 & \bar{\sigma} & 0 \\ 0 & 0 & \bar{\sigma} \end{bmatrix} + \begin{bmatrix} (\sigma_x - \bar{\sigma}) & \tau_{xy} & \tau_{xz} \\ \tau_{yx} & (\sigma_y - \bar{\sigma}) & \tau_{yz} \\ \tau_{zx} & \tau_{zy} & (\sigma_z - \bar{\sigma}) \end{bmatrix},$$

where $\bar{\sigma} = \dfrac{\sigma_x + \sigma_y + \sigma_z}{3}$.

In particular, and using the principal coordinate system:

$$[\sigma_{ij}] = \begin{bmatrix} \sigma_1 & 0 & 0 \\ 0 & \sigma_2 & 0 \\ 0 & 0 & \sigma_3 \end{bmatrix}$$

$$= \begin{bmatrix} \bar{\sigma} & 0 & 0 \\ 0 & \bar{\sigma} & 0 \\ 0 & 0 & \bar{\sigma} \end{bmatrix} + \begin{bmatrix} (\sigma_1 - \bar{\sigma}) & 0 & 0 \\ 0 & (\sigma_2 - \bar{\sigma}) & 0 \\ 0 & 0 & (\sigma_3 - \bar{\sigma}) \end{bmatrix},$$

where $\bar{\sigma} = \dfrac{\sigma_1 + \sigma_2 + \sigma_3}{3}$

and $\begin{bmatrix} (\sigma_1 - \bar{\sigma}) & 0 & 0 \\ 0 & (\sigma_2 - \bar{\sigma}) & 0 \\ 0 & 0 & (\sigma_3 - \bar{\sigma}) \end{bmatrix}$ corresponds to the distortional (or deviatoric) component.

If we substitute σ_x for $\sigma_1 - \bar{\sigma}$, σ_y for $\sigma_2 - \bar{\sigma}$, and σ_z for $\sigma_3 - \bar{\sigma}$ in (4.3), we obtain:

$$u = \frac{1}{2E}\{[(\sigma_1 - \bar{\sigma})^2 + (\sigma_2 - \bar{\sigma})^2 + (\sigma_3 - \bar{\sigma})^2] - 2\nu[(\sigma_1 - \bar{\sigma})(\sigma_2 - \bar{\sigma}) + (\sigma_1 - \bar{\sigma})(\sigma_3 - \bar{\sigma}) + (\sigma_2 - \bar{\sigma})(\sigma_3 - \bar{\sigma})]\}.$$

After algebraic manipulation, the above expression can be simplified and written as:

$$u = \frac{1+\nu}{6E}\left[(\sigma_1 - \sigma_2)^2 + (\sigma_1 - \sigma_3)^2 + (\sigma_2 - \sigma_3)^2\right]. \tag{4.4}$$

For a simple axial tensile test, we can use:

$$\sigma_1 = \sigma_{yield}$$

$$\sigma_2 = \sigma_3 = 0.$$

Therefore,

$$u = \frac{1+\nu}{6E}\left(2\sigma_{yield}^2\right) = \frac{1+\nu}{3E}\sigma_{yield}^2. \tag{4.5}$$

Comparing (4.4) to (4.5), we obtain the maximum distortion energy theory criterion

$$\sqrt{\frac{1}{2}\left[(\sigma_1 - \sigma_2)^2 + (\sigma_1 - \sigma_3)^2 + (\sigma_2 - \sigma_3)^2\right]} = \sigma_{yield},$$

which is precisely the same obtained in the octahedral shear stress theory. Indeed, the fact that theories four and five are identical with support from experimental observation made engineers choose von Mises criterion. It is the most popular theory, although the maximum shear stress theory (Tresca) is the most conservative.

4.4 Examples

Problem 4.4-1

The state of stress at a point is defined by the following (3×3) real symmetric matrix

$$\sigma_{ij} = \begin{bmatrix} 65 & 0 & 0 \\ 0 & 1 & 0 \\ 0 & 0 & -12 \end{bmatrix} (MPa).$$

Assuming $\sigma_{yield} = 90\ MPa$ and using a safety factor $\mathrm{SF} = 1.2$, determine whether failure by yielding occurs at the point for (a) the maximum shear stress theory and (b) the maximum distortion energy theory.

Solution

The principal stresses are the eigenvalues of $[\sigma_{ij}]$.

$$\sigma_1 = 65\ MPa$$

$$\sigma_2 = 1\ MPa$$

$$\sigma_3 = -12\ MPa$$

Notice that the principal stresses are arranged in descending order: $\sigma_1 \geq \sigma_2 \geq \sigma_3$.

a) $|\sigma_1 - \sigma_3| = 77\ MPa$

$$\frac{\sigma_{yield}}{\mathrm{SF}} = \frac{90\ MPa}{1.2} = 75\ MPa$$

Since $77\ MPa > 75\ MPa$, failure by yielding occurs according to the maximum shearing stress theory.

b) $\sqrt{\frac{1}{2}\left[(\sigma_1 - \sigma_2)^2 + (\sigma_1 - \sigma_3)^2 + (\sigma_2 - \sigma_3)^2\right]} = \sqrt{\frac{1}{2}\left[(65-1)^2 + (65+12)^2 + (1+12)^2\right]} = 71.4\ MPa$

Since $71.4\ MPa < 75\ MPa$, failure by yielding does not occur according to the maximum distortion energy theory.

Notice that, as mentioned in the previous section, the maximum shearing stress theory is more conservative than the maximum distortion energy theory.

Problem 4.4-2

A circular bar of tensile yield strength $\sigma_{yield} = 350\ MPa$ is subjected to a combined state of loading defined by the bending moment $M = 8\ kN \times m$ and torque $T = 24\ kN \times m$. Calculate the diameter d which the bar must have to achieve a factor of safety $SF = 2$. Apply the following theories: (a) maximum principal stress; (b) maximum shear stress; and (c) maximum energy of distortion.

Solution

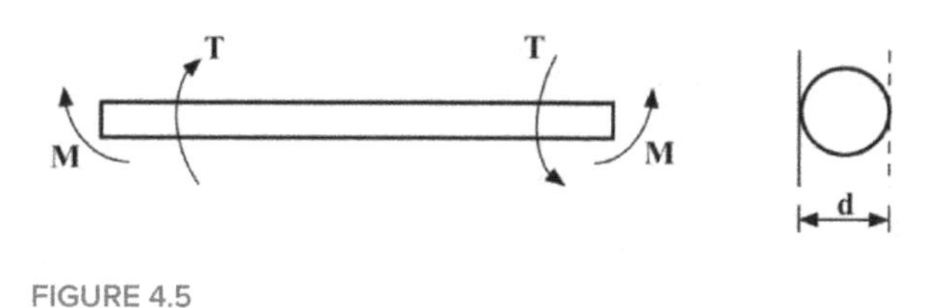

FIGURE 4.5

This problem is more challenging than the previous one. It differs from the previous one in two ways. First, in Problem 4.4-1, $[\sigma_{ij}]$ was given to us. In this problem, we need to establish $[\sigma_{ij}]$ at the most critical point in the structure. Therefore, we have to move from external loading to stress. Second, the unknown in this problem is the diameter d. It is a design problem rather than an analysis problem.

$$\sigma = -\frac{My}{I} = \frac{32M}{\pi d^3}$$

$$\tau = \frac{Tr}{J} = \frac{16T}{\pi d^3}$$

The principal stresses (at the most critical point) are:

$$\sigma_1 = \frac{\sigma}{2} + \frac{1}{2}\sqrt{\sigma^2 + 4\tau^2}$$

$$\sigma_2 = 0$$

$$\sigma_3 = \frac{\sigma}{2} - \frac{1}{2}\sqrt{\sigma^2 + 4\tau^2}$$

Notice again that the principal stresses we arranged in descending order, such that: $\sigma_1 \geq \sigma_2 \geq \sigma_3.$

Therefore,

$$\sigma_1 = \frac{16}{\pi d^3}\left(M + \sqrt{M^2 + T^2}\right)$$

$$\sigma_2 = 0$$

$$\sigma_3 = \frac{16}{\pi d^3}\left(M - \sqrt{M^2 + T^2}\right)$$

a) maximum principal stress theory:

$$\frac{16}{\pi d^3}\left(M + \sqrt{M^2 + T^2}\right) = \frac{\sigma_{yield}}{SF}$$

$$\Rightarrow d = 98.9 \text{ mm}$$

b) maximum shearing stress theory:

$$\frac{32}{\pi d^3}\sqrt{M^2 + T^2} = \frac{\sigma_{yield}}{SF}$$

$$\Rightarrow d = 113.7 \text{ mm}$$

c) maximum energy of distortion theory:

$$\sqrt{\sigma^2 + 3\tau^2} = \frac{\sigma_{yield}}{SF} \Rightarrow$$

$$\frac{16}{\pi d^3}\sqrt{4M^2 + 3T^2} = \frac{\sigma_{yield}}{SF}$$

$$\Rightarrow d = 109 \text{ mm}$$

Notice again that the maximum shearing stress theory is the most conservative among all three theories.

4.5 Final Remarks

We only covered failure by yielding in this chapter. However, it is important to mention that there are other types of failure in structural engineering that can be more catastrophic, such as failure by structural instability (buckling), failure by excessive deformation (jamming), or failure by fracture. Buckling will be covered in detail in chapter 9.

Problems

4.1. The state of stress at a point is defined by the following (3×3) matrix:

$$\sigma_{ij} = \begin{bmatrix} 70 & 0 & 0 \\ 0 & -30 & 0 \\ 0 & 0 & 10 \end{bmatrix} (MPa).$$

Assuming $\sigma_{yield} = 110\ MPa$ and using a safety factor $SF = 1.25$, determine whether failure occurs at the point for (a) the maximum shear stress theory and (b) the maximum distortion energy theory.

4.2. At a point in a structural member, the state of stress in reference to an *xyz*-coordinate system is defined by the (3×3) real symmetric matrix:

$$\sigma_{ij} = \begin{bmatrix} 0 & 30 & 0 \\ 30 & 60 & -70 \\ 0 & -70 & 0 \end{bmatrix} (MPa).$$

Assuming $\sigma_{yield} = 150\ MPa$, determine whether failure by yielding occurs at the point for (a) the maximum principal stress theory, (b) the maximum distortion energy theory, and (c) the maximum shear stress theory.

4.3. At a point on the hub of a flywheel, the state of stress is defined by the following (3×3) real symmetric matrix

$$\sigma_{ij} = \begin{bmatrix} 125 & 75 & 0 \\ 75 & -15 & 0 \\ 0 & 0 & 0 \end{bmatrix} (MPa).$$

Assuming the flywheel material has a yield stress of $\sigma_{yield} = 300\ MPa$,

a) determine the factor of safety according to the maximum shear stress theory (Tresca)
b) determine the factor of safety according to the maximum distortion energy theory (von Mises)
c) determine which criterion, Tresca or von Mises, is more conservative

4.4. A circular cylindrical shaft is made of steel with yield stress $\sigma_{yield} = 280\ MPa$. The shaft is subjected simultaneously to a static bending moment $M = 10\ kN \times m$ and a static torsion moment $T = 15\ kN \times m$. Using a factor of safety of 1.50, determine the minimum safe diameter for the shaft (a) according to the octahedral shear stress theory and (b) according to the maximum shear stress theory.

4.5. A 30-mm diameter rod made of a ductile material with a yield strength of 350 MPa is subjected to a bending moment of 175 $N \times m$ and to a torque of 125 $N \times m$. An axial tensile force is then gradually applied. What is the value of the axial force when yielding of the rod occurs? Solve the problem in two ways: using (a) the maximum shear stress theory and (b) the maximum distortion energy theory.

4.6.

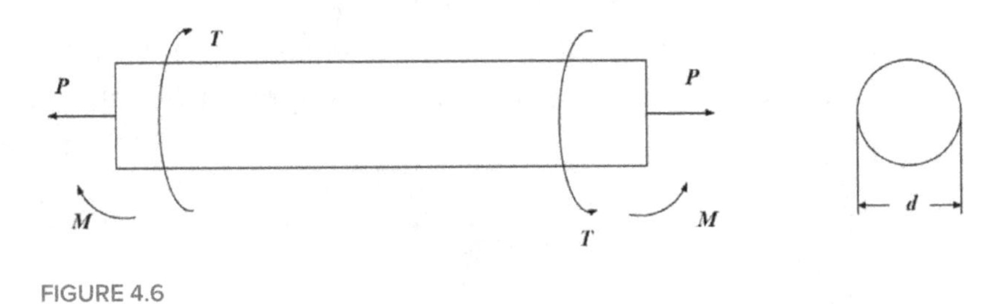

FIGURE 4.6

A circular shaft of 0.10 m diameter is subjected to end loads $P = 50\ kN$, $M = 5\ kN \cdot m,\ and\ T = 10\ kN \cdot m$. Let $\sigma_{yield} = 280\ MPa$. What is the factor of safety? Assume that failure occurs according to the octahedral shear stress theory.

4.7.

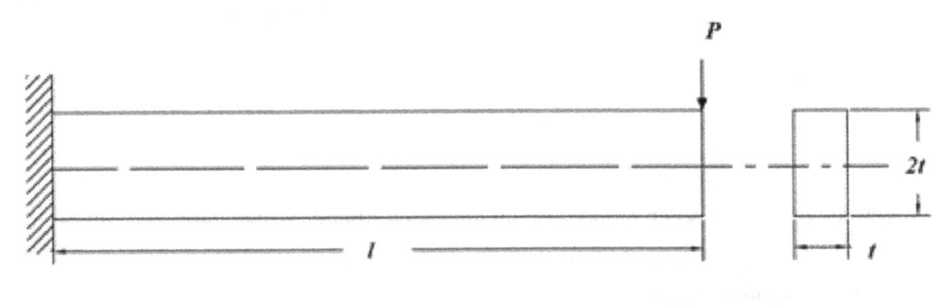

FIGURE 4.7

Determine the width t of the cantilever beam of height 2t and length $l = 0.50\ m$ subjected to concentrated load $P = 500\ N$ at its free end. Apply the maximum energy of distortion theory. The tensile and compressive strengths of the material are the same: $\sigma_{yield} = 280\ MPa$.

4.8. A circular shaft is subjected to a combined state of loading defined by bending moment $M = 10\ kN \cdot m$ and torque $T = 25\ kN \cdot m$. Calculate the required shaft diameter d in order to achieve a factor of safety $SF = 2.1$. Apply (a) the maximum shear stress theory and (b) the maximum distortion energy theory.

Assume $\sigma_{yield} = 350\ MPa$ for the shaft material.

4.9. A solid cylinder of radius 60 mm is subjected to a twisting moment T and axial load P. Assume that the maximum distortion energy theory governs and that the yield strength of the material is $\sigma_{yield} = 280\ MPa$. Determine the maximum twisting moment consistent with elastic behavior of the bar for (a) $P = 0$ and (b) $P = 500\pi\ kN$.

4.10. The state of stress at a point is defined by:

$$\sigma_{ij} = \begin{bmatrix} 100 & 70 & \tau \\ 70 & -50 & 0 \\ \tau & 0 & 65 \end{bmatrix} (MPa),$$

where τ is an unknown positive ($\tau > 0$). Assume $\sigma_{yield} = 350\ MPa$.

a) Find the value of τ for a safety factor of 1.25 according to the maximum distortion energy theory (von Mises).
b) For the value of τ found in (a), what is the safety factor according to the maximum shear stress theory of failure?

References

Budynas, Richard G. *Advanced Strength and Applied Stress Analysis.* New York City: McGraw-Hill, 1977.

Curtis, H. D. *Fundamentals of Aircraft Structural Analysis.* New York City: McGraw-Hill, 1997.

Ugural, Ansel. C. *Mechanical Design: An Integrated Approach.* New York City: McGraw-Hill, 2004.

Ugural, Ansel C., and Saul K. Fenster. *Advanced Mechanics of Materials and Applied Elasticity.* 5th ed. Upper Saddle River: Prentice Hall, 2012.

CHAPTER 5

Bending of Beams

5.1 Introduction

We will discuss in this chapter beam bending. We will focus on Euler–Bernoulli* beams. An Euler–Bernoulli beam is a straight one characterized by a very large span compared to its cross section. The ratio between the largest dimension of the cross section and the span must be less than 1/20. In structural engineering, one can encounter other types of beams, such as Timoshenko beams**. A Timoshenko beam is a stubby straight beam in which the span is not very large compared to the cross section. In addition to straight beams, one can encounter curved beams.

5.2 Pure Symmetric Bending

In beam analysis, when investigating the internal forces at a cross section of a beam subject to external loading, such as the one shown in the figure below.

---

* Named after Leonhard Euler (1707–1783), a prolific Swiss mathematician who contributed enormously to applied mechanics. Bernoulli is a member of the Bernoulli family that, for generations, held prominent teaching positions at Basel University in Switzerland. Indeed, Euler himself studied under the supervision of Johann Bernoulli at Basel University.

** Named after Stephen Timoshenko. He was a famous engineer born in Ukraine in 1878. He immigrated to Yugoslavia after the Bolshevik revolution and finally settled at Stanford University in California. He died on May 29, 1972. Timoshenko is considered the most prominent contributor to solid mechanics in the 20th century.

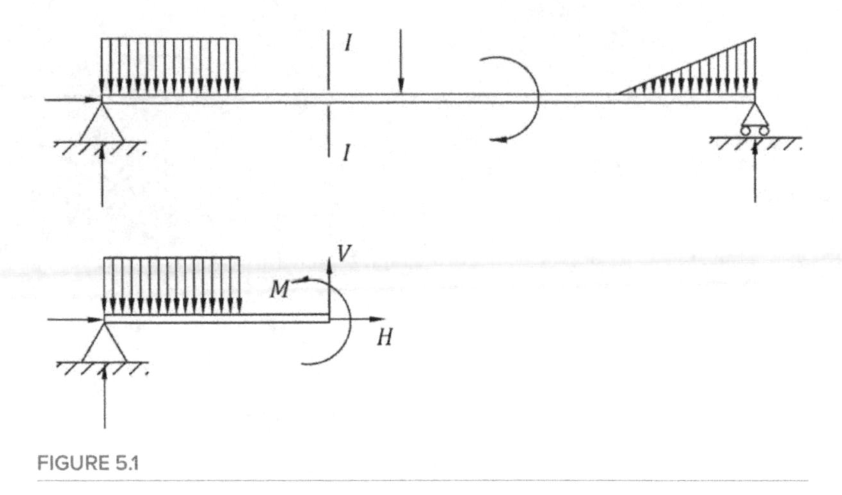

FIGURE 5.1

Three internal resultant forces are observed at the beam cross section upon making cut I-I. These are the bending moment M, the shear force V, and the axial force H. Pure bending refers to the case when bending moment is observed at the cross section, but the shear force is not there. An example of pure bending is shown in the cantilever beam in **figure 5.2**.

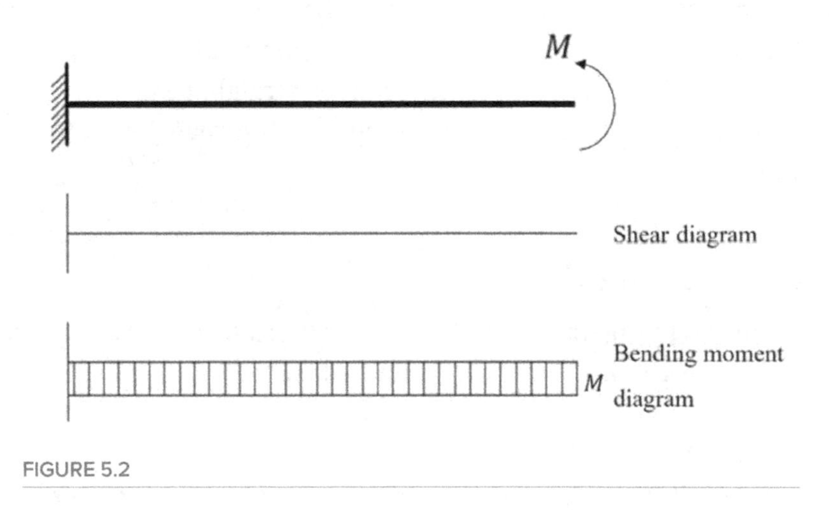

FIGURE 5.2

Symmetric bending refers to a symmetric cross section—one that possesses an axis of symmetry. Examples of a symmetric cross section are shown in **figure 5.3**.

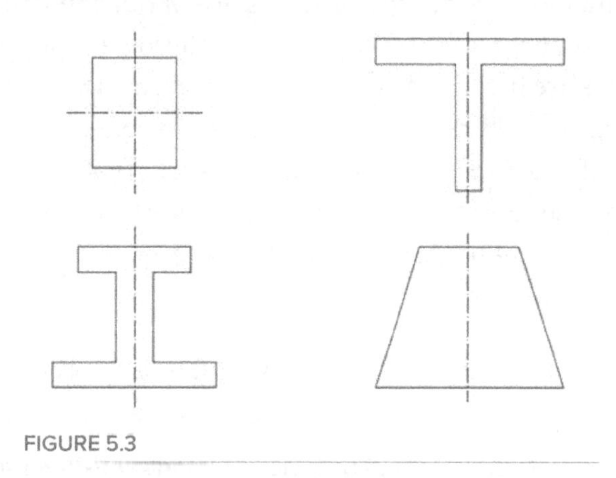

FIGURE 5.3

When the cross section is unsymmetric, such as in **figure 5.4**, bending is called unsymmetric bending.

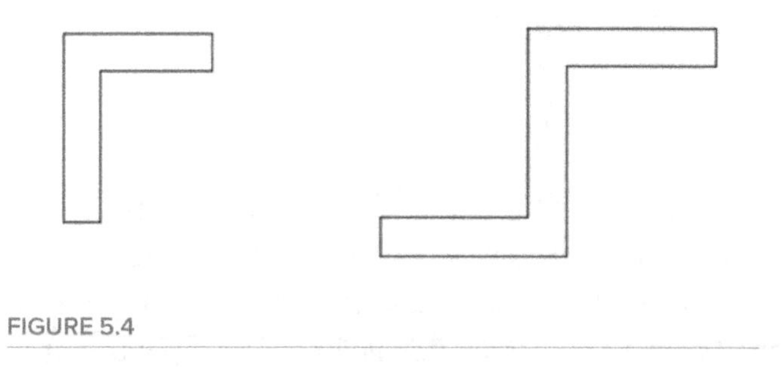

FIGURE 5.4

5.3 Neutral Axis

The following sign convention, adopted in the United States, is shown in **figure 5.5**.

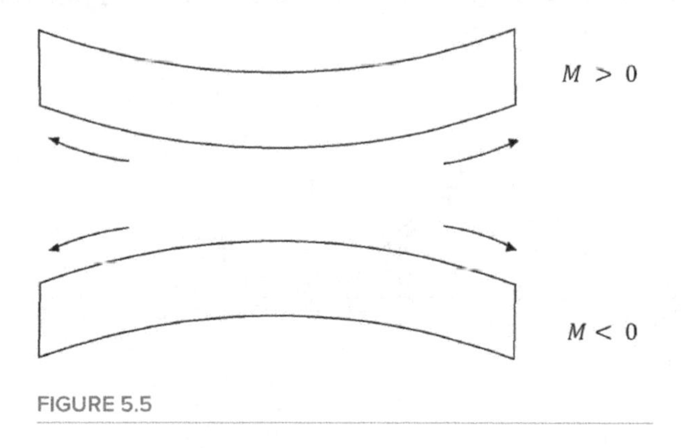

FIGURE 5.5

In a positive bending moment, the lower fibers are in tension while the upper fibers are in compression. In a negative bending moment, the lower fibers are in compression while the upper fibers are in tension. It seems intuitive from the above that there should be fibers in-between that are neither in tension nor in compression. The neutral surface is defined to be the locus or set of points in the space that will be neither in tension nor in compression. The intersection of the neutral surface with the cross section of the beam is said to be the neutral axis (N.A.). Along the neutral axis, the stress is zero.

5.4 Stress Formula for Pure Symmetric Bending

Our objective is to establish the state of stress at a point in the cross section of a beam subject to pure symmetric bending. We will use the so called semi-inverse method. The state of stress at a specific point is completely defined by the (3×3) real symmetric matrix:

$$[\sigma_{ij}] = \begin{bmatrix} \sigma_x & \tau_{xy} & \tau_{xz} \\ \tau_{yx} & \sigma_y & \tau_{yz} \\ \tau_{zx} & \tau_{zy} & \sigma_z \end{bmatrix}_{(3\times3)}.$$

We will assume that $\sigma_y = \sigma_z = \tau_{xy} = \tau_{xz} = \tau_{yz} = 0$. Indeed, the theory of elasticity verifies that our assumption is well justified when studying pure symmetric bending in an Euler–Bernoulli beam. Furthermore, we will assume that the normal bending stress σ_x at a particular fiber in the cross section is directly proportional to the distance y of the fiber from the neutral axis (i.e., $\sigma_x = ky$ where k is a proportionality constant yet to be determined).

For symmetric bending (i.e., when the cross section has an axis of symmetry) it seems intuitive that σ_x is a function of y only. We will see later in this chapter that this is not true for unsymmetric bending. In such a case, σ_x will be a function of both y and z.

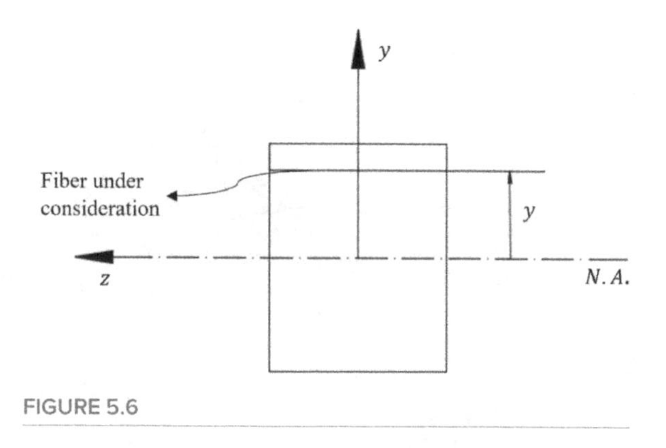

FIGURE 5.6

From statics, we know

$$\sum F_x = 0 \Rightarrow$$

$$\int_A \sigma_x dA = 0 \Rightarrow$$

$$\int_A kydA = 0 \Rightarrow$$

$$k\int_A ydA = 0 \Rightarrow$$

$$\int_A ydA = 0,$$

which shows that the neutral axis, indeed, must pass through the centroid of the cross section. Therefore, the neutral axis is a centroidal axis.

Also from statics, we know:

$$\sum M_z = 0 \Rightarrow$$

$$\int_A y\sigma_x dA + M = 0 \Rightarrow$$

$$\int_A ykydA + M = 0 \Rightarrow$$

$$k\int_A y^2 dA = -M \Rightarrow$$

$$k = -\frac{M}{I}.$$

We conclude that:

$$\sigma = -\frac{My}{I}.$$

The above formula gives us the normal bending stress for pure symmetric bending. In the SI system of units, the unit of M is N×m*, the unit of y is m, and the unit of I is m^4. Therefore, the unit of σ will be $Nmm / m^4 = N / m^2 = Pa$. One Pa is very small in structural engineering. We usually express σ in MPa. The "—" sign in the formula automatically takes care of the sign of the stress.

A positive σ corresponds to tensile stress, while a negative σ corresponds to compressive stress. Notice also that, implicitly, in the above formula, we meant:

$$\sigma_x = -\frac{M_z y}{I_z}.$$

We were able to drop the subscripts, since there was no way for any confusion to arise in this case.

EXAMPLE

Draw the stress distribution for the following pure symmetric bending when the beam cross section is rectangular.

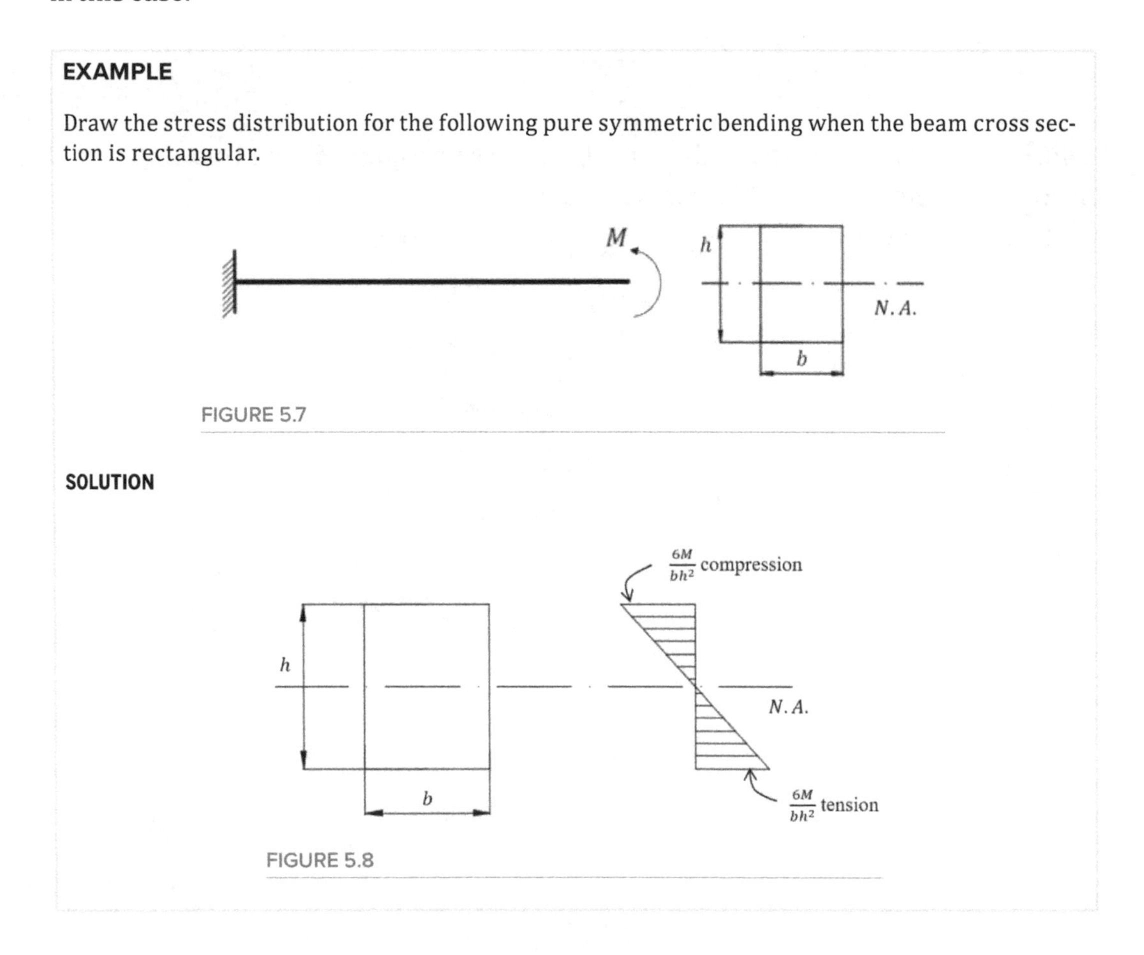

FIGURE 5.7

SOLUTION

FIGURE 5.8

* The SI convention is to write N·m; however, I am using N × m to emphasize that this is a moment and not work Nm = Joule.

EXAMPLE

Draw the stress distribution for the following pure symmetric bending when the beam cross section is as shown in **figure 5.9**.

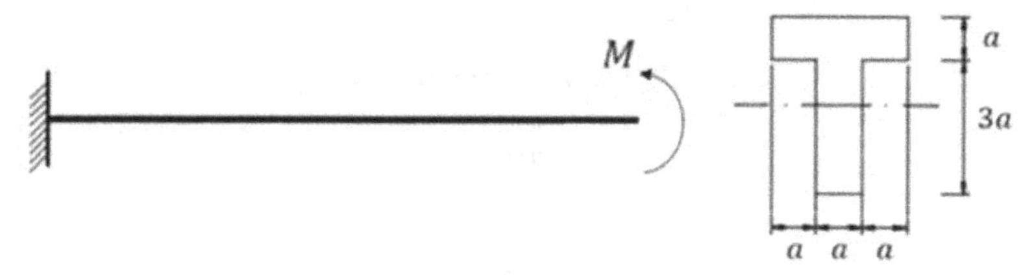

FIGURE 5.9

SOLUTION First, we need to determine the location of the neutral axis.

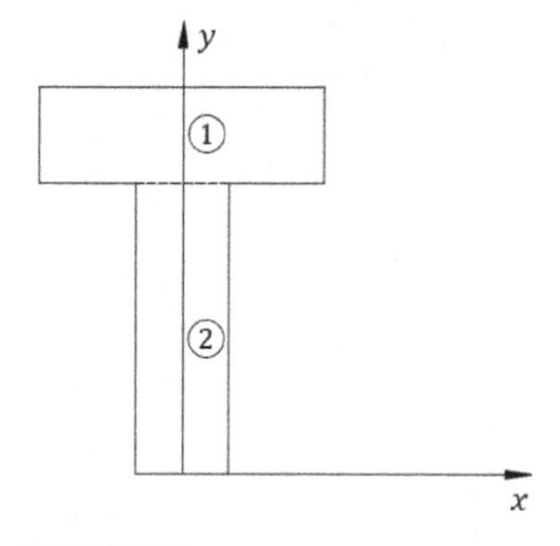

FIGURE 5.10

$$A_1 = 3a^2; \bar{y}_1 = 3.5a;$$

$$A_2 = 3a^2; \bar{y}_2 = 1.5a;$$

$$\bar{y} = \frac{A_1\bar{y}_1 + A_2\bar{y}_2}{A_1 + A_2} = \frac{(3a^2)(3.5a) + (3a^2)(1.5a)}{3a^2 + 3a^2} = 2.5a$$

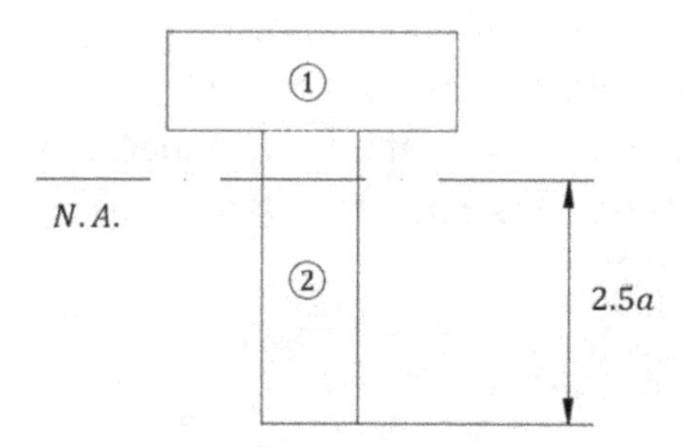

FIGURE 5.11

Next, we need to compute the area moment of inertia I about the neutral axis.

$$I = I_{①} + I_{②}$$

$$I_{①} = \frac{1}{12}(3a)(a)^3 + (3a)(a)(a)^2 = 3.25a^4$$

$$I_{②} = \frac{1}{12}(a)(3a)^3 + (a)(3a)(a)^2 = 5.25a^4$$

$$\Rightarrow \quad I = 8.5a^4$$

$$\sigma_{max(tensile)} = \frac{M(2.5a)}{8.5a^4} = \frac{5}{17}\frac{M}{a^3}$$

$$\sigma_{max(compressive)} = \frac{M(1.5a)}{8.5a^4} = \frac{3}{17}\frac{M}{a^3}$$

The stress distribution is shown in **figure 5.12**.

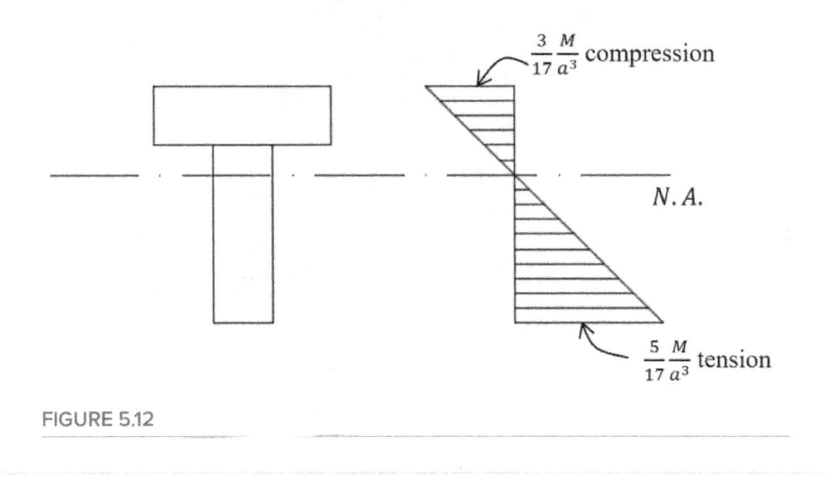

FIGURE 5.12

5.5 Unsymmetrical Bending

In the previous section, we found that, for pure symmetric bending, $\sigma_x = -\frac{M_z y}{I_z}$, which means that a bending moment about the *z*-axis (M_z) is applied. Unsymmetric bending takes place in one of these two scenarios: The first case is when the cross section is still symmetric, but the bending moment is now oblique. It is neither applied about the *z*-axis nor applied about the *y*-axis. The second case occurs when the cross section is unsymmetrical to begin with.

Case (1): Unsymmetric Bending (Symmetric Cross Section)

This is the case when M is neither applied about the *z*-axis nor applied about the *y*-axis. The principle of superposition can be used.

$$\sigma = -\frac{M_z}{I_z}y + \frac{M_y}{I_y}z$$

EXAMPLE

For the unsymmetrical bending shown in the figure below:

i. Determine the stress σ_x at point A.
ii. Determine the orientation of the neutral axis (N.A.).

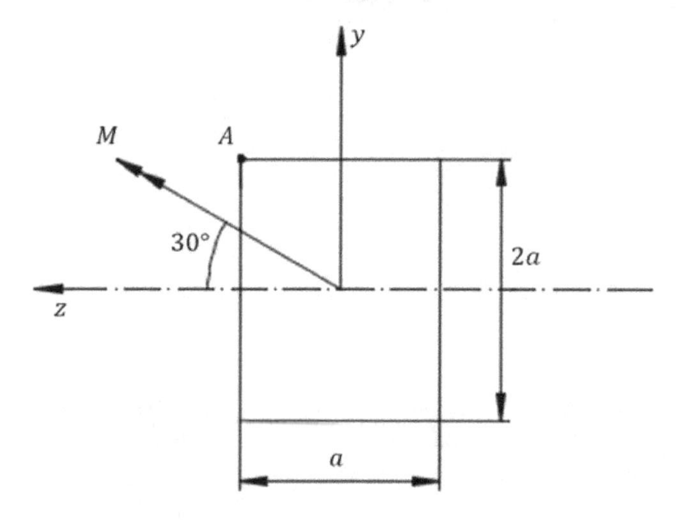

FIGURE 5.13

SOLUTION Notice that for unsymmetric bending, is a function of y and z.

i. stress at point A:

$$\sigma_{x_A} = -\frac{(M)(\cos 30^\circ)}{\frac{1}{12}(a)(2a)^3}(a) + \frac{(M)(\sin 30^\circ)}{\frac{1}{12}(2a)(a)^3}\left(\frac{a}{2}\right) = 0.201\frac{M}{a^3}$$

Since σ_{xA} is positive, this means it is tensile.

ii. orientation of the neutral axis:

The orientation of the neutral axis is determined by setting $\sigma_x = 0$:

$$\sigma_x = -\frac{M_z}{I_z}y + \frac{M_y}{I_y}z = 0$$

$$\Rightarrow \qquad y = \left(\frac{I_z}{I_y}\right)\left(\frac{M_y}{M_z}\right)z$$

$$\Rightarrow \qquad y = \left[\frac{\frac{1}{12}(a)(2a)^3}{\frac{1}{12}(2a)(a)^3}\right]\frac{(M\sin 30^\circ)}{(M\cos 30^\circ)}(z)$$

$$\Rightarrow \qquad y = (4\tan 30^\circ)z.$$

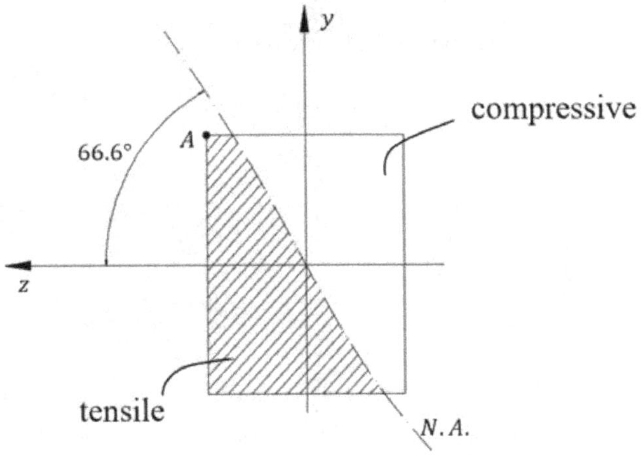

FIGURE 5.14

Notice that the neutral axis is still passing through the centroid of the cross section. However, it is now neither the *z*-axis nor the *y*-axis. The neutral axis still splits the cross section into two regions, one tensile and one compressive.

Case (2): Unsymmetric Bending (Unsymmetric Cross Section)

We will also be using the so-called semi-inverse method in order to derive the general flexural formula. In order to determine the state of stress at a specific point for unsymmetric bending, we will also assume that $\sigma_y = \sigma_z = \tau_{xy} = \tau_{xz} = \tau_{yz} = 0$. Furthermore, we will assume that:

$$\sigma_x = c_1 + c_2 y + c_3 z,$$

where c_1, c_2, and c_3 are three constants yet to be determined. Notice that the above is the most general linear expression of σ_x as a function of y and z.

From statics, we know:

$$\sum F_x = 0 \quad \Rightarrow$$

$$\int_A \sigma_x dA = 0 \Rightarrow$$

$$\int_A (c_1 + c_2 y + c_3 z) dA = 0 \Rightarrow$$

$$c_1 A + c_2 \int_A y dA + c_3 \int_A z dA = 0.$$

It is always possible to choose the origin of the coordinate system at the centroid of the cross section, thus forcing $\int_A y dA$ and $\int_A z dA$ to become zero.

Therefore,

$$c_1 A = 0 \Rightarrow \quad c_1 = 0.$$

Also from statics, we know:

$$\sum M_z = 0 \Rightarrow \quad \int_A y(c_2 y + c_3 z) dA + M_z = 0$$

$$\Rightarrow c_2 \int_A y^2 dA + c_3 \int_A yz dA = -M_z$$

$$\Rightarrow c_2 I_z - c_3 I_{yz} = -M_z.$$

Also from statics, we know:

$$\sum M_y = 0 \Rightarrow \quad \int_A z(c_2 y + c_3 z) dA + M_y = 0$$

$$\Rightarrow c_2 \int_A yz dA + c_3 \int_A z^2 dA = M_y$$

$$\Rightarrow -c_2 I_{yz} + c_3 I_y = M_y.$$

Solving the above two linear equations simultaneously, we obtain:

$$c_2 = \frac{M_y I_{yz} - M_z I_y}{I_y I_z - I_{yz}^2}$$

$$c_3 = \frac{M_y I_z - M_z I_{yz}}{I_y I_z - I_{yz}^2}.$$

Therefore,

$$\sigma_x = \frac{\left(M_y I_{yz} - M_z I_y\right)y + \left(M_y I_z - M_z I_{yz}\right)z}{I_y I_z - I_{yz}^2}.$$

The above is the general flexural formula.

Notice that in deriving the above formula, we used the definitions in appendix D, where:

$$I_y = \int_A z^2 dA$$

$$I_z = \int_A y^2 dA$$

$$I_{yz} = -\int_A yz dA.$$

Many textbooks define the product of inertia without the (–) sign. In this case, the general flexural formula will be slightly modified.

EXAMPLE

For the cross section and loading shown in the figure below, compute the bending stress at point A. Also determine the orientation of the neutral axis. C is the centroid of the slender angle.

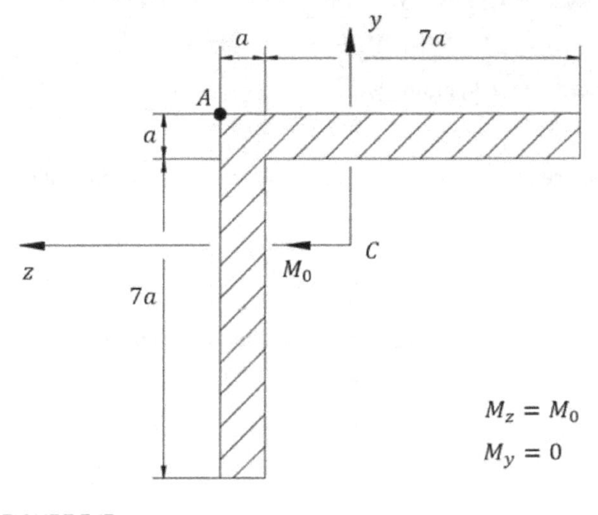

FIGURE 5.15

SOLUTION To work out the problem, the following steps will be taken.
Determination of the location of the centroid of the cross section is shown in **figure 5.16**.

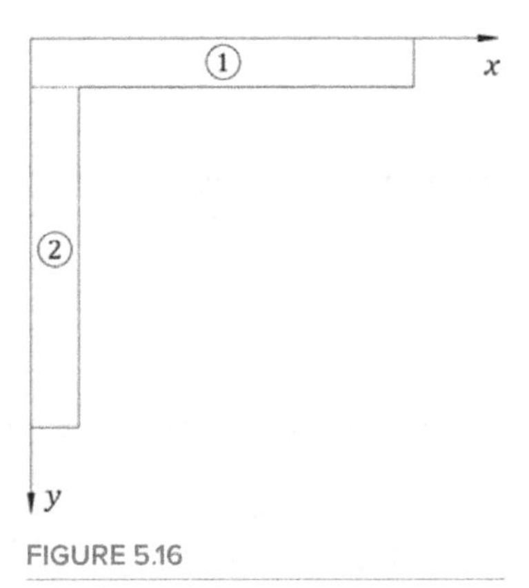

FIGURE 5.16

Notice that in the figure above, the xy-coordinate system is not the original coordinate system. It is a transient temporary system used to determine the location of the centroid. It will be dropped after being used.

$$A_1 - 8a^2;\ \overline{x_1} = 4a;\ \overline{y_1} = 0.5a;$$

$$A_2 = 7a^2;\ \overline{x_2} = 0.5a;\ \overline{y_2} = 4.5a;$$

$$\bar{x} = \frac{A_1\bar{x}_1 + A_2\bar{x}_2}{A_1 + A_2} = \frac{(8a^2)(4a) + (7a^2)(0.5a)}{8a^2 + 7a^2} = 2.367a$$

$$\bar{y} = \frac{A_1\bar{y}_1 + A_2\bar{y}_2}{A_1 + A_2} = \frac{(8a^2)(0.5a) + (7a^2)(4.5a)}{8a^2 + 7a^2} = 2.367a$$

Therefore, as predicted due to symmetry,

$$\bar{x} = \bar{y} = 2.367a.$$

Determination of the area moment of inertia I_x, I_y and the area product of inertia I_{xy}.

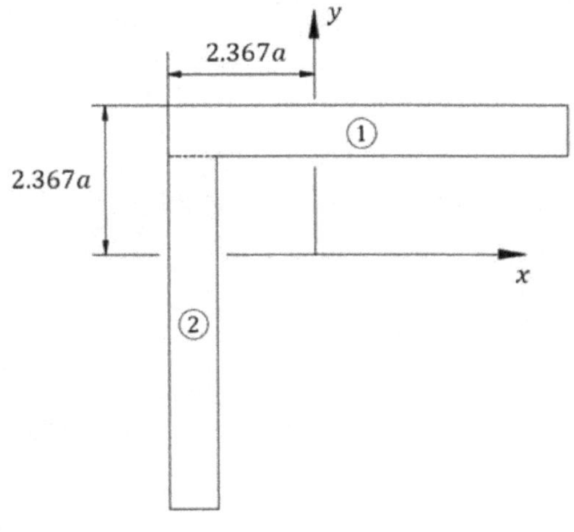

FIGURE 5.17

Again, notice that the xy-coordinate system is not the original coordinate system. It is only a transient temporary system that needs to be dropped later on.

$$I_x = I_{x①} + I_{x②}$$

$$I_{x①} = \frac{1}{12}(8a)(a)^3 + (8a)(a)(1.867a)^2$$

$$= 28.55a^4$$

$$I_{x②} = \frac{1}{12}(a)(7a)^3 + (a)(7a)(2.133a)^2$$

$$= 60.43a^4$$

$$\Rightarrow \quad I_x = 88.98a^4$$

$$I_y = I_{y①} + I_{y②}$$

$$I_{y①} = \frac{1}{12}(a)(8a)^3 + (a)(8a)(1.633a)^2$$

$$= 64.00a^4$$

$$I_{y②} = \frac{1}{12}(7a)(a)^3 + (7a)(a)(1.867a)^2$$

$$= 24.98a^4$$

$$\Rightarrow \quad I_y = 88.98a^4$$

Notice that $I_x = I_y$, which is not surprising (due to symmetry).

$$I_{xy} = I_{xy①} + I_{xy②}$$

$$I_{xy①} = 0 - (1.633a)(1.867a)(8a)(a)$$

$$= -24.39a^4$$

$$I_{xy②} = 0 - (-1.867a)(-2.133a)(7a)(a)$$

$$= -27.88a^4$$

$$\Rightarrow \quad I_{xy} = -52.27a^4$$

Therefore,

$$I_x = 88.98a^4$$

$$I_y = 88.98a^4$$

$$I_{xy} = -52.27a^4.$$

Determination of the area moment of inertia I_x, I_x and the area product of inertia I_{xy} is shown below:

$$I_y = 88.98a^4$$

$$I_z = 88.98a^4$$

$$I_{yz} = 52.27a^4.$$

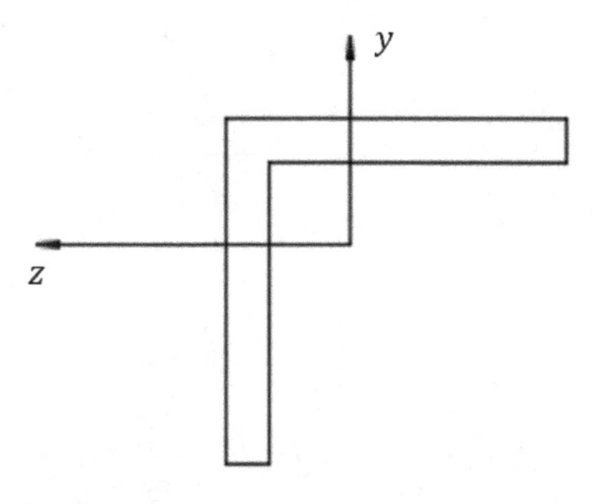

FIGURE 5.18

Calculation of σ_x at point A, using the general flexural formula is as follows:

$$\sigma_x = \frac{\left(M_y I_{yz} - M_z I_y\right)y + \left(M_y I_z - M_z I_{yz}\right)z}{I_y I_z - I_{yz}^2}$$

$$= \frac{-(M_0)(88.98a^4)(2.367a) - (M_0)(52.27a^4)(2.367a)}{(88.98a^4)(88.98a^4) - (52.27a^4)^2}$$

$$= \frac{-210.61566M_0a^5 - 334.33875M_0a^5}{5185.2875a^8}$$

$$= -0.0645\frac{M_0}{a^3}.$$

Notice that now yz-coordinate is the original coordinate system of the problem.

The negative sign means compressive.

In order to determine the orientation of the neutral axis, we set $\sigma_x =$ ⍰:

$$\left(M_y I_{yz} - M_z I_z\right)y + \left(M_y I_z - M_z I_{yz}\right)z = 0$$

$$\Rightarrow \quad -\left(M_0 I_y\right)y - \left(M_0\right)\left(I_{yz}\right)z = 0$$

$$\Rightarrow \quad yI_y + zI_{yz} = 0$$

$$\Rightarrow \quad y = -\frac{I_{yz}}{I_y}z$$

$$= -\frac{52.27a^4}{88.98a^4}z$$

$$y = -0.5874z.$$

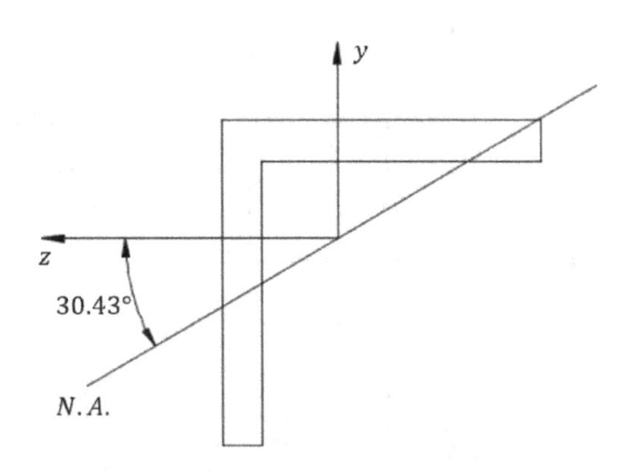

FIGURE 5.19

Notice that the neutral axis (N.A.) again passes through the centroid. It splits the cross section into two regions: one compressive and one tensile.

Alternatively, we can do the problem by first rotating the original coordinate system and switching to the principal coordinate system.

Determination of the principal coordinate system is shown in **figure 5.20**.

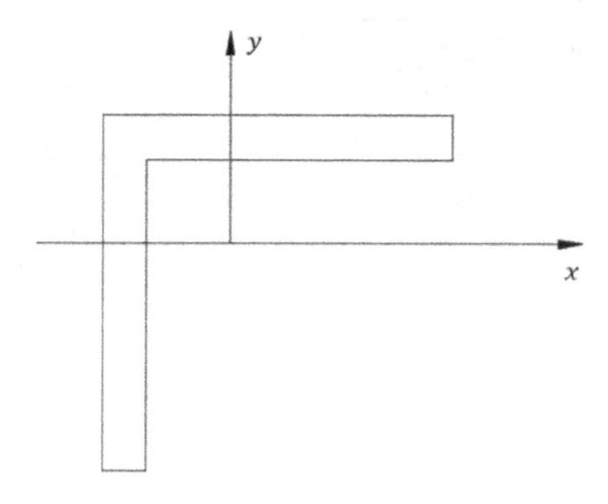

FIGURE 5.20

$$I_{\min}^{\max} = \frac{I_x + I_y}{2} \pm \frac{1}{2}\sqrt{\left(I_x - I_y\right)^2 + 4I_{xy}^2}$$

$$\Rightarrow I_{max} = 88.98a^4 + 52.27a^4 = 141.25a^4$$

$$I_{min} = 88.98a^4 - 52.27a^4 = 36.71a^4$$

$$\tan 2\theta = \frac{2I_{xy}}{I_x - I_y}$$

$$\Rightarrow \theta = 45^\circ \text{ or } \theta = 135^\circ$$

To find out which axis corresponds to I_{max} and which corresponds to I_{min}, we use:

$$I_{x'}(\theta) = \frac{I_x + I_y}{2} + \frac{I_x - I_y}{2}\cos 2\theta + I_{xy}\sin 2\theta$$

$$I_{x'}(45^\circ) = 88.98a^4 - 52.27a^4 = 36.71a^4.$$

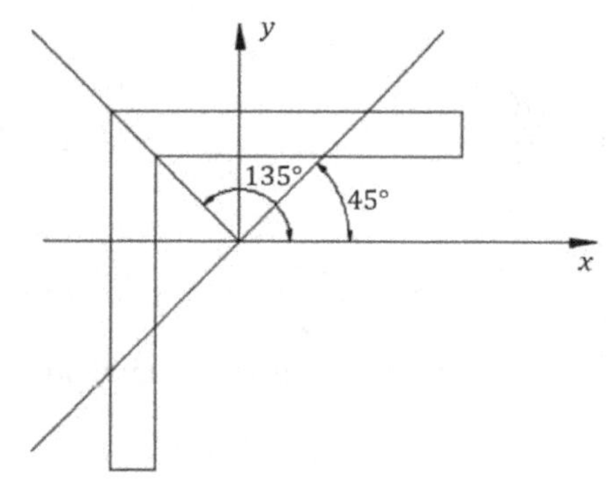

FIGURE 5.21

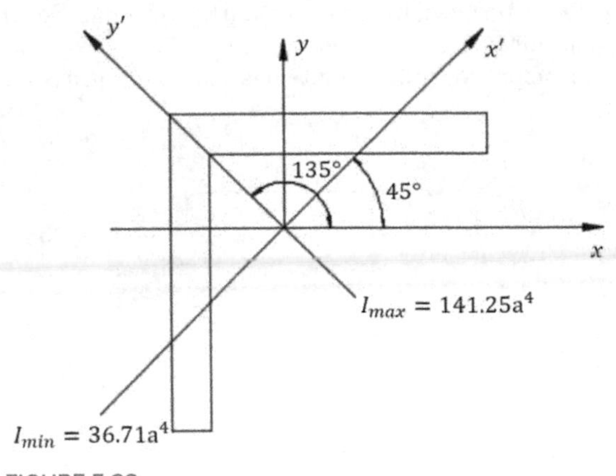

FIGURE 5.22

In the new primed principal coordinate system, $I_{y'z'} = 0$.
Therefore, we can now use the shortcut formula:

$$\sigma_x = -\frac{M_{z'}}{I_{z'}}y' + \frac{M_{y'}}{I_{y'}}z'.$$

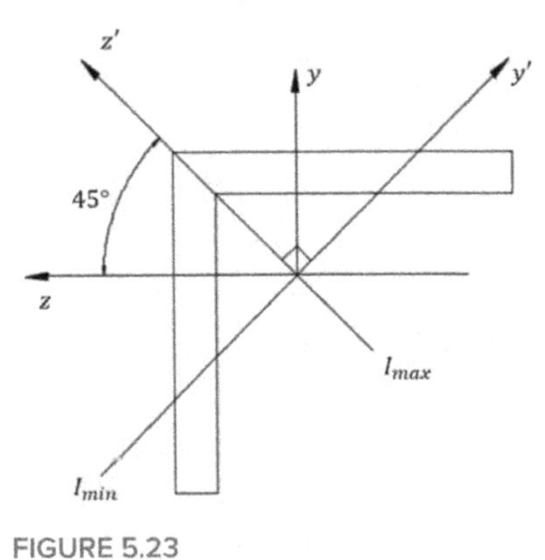

FIGURE 5.23

At point A:

$$\sigma_{x_A} = -\frac{(M_0)(1/\sqrt{2})}{141.25a^4}(0) + \frac{-(M_0)(1/\sqrt{2})}{36.71a^4}(2.367a)(\sqrt{2})$$

$$= -0.0645\frac{M_0}{a^3}.$$

This is exactly the same result obtained using the previous method.

Determination of the orientation of the neutral axis is as follows:

$$\sigma_x = 0 \;\Rightarrow\; -\frac{M_{z'}}{I_{z'}}y' + \frac{M_{y'}}{I_{y'}}z' = 0$$

$$\Rightarrow \frac{M_{z'}}{I_{z'}}y' = \frac{M_{y'}}{I_{y'}}z'$$

$$\Rightarrow y' = \frac{I_{z'}}{I_{y'}}\frac{M_{y'}}{M_{z'}}z' = \frac{141.25a^4}{36.71a^4}\left(\frac{-M_0\frac{1}{\sqrt{2}}}{M_0\frac{1}{\sqrt{2}}}\right)z'$$

$$\Rightarrow y' = -3.8477z'.$$

Therefore, the angle that the neutral axis makes with the z-axis is:

$$\tan^{-1}(3.8477) - 45° = 75.43° - 45°$$

$$= 30.43°.$$

This is exactly the same result obtained in the previous method.

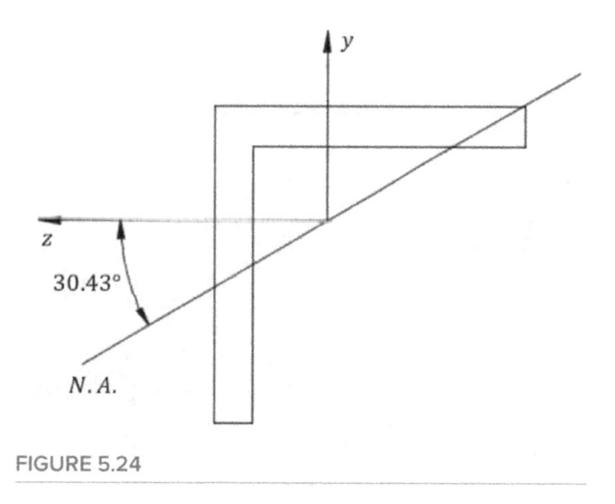

FIGURE 5.24

Problems

5.1–5.3

For the cantilevered beam subject to pure bending M as shown in the figure below and for the given cross sections, determine the location and the value of the maximum tensile normal stress. Also, determine the location and the value of the maximum compressive normal stress.

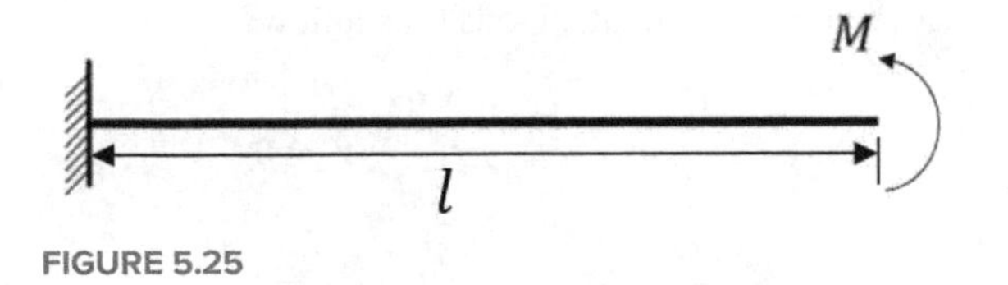

FIGURE 5.25

5.1.

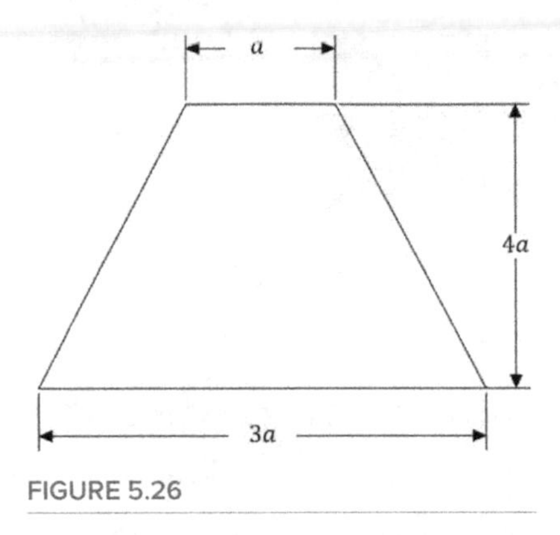

FIGURE 5.26

5.2.

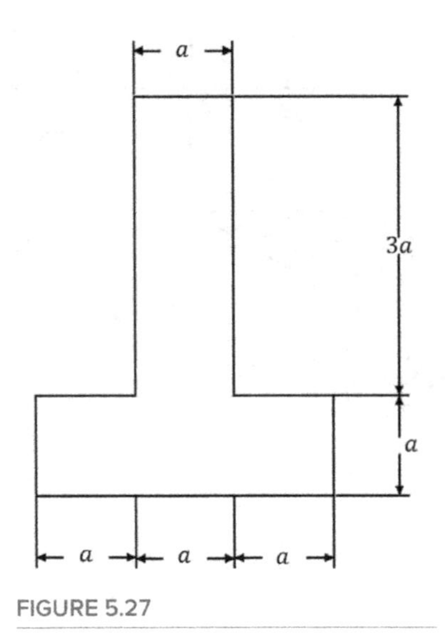

FIGURE 5.27

5.3.

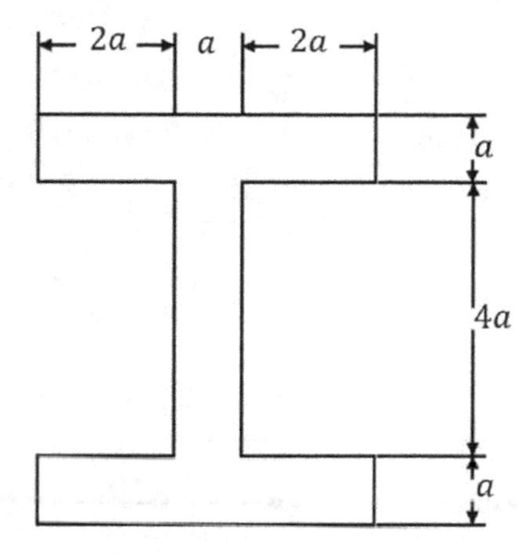

FIGURE 5.28

5.4. For the state of unsymmetric bending shown in the figure below:

a) Determine the stress σ_x at point A.
b) Determine the orientation of the neutral axis (N.A.).

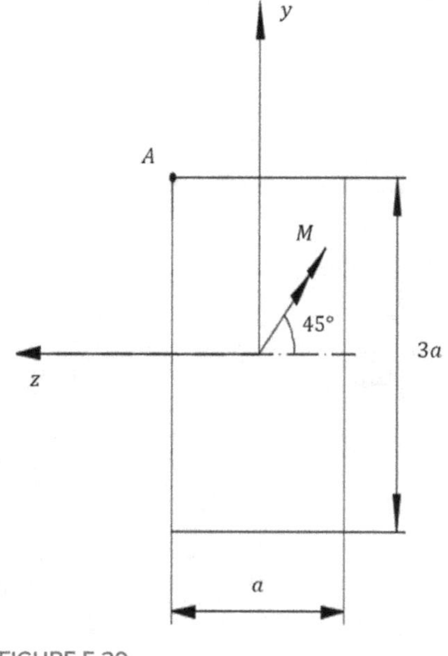

FIGURE 5.29

5.5. For the state of unsymmetric bending shown in the figure below, determine σx at point A and the orientation of the neutral axis (N.A.). C is the centroid of the cross section.

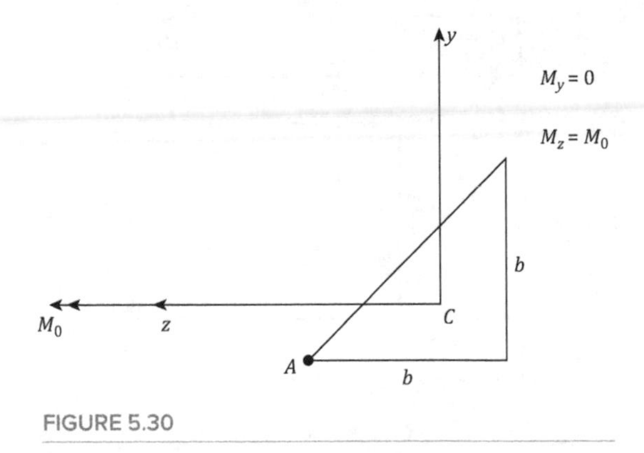

FIGURE 5.30

5.6. A couple of magnitude M_0 acting in a vertical plane is applied to a beam having the Z-shaped cross section shown below. Determine:

a) the stress at point *A*
b) the angle that the neutral axis forms with the horizontal plane

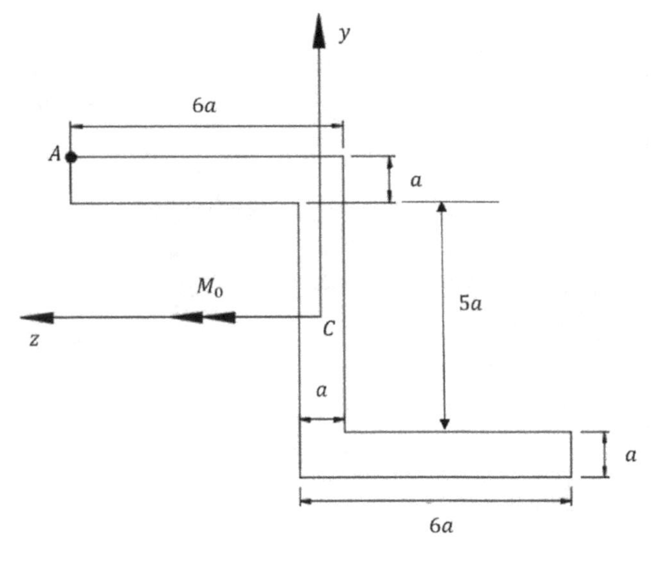

FIGURE 5.31

5.7. For the state of unsymmetric bending shown in the figure below (C is the centroid of the cross section):

a) Compute the normal stress σ_x at point A.

a) Determine the orientation of the neutral axis.

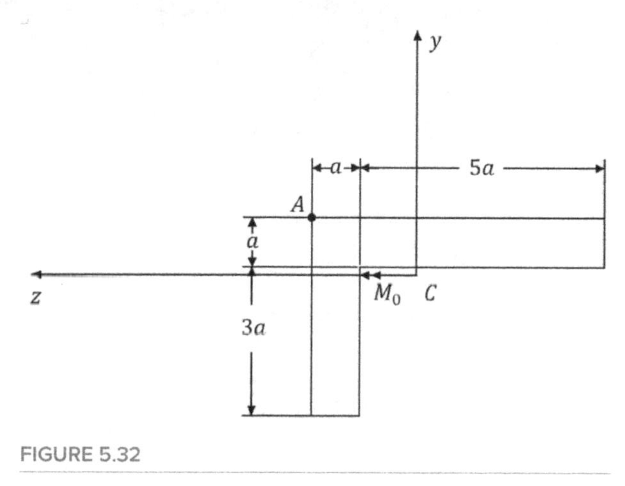

FIGURE 5.32

References

Beer, Ferdinand P., E. Russell Johnston, Jr., John T. DeWolf, and David. F. Mazurek. *Mechanics of Materials.* 7th ed. New York City: McGraw-Hill, 2015.

Ugural, Ansel C., and Saul K. Fenster. *Advanced Mechanics of Materials and Applied Elasticity.* 5th ed. Upper Saddle River: Prentice Hall, 2012.

CHAPTER 6

Torsion

6.1 Introduction

Torsion of prismatic bars will be discussed in this chapter. First, we will review torsion of circular rods, which is usually covered in an elementary course of mechanics of deformable bodies. Then, we will discuss torsion of noncircular rods. In this case, warping (out-of-plane deformation) takes place, and the method used to formulate the problem is more complex.

6.2 Torsion of Circular Rods

Our objective in this section is to investigate stress and strain (deformation) in a twisted rod that has a circular cross section (solid or hollow). Transmission shafts are usually circular. The so-called semi-inverse method will be used to approach the problem, and the following assumptions will be made:

i. Plane cross sections perpendicular to the longitudinal axis of the rod before deformation remain plane and perpendicular to the longitudinal axis of the rod after deformation. In other words, no warping (out-of-plane deformation) occurs.
ii. The shear stress τ at a specific point of the circular cross section varies linearly with r the distance from the center of the circular cross section to the point under consideration. In other words, $\tau = kr$, where k is a proportionality constant yet to be determined. The assumption that τ is a function of r is intuitive due to circular symmetry.
iii. We will assume that the material is homogeneous, isotropic, and behaving in the linearly elastic range, thus obeying Hooke's generalized laws.

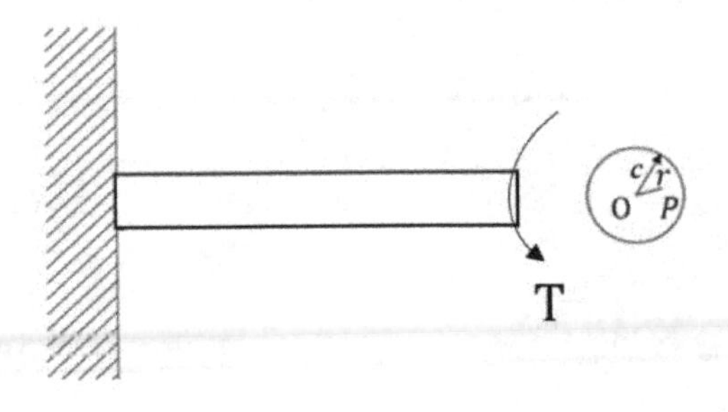

FIGURE 6.1

We know from statics

$$\sum M = 0$$

$$\Rightarrow \int_A r\tau dA = \int_A rkrdA$$

$$= k\int_A r^2 dA$$

$$= kJ = T$$

$$\Rightarrow k = \frac{T}{J},$$

and we conclude that

$$\tau = \frac{Tr}{J},$$

where:

- τ is the shear stress at a specific point $P\left(\frac{N}{m^2}\right)$;
- r is the distance from the center O to the point P (m);
- J is the area polar moment of inertia of the cross section (m^4); and
- T is the torque or twisting moment ($N \times m$).

For a solid circular cross section with radius c (and diameter d = 2c):

$$J = \int_A r^2 dA = \int_{r=0}^{c} r^2(2\pi r)dr = 2\pi\int_{r=0}^{c} r^3 dr = (2\pi)\left(\frac{1}{4}c^4\right) = \frac{\pi}{2}c^4 = \frac{\pi}{32}d^4.$$

For a hollow circular cross section with inner radius c_i and outer radius of c_o:

$$J = \int_A r^2 dA = \int_{r=c_i}^{c_o} r^2(2\pi r)dr = (2\pi)\left(\frac{1}{4}\right)(c_0^4 - c_i^4) = \frac{\pi}{2}(c_0^4 - c_i^4) = \frac{\pi}{32}(d_0^4 - d_i^4).$$

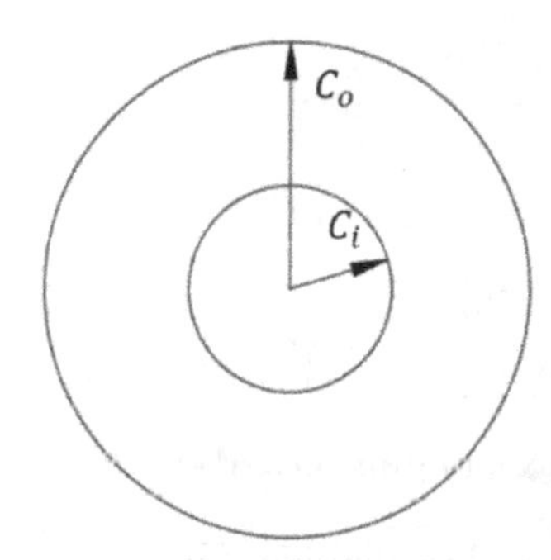

FIGURE 6.2 Hollow circular cross section

For a solid circular cross section with radius c:

$$\tau_{max} = \frac{Tc}{\frac{\pi}{2}c^4} = \frac{2T}{\pi c^3} = \frac{16T}{\pi d^3}.$$

6.3 Angle of Twist

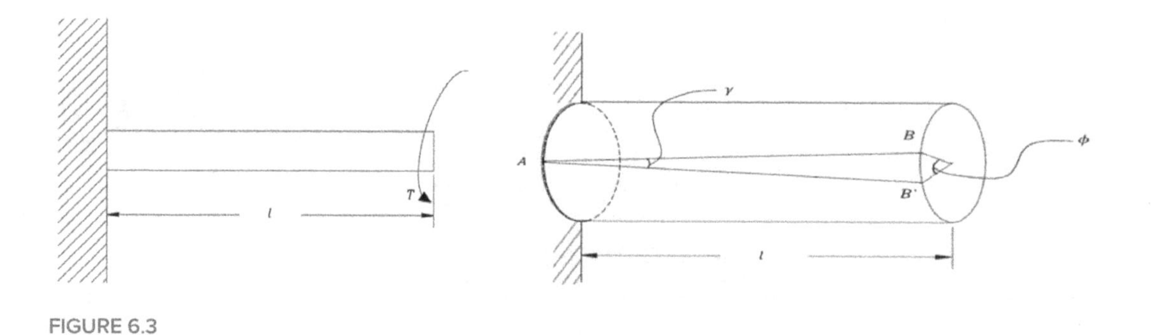

FIGURE 6.3

Consider a circular rod with uniform cross section subject to a twisting moment T at the free end. The rod is assumed to be fixed at the other end, as shown in **figure 6.3** above. Our objective is to find an expression for the angle of twist ϕ shown in the figure.

For small deformation, the shear angle γ and the angle of twist ϕ are small, and the arc length BB′ can be approximated to a line segment in triangle ABB′.

$$\overline{BB'} = l(\tan\gamma) = l\gamma = c\phi \Rightarrow l\frac{\tau}{G} = c\phi \Rightarrow l\frac{Tc}{JG} = c\phi \Rightarrow \phi = \frac{Tl}{GJ}$$

In the above expression:

- T is the torque or twisting moment $(N \times m)$
- l is the length of the rod (m)
- G is shear modulus of elasticity $\left(\frac{N}{m^2}\right)$
- J is the area polar moment of inertia (m^4)
- ϕ is the angle of twist (radian or unitless)

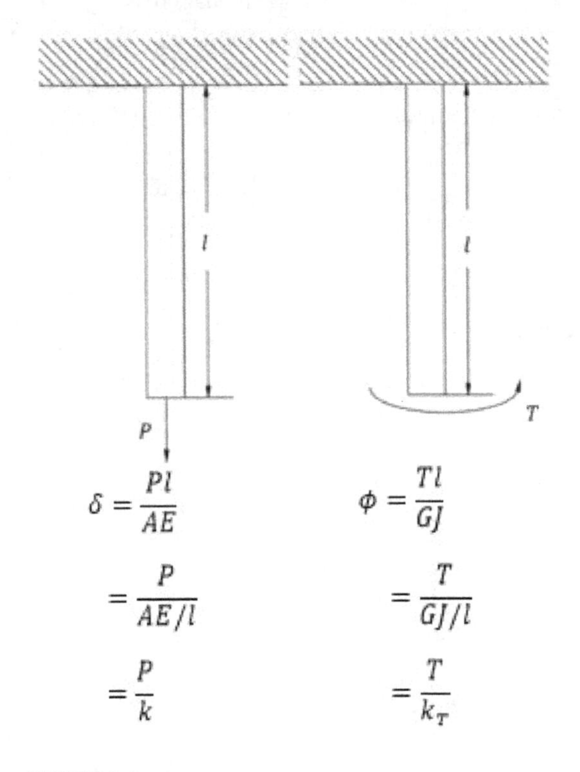

$$\delta = \frac{Pl}{AE} = \frac{P}{AE/l} = \frac{P}{k} \qquad \phi = \frac{Tl}{GJ} = \frac{T}{GJ/l} = \frac{T}{k_T}$$

FIGURE 6.4

Notice the similarity between the expression, we encountered in chapter 1, describing the axial deformation of a bar subject to axial loading and the expression in this chapter describing the angle of twist of a circular rod subject to twisting. *P* is now replaced by T; A is replaced by J; and E is replaced by G.

In chapter 1, we said that a prismatic bar subject to axial loading, as long as it is still behaving in linearly elastic range, will behave like a linear spring with spring constant:

$$k = \frac{AE}{l}.$$

Similarly, a circular rod subject to twisting, as long as it is still behaving in the linearly elastic range, will behave like a torsional spring with torsional spring constant:

$$k_T = \frac{GJ}{l}.$$

The unit of k_T in the SI system is $\frac{Nm}{rad}$

$$\theta = \frac{\phi}{l} = \frac{T}{GJ}$$

and is called the angle of twist per unit length (*rad/m* in SI system).

The torsional rigidity, commonly denoted by C, is defined to be:

$$C = \frac{T}{\theta}.$$

For a circular cross section with radius c, the torsional rigidity is:

$$C = \frac{\pi G c^4}{2}.$$

6.4 Practice Problems

EXAMPLE 6.1

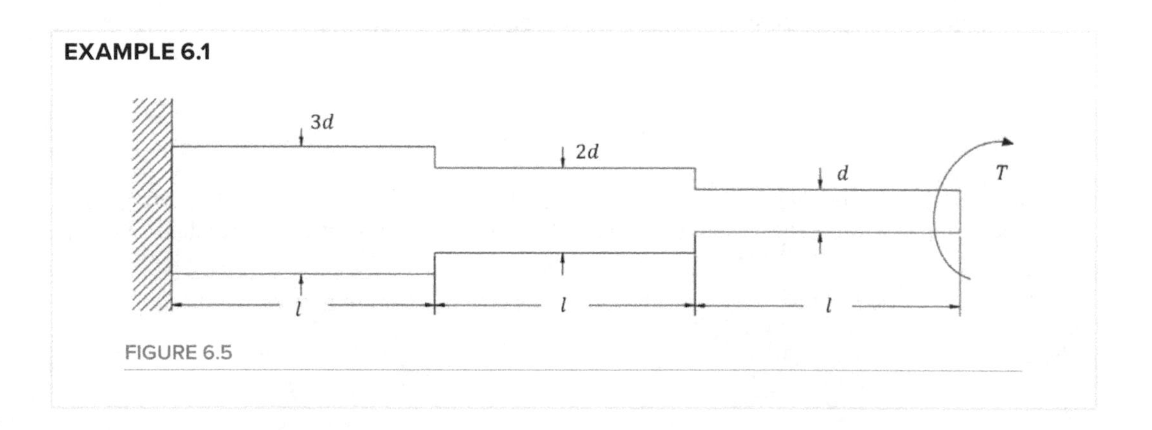

FIGURE 6.5

For the stepped rod shown in the figure above, compute the angle of twist ϕ at the free end. The rod is solid circular with different diameters as shown. Assume G to be constant throughout.

SOLUTION

$$\phi = \sum_{i=1}^{3} \frac{T l_i}{G J_i} = \frac{Tl}{G\frac{\pi d^4}{32}} + \frac{Tl}{G\frac{\pi (2d)^4}{32}} + \frac{Tl}{G\frac{\pi (3d)^4}{32}} = \frac{2786}{81\pi}\frac{Tl}{Gd^4} \approx 10.948\frac{TL}{Gd^4}$$

EXAMPLE 6.2

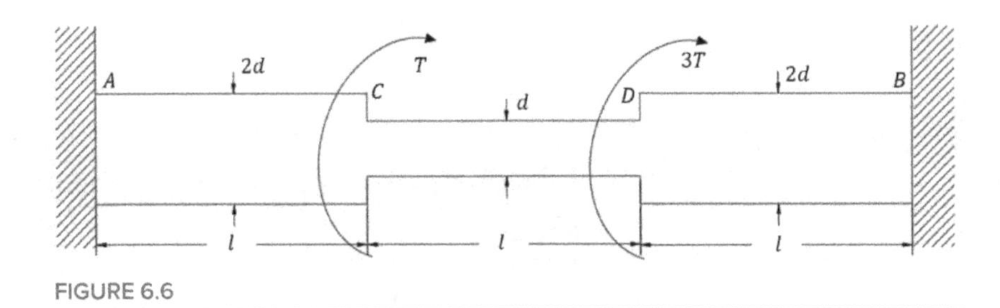

FIGURE 6.6

For the structure shown in the figure above, determine the moment reactions T_A and T_B at the fixed end supports. The rod is solid circular with different diameters as shown. Assume G to be constant throughout.

SOLUTION

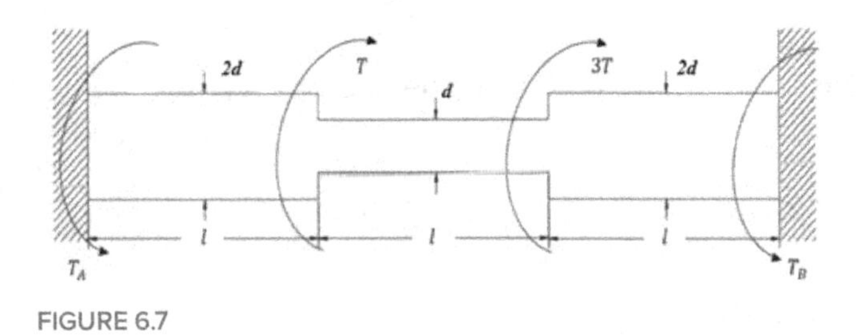

FIGURE 6.7

The problem is statically indeterminate to the first degree (i.e., the degree of indeterminate is one).

We know from statics:

$$\sum M = 0 \Rightarrow T_A + T_B = 4T.$$

This is the only equation you can obtain from statics. A second equation is needed to solve for the two unknowns T_A and T_B. The second equation will be derived from the geometry of deformation.

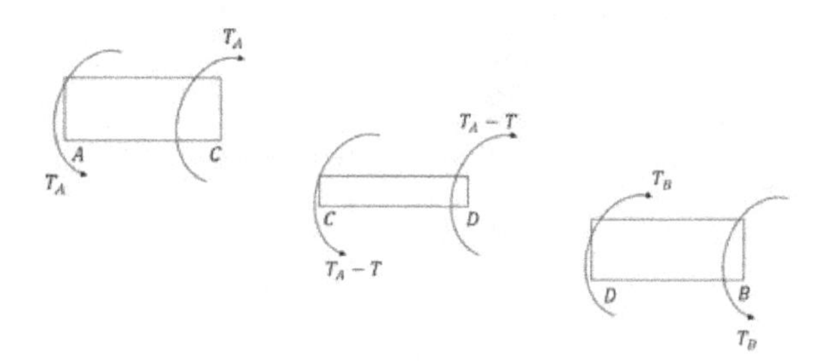

FIGURE 6.8

The compatibility equation is as follows:

$$\sum \phi = 0 \Rightarrow \frac{T_A l}{G\frac{\pi(2d)^4}{32}} + \frac{(T_A - T)l}{G\frac{\pi d^4}{32}} - \frac{T_B l}{G\frac{\pi(2d)^4}{32}} = 0 \Rightarrow \frac{T_A}{16} + \frac{T_A - T}{1} - \frac{T_B}{16} = 0 \Rightarrow 17T_A - T_B = 16T.$$

Notice that the above equation, called compatibility equation, was derived from the geometry of deformation and had nothing to do with statics.

Solving the two equations with two unknowns simultaneously, we obtain:

$$T_A = \frac{10}{9}T; T_B = \frac{26}{9}T.$$

EXAMPLE 6.3

A solid circular shaft AB is fixed to rigid walls at both ends. It is subjected to a torque T at section C, as shown in the figure below. The shaft diameters are d_a and d_b for segments AC and CB, respectively. Knowing that $d_a = 15mm$, $d_b = 10mm$, and $l = 500mm$, determine the length a and b if the maximum shearing stress in both shaft segments is to be the same. Assume G to be constant throughout.

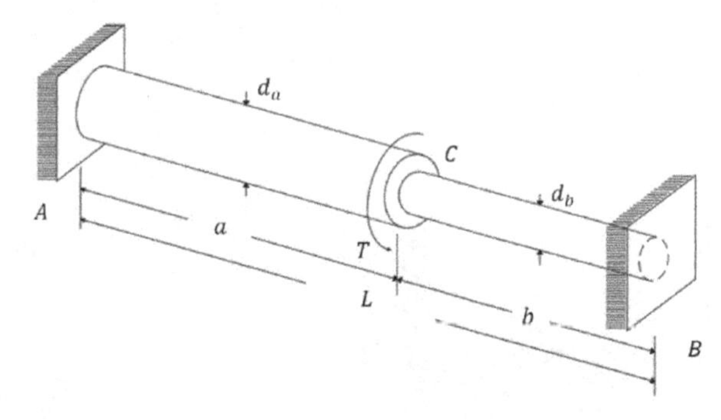

FIGURE 6.9

SOLUTION

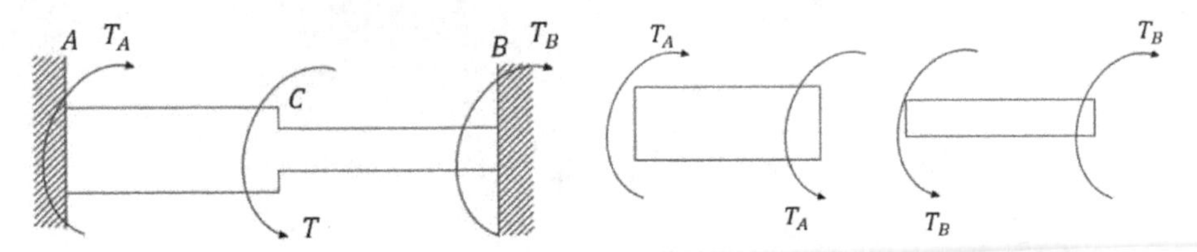

FIGURE 6.10

Maximum shearing stress in both shaft segments is the same; therefore,

$$\frac{16T_A}{\pi d_a^3} = \frac{16T_B}{\pi d_b^3} \Rightarrow \frac{T_A}{T_B} = \left(\frac{d_a}{d_b}\right)^3.$$

The compatibility equation is as follows:

$$\frac{T_A a}{G\frac{\pi d_a^4}{32}} = \frac{T_B b}{G\frac{\pi d_b^4}{32}} \Rightarrow \frac{T_A}{T_B} = \frac{b d_a^4}{a d_b^4} = \left(\frac{b}{a}\right)\left(\frac{d_a}{d_b}\right)^4.$$

We conclude that:

$$\left(\frac{d_a}{d_b}\right)^3 = \left(\frac{b}{a}\right)\left(\frac{d_a}{d_b}\right)^4 \Rightarrow \left(\frac{d_a}{d_b}\right)\left(\frac{b}{a}\right) = 1 \Rightarrow \frac{b}{a} = \frac{d_b}{d_a} = \frac{10}{15} = \frac{2}{3} \Rightarrow 2a = 3b \Rightarrow b = \frac{2}{3}a$$

$$a + b = l = 500\text{mm} \Rightarrow a + \frac{2}{3}a = 500 \Rightarrow \frac{5}{3}a = 500 \Rightarrow a = 300\text{mm},\ b = 200\text{mm}.$$

6.5 General Solution of the Torsion Problem

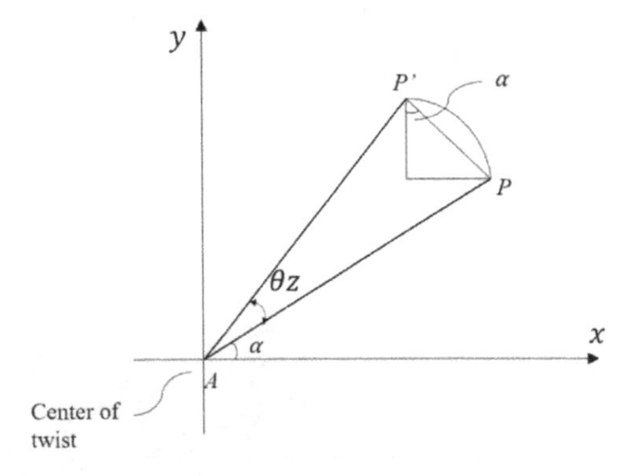

FIGURE 6.11

When the cross section of the rod subjected to twisting moment is non-circular, warping (i.e., out-of-plane deformation) will take place, and the approach to the problem will be different. The *z*-axis is chosen to be the longitudinal axis of the twisted rod, while the xy-coordinate system shown in the figure above refers to the plane of the cross section. The origin of the coordinate system is chosen to be A—the center of twist. It is the center about which the cross section rotated during twisting. Notice that A remains at rest in every cross section of a rod when one end is fixed, while the other is twisted by T.

Let u, v, and w denote the components of the displacement field in the x, y, and z directions, respectively. We will make the following two assumptions:

a) $w = f(x,y)$, which means that the warping deformation is independent of axial location.
b) The angle of twist per unit length θ is constant.

We can write:

$$u = -(r\theta z)\ sin\alpha = -y\theta z$$

$$v = (r\theta z)\ cos\alpha = x\theta z$$

$$w = f(x,y).$$

Next, we establish the strain tensor:

$$\varepsilon_x = \frac{\partial u}{\partial x} = 0$$

$$\varepsilon_y = \frac{\partial v}{\partial y} = 0$$

$$\varepsilon_z = \frac{\partial w}{\partial z} = 0$$

$$\gamma_{xy} = \frac{\partial u}{\partial y} + \frac{\partial v}{\partial x} = 0$$

$$\gamma_{xz} = \frac{\partial u}{\partial z} + \frac{\partial w}{\partial x} = \frac{\partial w}{\partial x} - y\theta$$

$$\gamma_{yz} = \frac{\partial v}{\partial z} + \frac{\partial w}{\partial y} = \frac{\partial w}{\partial y} + x\theta.$$

Using Hooke's generalized laws, we can now establish the stress tensor:

$$\sigma_x = \sigma_y = \sigma_z = \tau_{xy} = 0$$

$$\tau_{zx} = G\left(\frac{\partial w}{\partial x} - y\theta\right)$$

$$\tau_{zy} = G\left(\frac{\partial w}{\partial y} + x\theta\right)$$

$$\Rightarrow \frac{\partial \tau_{zx}}{\partial y} - \frac{\partial \tau_{zy}}{\partial x} = -2G\theta = H \text{ (a constant).}$$

Introducing ϕ, called Prandtl stress function, such as

$$\tau_{zx} = \frac{\partial \phi}{\partial y}; \tau_{zy} = -\frac{\partial \phi}{\partial x}, \tag{6-1}$$

we obtain:

$$\frac{\partial^2 \phi}{\partial x^2} + \frac{\partial^2 \phi}{\partial y^2} = H = -2G\theta. \tag{6-2}$$

The above equation is a second order partial differential equation called Poisson's equation.

Also, it can be shown that on the boundary

$$\frac{\partial \phi}{\partial y}\frac{dy}{ds} + \frac{\partial \phi}{\partial x}\frac{dx}{ds} = \frac{d\phi}{ds} = 0$$

$\Rightarrow$ ϕ must be constant on the boundary. It is customary to choose $\phi = 0$ on the boundary.

Using statics, we can show that:

$$T = 2\int \phi dA. \tag{6-3}$$

We will illustrate such an approach by applying it in order to solve the elliptical cross section problem. Our objective is to determine the valve and location of the maximum shear stress in a uniform bar subject to a twisting moment T when the cross section is elliptical as shown in **figure 6.12**.

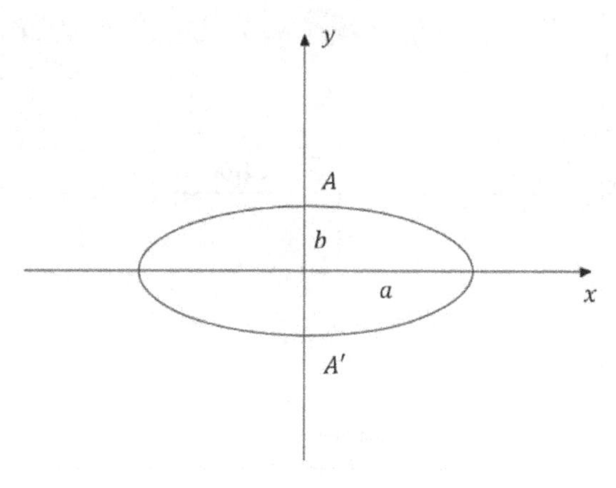

FIGURE 6.12

We start by assuming a Prandtl stress function,

$$\phi = k\left(\frac{x^2}{a^2} + \frac{y^2}{b^2} - 1\right),$$

where k is a constant yet to be determined. Notice that by starting with ϕ defined as such, we are forcing ϕ to be zero on the boundary of the elliptical cross section.

Next, we use Poisson's differential equation:

$$\frac{\partial \phi}{\partial x} = \frac{2kx}{a^2} \Rightarrow \frac{\partial^2 \phi}{\partial x^2} = \frac{2k}{a^2}$$

$$\frac{\partial \phi}{\partial y} = \frac{2ky}{b^2} \Rightarrow \frac{\partial^2 \phi}{\partial y^2} = \frac{2k}{b^2}.$$

Therefore,

$$k = -\frac{G\theta a^2 b^2}{a^2 + b^2}$$

$$\Rightarrow \qquad \phi = -\frac{G\theta a^2 b^2}{a^2 + b^2}\left(\frac{x^2}{a^2} + \frac{y^2}{b^2} - 1\right).$$

Next, we use (6-3) in order to express ϕ in terms of T.

$$T = 2\int \phi dA = 2\int -\frac{G\theta a^2b^2}{a^2+b^2}\left(\frac{x^2}{a^2}+\frac{y^2}{b^2}-1\right)dA = -\frac{2G\theta a^2b^2}{a^2+b^2}\int\left(\frac{x^2}{a^2}+\frac{y^2}{b^2}-1\right)dA$$

$$= -\frac{2G\theta a^2b^2}{a^2+b^2}\left(\frac{\frac{\pi}{4}a^3b}{a^2}+\frac{\frac{\pi}{4}ab^3}{b^2}-\pi ab\right) = -\frac{2G\theta a^2b^2}{a^2+b^2}\left(\frac{\pi}{4}ab+\frac{\pi}{4}ab-\pi ab\right) = \frac{\pi G\theta a^3b^3}{a^2+b^2}$$

We conclude that:

$$T = \frac{\pi G\theta a^3b^3}{a^2+b^2}$$

$$\Rightarrow \phi = -\frac{T}{\pi ab}\left(\frac{x^2}{a^2}+\frac{y^2}{b^2}-1\right).$$

Using (6-1),

$$\tau_{zx} = \frac{\partial\phi}{\partial y} = -\frac{2Ty}{\pi ab^3}$$

$$\tau_{zy} = -\frac{\partial\phi}{\partial x} = \frac{2Tx}{\pi a^3b}.$$

Thus, the resulting shearing stress τ is:

$$\tau = \sqrt{\tau_{zx}^2+\tau_{zy}^2} = \sqrt{\frac{4T^2y^2}{\pi^2a^2b^6}+\frac{4T^2x^2}{\pi^2a^6b^2}} = \frac{2T}{\pi ab}\sqrt{\frac{x^2}{a^4}+\frac{y^2}{b^4}}.$$

The above expression will give us the shear stress at each point in the cross section. Notice that $\tau = 0$ at the center of the ellipse ($x = y = 0$). It can be easily shown that τ_{max} takes place at point A (or point A'):

$$\tau_{max} = \frac{2T}{\pi ab^2}.$$

The angle of twist per unit length θ is:

$$\theta = \frac{\left(a^2+b^2\right)T}{\pi a^3b^3G}.$$

The torsional rigidity, denoted by C, is:

$$C = \frac{T}{\theta} = \frac{\pi a^3 b^3}{a^2 + b^2} G.$$

Notice that the above results are consistent with those previously obtained for a circular cross section.

- special case: $a = b = c$ (circular cross section)

$$\tau_{\max} = \frac{2T}{\pi c^3}$$

$$\theta = \frac{2T}{\pi c^4 G}$$

$$C = \frac{T}{\theta} = \frac{\pi c^4 G}{2}$$

6.6 Practice Problem

Determine the value and location of the maximum shear stress τ_{max} for an equilateral cross-sectional solid bar subject to a twisting moment T. Also, determine the angle of twist per unit length θ. The cross section is shown in the figure below.

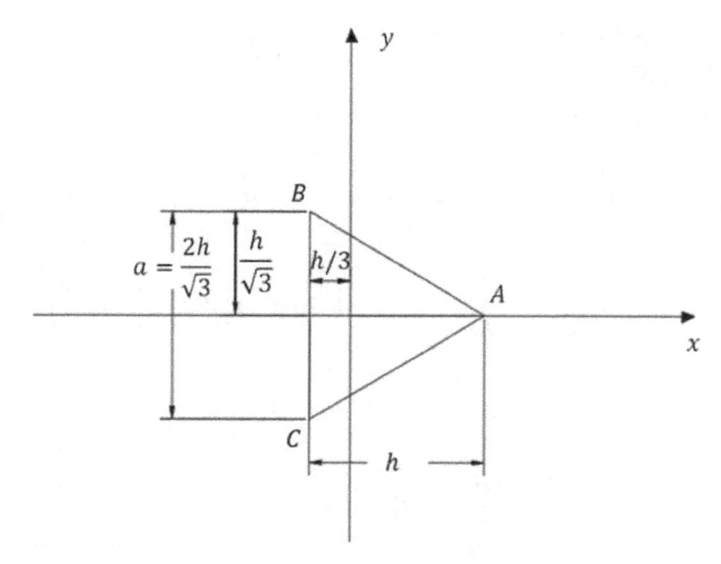

FIGURE 6.13

Solution

We will follow precisely the same steps used in the elliptical cross section problem.

First, we need to assume a Prandtl stress function ϕ.

In the xy-coordinate system, the equation of the line passing through B and C is:

$$x + \frac{1}{3}h = 0.$$

The equation of the line passing through A and B is:

$$x + \sqrt{3}y - \frac{2}{3}h = 0.$$

The equation of the line passing through A and C is:

$$x - \sqrt{3}y - \frac{2}{3}h = 0.$$

Therefore, assume a stress function of the form

$$\phi = k\left(x - \sqrt{3}y - \frac{2}{3}h\right)\left(x + \sqrt{3}y - \frac{2}{3}h\right)\left(x + \frac{1}{3}h\right),$$

where k is a constant yet to be determined.

Notice that, by assuming ϕ as such, we are forcing ϕ to be zero on the boundary of the equilateral triangular section.

Next, we insert ϕ in Poisson's partial differential equation.

$$\phi = k\left(x - \sqrt{3}y - \frac{2}{3}h\right)\left(x + \sqrt{3}y - \frac{2}{3}h\right)\left(x + \frac{1}{3}h\right) = k\left(x^3 - hx^2 - 3xy^2 + \frac{4}{27}h^3 - hy^2\right)$$

$$\Rightarrow \frac{\partial \phi}{\partial x} = k\left(3x^2 - 2hx - 3y^2\right)$$

$$\frac{\partial^2 \phi}{\partial x^2} = k(6x - 2h)$$

$$\frac{\partial \phi}{\partial y} = k(-6xy - 2hy)$$

$$\frac{\partial^2 \phi}{\partial y^2} = k(-6x - 2h)$$

Therefore,

$$k(-4h) = -2G\theta \Rightarrow k = \frac{G\theta}{2h} \Rightarrow \phi = \frac{G\theta}{2h}\left(x^3 - hx^2 - 3xy^2 + \frac{4}{27}h^3 - hy^2\right).$$

Next, we will use (6-3):

$$T = 2\int \phi dA = \frac{G\theta}{h}\int\left(x^3 - hx^2 - 3xy^2 + \frac{4}{27}h^3 - hy^2\right)dA$$

$$\int x^2 dA = I_y = \frac{1}{36}\left(\frac{2h}{\sqrt{3}}\right)h^3 = \frac{h^4}{18\sqrt{3}}$$

$$\int y^2 dA = I_x = 2\left(\frac{1}{12}\right)h\left(\frac{h}{\sqrt{3}}\right)^3 = \frac{h^4}{18\sqrt{3}}$$

$$\int dA = A = \frac{1}{2}\left(\frac{2h}{\sqrt{3}}\right)h = \frac{h^2}{\sqrt{3}}$$

$$\int x^3 dA = 2\int_{x=-\frac{h}{3}}^{\frac{2h}{3}}\int_{y=0}^{\frac{2h}{3\sqrt{3}}-\frac{x}{\sqrt{3}}} x^3 dy dx = \frac{h^5}{135\sqrt{3}}$$

$$\int xy^2 dA = 2\int_{x=-\frac{h}{3}}^{\frac{2h}{3}}\int_{y=0}^{\frac{2h}{3\sqrt{3}}-\frac{x}{\sqrt{3}}} xy^2 dy dx = -\frac{h^5}{135\sqrt{3}}$$

$$\Rightarrow T = \frac{G\theta}{h}\left(\frac{h^5}{135\sqrt{3}} - \frac{h^5}{18\sqrt{3}} + \frac{h^5}{45\sqrt{3}} + \frac{4h^5}{27\sqrt{3}} - \frac{h^5}{18\sqrt{3}}\right) = \frac{G\theta}{h}\left(\frac{h^5}{15\sqrt{3}}\right) = \frac{G\theta h^4}{15\sqrt{3}}$$

$$\Rightarrow \phi = \frac{15\sqrt{3}T}{2h^5}\left(x^3 - hx^2 - 3xy^2 + \frac{4}{27}h^3 - hy^2\right)$$

$$\tau_{xz} = \frac{\partial \phi}{\partial y} = \frac{15\sqrt{3}T}{2h^5}(-6xy - 2hy)$$

$$\tau_{yz} = -\frac{\partial \phi}{\partial x} = -\frac{15\sqrt{3}T}{2h^5}(3x^2 - 2hx - 3y^2)$$

$$\tau = \sqrt{\tau_{xz}^2 + \tau_{yz}^2}$$

$$\tau_{min} \text{ is at } x = y = 0 \Rightarrow \tau_{min} = 0$$

$$\tau_{max} \text{ is at } x = -\frac{h}{3}; y = 0 \Rightarrow \tau_{max} = \frac{15\sqrt{3}T}{2h^3}$$

$$h = \frac{a\sqrt{3}}{2} \Rightarrow h^3 = \frac{3\sqrt{3}a^3}{8} \Rightarrow \tau_{max} = \frac{20T}{a^3}.$$

Also, $\theta = \frac{15\sqrt{3}T}{Gh^4} \Rightarrow \theta = \frac{80\sqrt{3}T}{3Ga^4}$ is the angle of twist per unit length.

Problems

6.1. Determine the torque T that causes a maximum shearing stress of 75 MPa in a hollow steel cylindrical shaft of outer radius 15 mm and inner radius 10 mm.

6.2. Determine the maximum shearing stress in a solid transmits cylindrical shaft of 15 mm diameter as it transmits 5 kW at a frequency of (a) 30 Hz and (b) 60 Hz.

6.3. The mass moment of inertia of a gear is to be determined experimentally by using a torsional pendulum consisting of a 5 ft steel wire. Determine the required diameter of the wire for which the torsional spring constant will be $5\frac{lb_f \times ft}{rad}$. Assume $G_{steel} = 11,200\ ksi$.

6.4. The truncated cone shown in the figure below has radius c at the free end and radius $2c$ at the fixed end. It is subject to a twisting moment T at the free end. Determine the angle of twist ϕ at the free end. Assume the modulus of rigidity of the material to be G. Express your answer in terms of T, l, c and G.

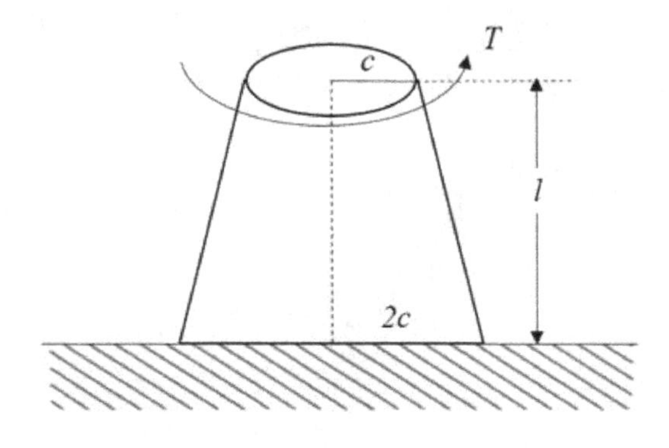

FIGURE 6.14

6.5. A stepped solid circular rod is loaded as shown in the figure below. Segment AB has modulus of rigidity G, while segment BC has modulus rigidity $1.25G$.

a) Compute the angle of twist ϕ at the free end C.
b) Determine the maximum shear stress τ_{max} in the structure.

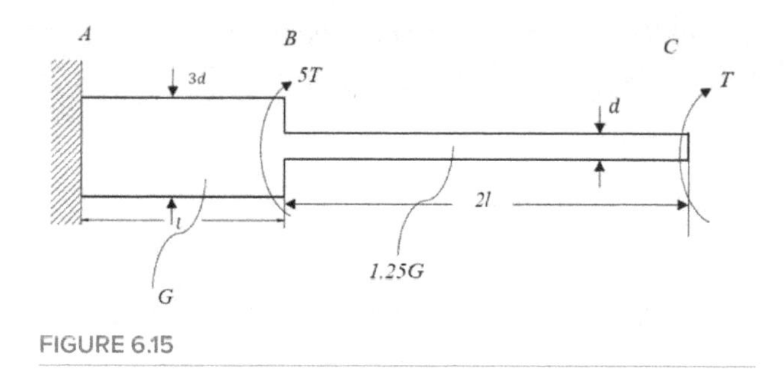

FIGURE 6.15

6.6. A stepped solid circular rod is loaded as shown in the figure below. Assume the shear modulus of elasticity G to be uniform throughout. Determine the angle of twist at C and the angle of twist at D.

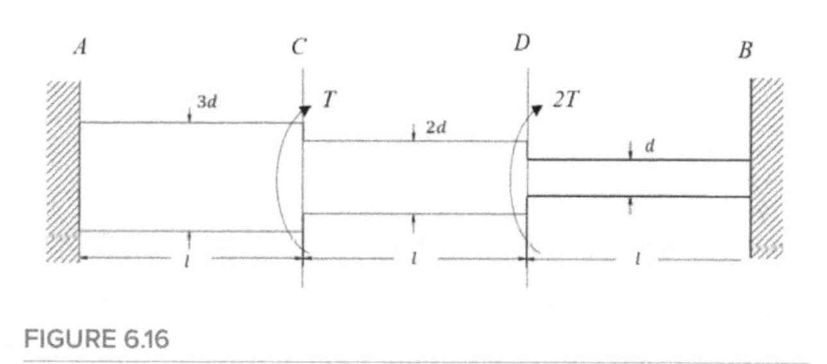

FIGURE 6.16

6.7. The torsional rigidity of a circle, an ellipse, and an equilateral triangle are denoted by C_c, C_e, and C_t, respectively. Assume the circle, the ellipse, and the triangle to have the same area. Evaluate (a) $\frac{C_e}{C_c}$ and (b) $\frac{C_t}{C_c}$.

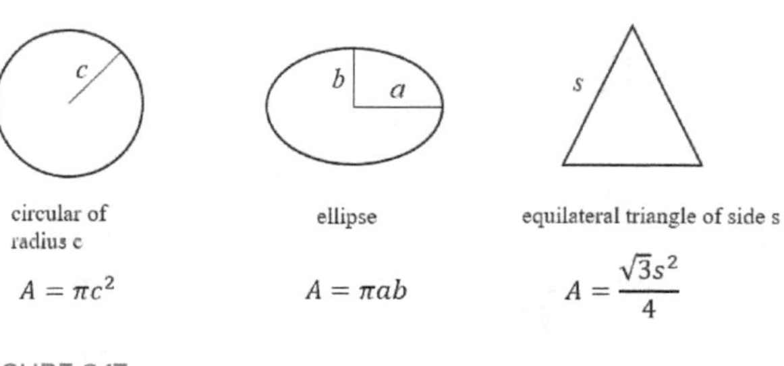

FIGURE 6.17

References

Beer, Ferdinand P., E. Russell Johnston, Jr., John T. DeWolf, and David. F. Mazurek. *Mechanics of Materials.* 7th ed. New York City: McGraw-Hill, 2015.

Budynas, Richard G. *Advanced Strength and Applied Stress Analysis.* New York City: McGraw-Hill, 1977.

Ugural, Ansel C., and Saul K. Fenster. *Advanced Mechanics of Materials and Applied Elasticity.* 5th ed. Upper Saddle River: Prentice Hall, 2012.

CHAPTER 7

Energy Methods

7.1 Introduction

Let us revisit the uniaxial state of tensile stress. Consider the prismatic bar shown in **figure 7.1** loaded axially with a load *P*. This is the simplest type of loading in structural engineering.

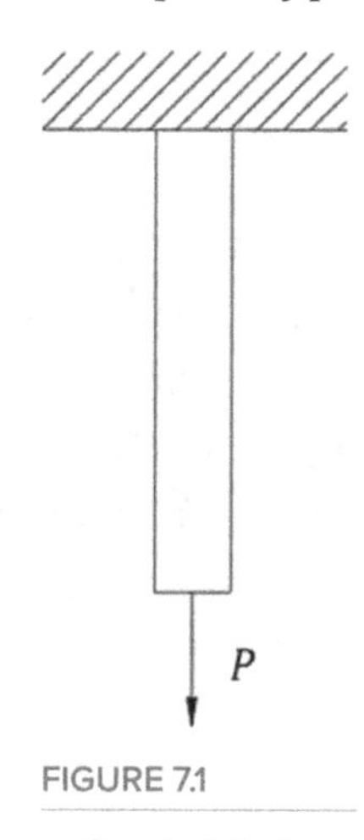

FIGURE 7.1

We saw in chapter 2 that the amount of axial deformation of the bar (i.e., the increase in the length of the bar) is given by:

$$\delta = \frac{Pl}{AE}. \tag{7.1}$$

We also showed in chapter 2 that the strain energy U stored in this prismatic bar is:

$$U = \frac{P^2 l}{2AE}. \tag{7.2}$$

Notice that if we take the partial derivative of U with respect to P (i.e., $\frac{\partial U}{\partial P}$):

$$\frac{\partial U}{\partial P} = \frac{Pl}{AE}, \tag{7.3}$$

which is precisely δ. This is not a matter of coincidence. Indeed, this is a special case of Castigliano's theorem.

7.2 Castigliano's Theorem

Consider a body, as shown in **figure 7.2**, subject to a system of forces. The term "forces" here does not mean necessarily "linear forces" (N, lb_f, kips, etc.). It can also include moments or torques (N × m, lb_f × ft, kips × in, etc.).

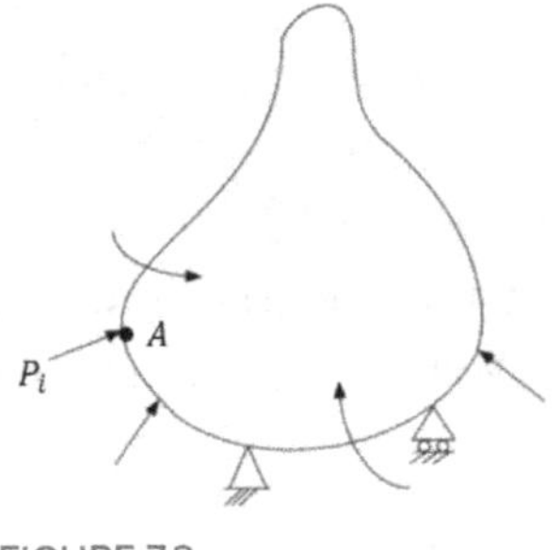

FIGURE 7.2

This body can be any structure (e.g., a beam, frame, arch, truss, plate, shell, three-dimensional machine part, etc.). Since the body is deformable (i.e., not rigid), there will be strain energy U stored in it due to such loading. The partial derivative of U with respect to load P_i at point A gives the deflection δ_i of point A in the direction of P_i. Similarly, the term "deflection" here can mean linear deflection (m, ft, in, etc.) or angular deflection (radian or unitless):

$$\frac{\partial U}{\partial P_i} = \delta_i. \tag{7.4}$$

This is Castigliano's theorem, named after Carlo Alberto Castigliano.[1]

---

1 Carlo Alberto Castigliano (1847–1884) was an Italian mathematician, physicist, and engineer. Castigliano's theorem was first published as a dissertation in 1873. Castigliano died at an early age in his 30s.

When applying Castigliano's theorem in a problem, we need to compute the strain energy U in the structure. Below are expressions of U for simple structures and loadings—those commonly encountered in an elementary course of Mechanics of Materials.

The axial loading is shown in **figure 7.3**.

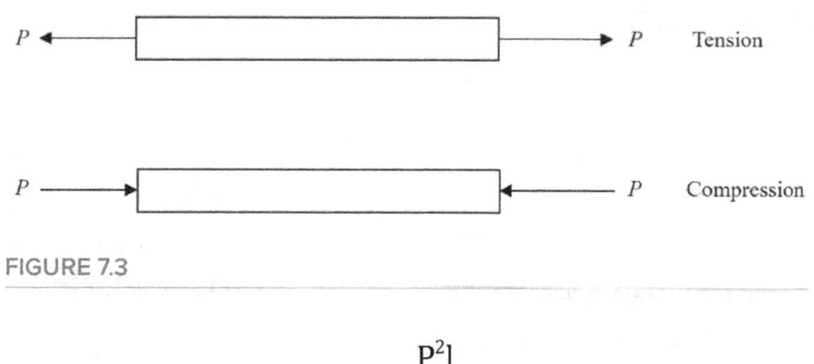

FIGURE 7.3

$$U = \frac{P^2 l}{2AE}$$

The torsion of a circular rod is shown in **figure 7.4**.

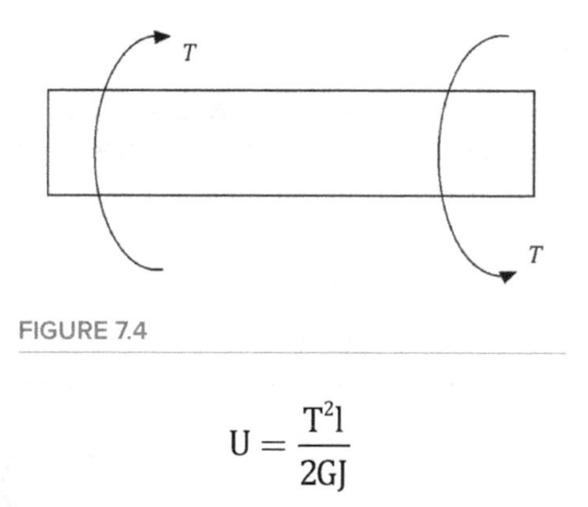

FIGURE 7.4

$$U = \frac{T^2 l}{2GJ}$$

The bending of an Euler-Bernoulli beam element is shown in **figure 7.5**.

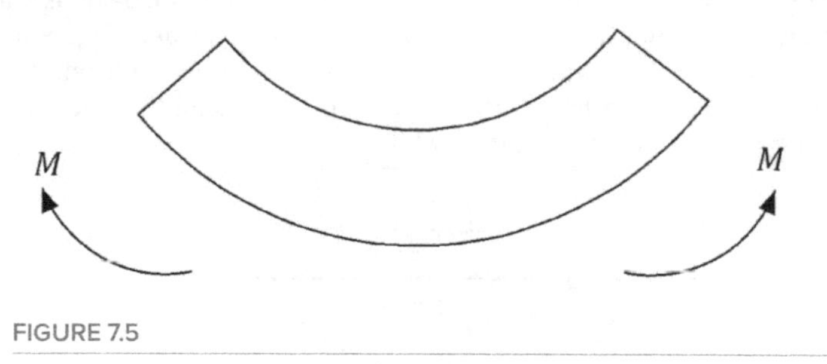

FIGURE 7.5

$$U = \int \frac{M_{(x)}^{\ 2} dx}{2EI}$$

For more complicated structures and loadings, the total strain energy U in the structure can be calculated using the following formula:

$$U = \int u_{(x,y,z)} dV. \tag{7.5}$$

Notice that the above integral is a triple integral and must be evaluated over the entire volume. $u_{(x,y,z)}$ is the strain energy density ($\frac{N}{m^2}$ or Pa). Strain energy density, like stress and strain, is a point function. Obviously, evaluating the triple integral in (7.5) in general is not easy and requires knowledge of the stress distribution in the structure.

Notice also that the strain energy U is always positive.

7.3 Application of Castigliano's Theorem to Beams

EXAMPLE 7.1

For the cantilevered beam shown in the figure below, compute the vertical displacement under load *P*. Use energy methods. Assume that the total strain energy is due to bending only. Assume EI to be constant throughout.

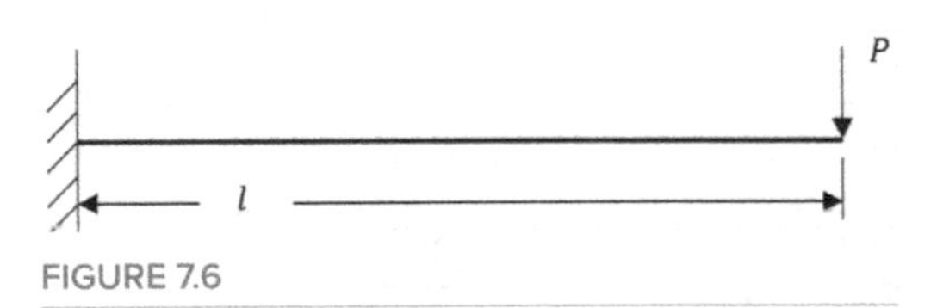

FIGURE 7.6

SOLUTION

We will first compute the strain energy U in the entire beam. We can then apply Castigliano's theorem in order to determine the vertical deflection under load *P*. The beam is statically determinate. Therefore, we can compute the reactions and determine the bending moment at each and every station. However, there is no need to compute the reactions here. We will choose the origin at the free end (in order to avoid computing the reactions and to simplify calculus). One cut is needed to determine $M_{(x)}$ (as shown in **figure 7.7**).

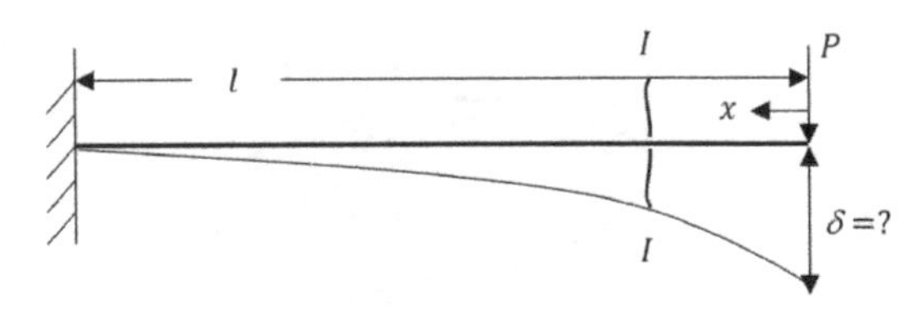

FIGURE 7.7

The bending moment at section I–I is:

$$M_{(x)} = -Px.$$

The strain energy is:

$$U = \int \frac{M_{(x)}^2 dx}{2EI} = \int_{x=0}^{l} \frac{P^2x^2dx}{2EI} = \frac{P^2}{2EI}\int_{x=0}^{l} x^2dx = \frac{P^2}{2EI}\left(\frac{l^3}{3}\right) = \frac{P^2l^3}{6EI}.$$

Notice that the strain energy U, as expected, has the dimension of energy (joule, $lb_f \times ft$, kips $\times$ in, etc.).

Applying Castigliano's theorem, the vertical deflection under load P is:

$$\delta = \frac{\partial U}{\partial P} = \frac{Pl^3}{3EI} \qquad \downarrow \text{(downward)}.$$

EXAMPLE 7.2

For the simply supported beam shown in the figure below, compute the vertical deflection under load P. Use energy methods. Assume that the total strain energy is due to bending only. Assume EI to be constant throughout.

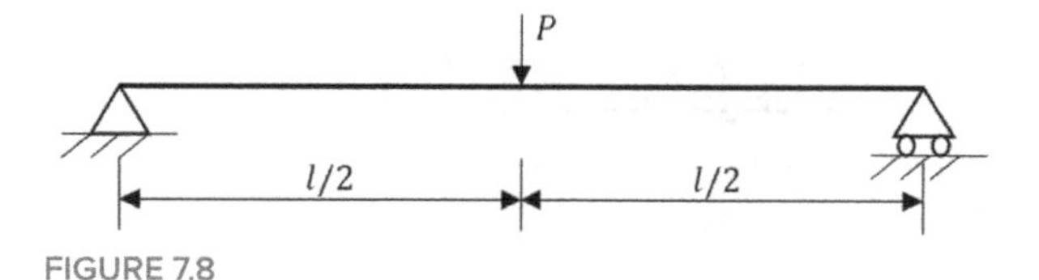

FIGURE 7.8

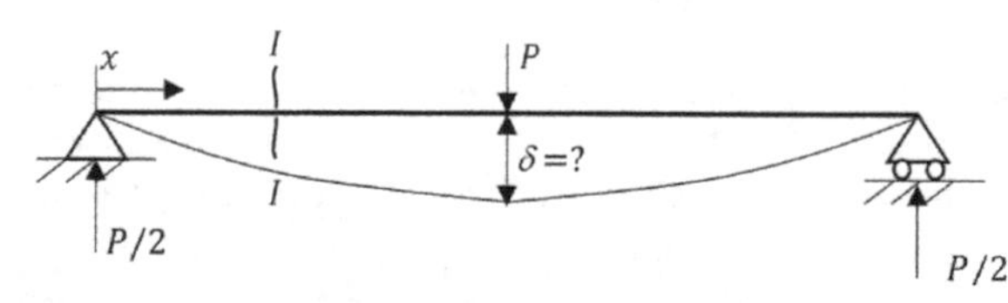

FIGURE 7.9

The beam is statically determinate, and the reactions can be easily determined. We need two cuts in order to determine the bending moment $M_{(x)}$ at each and every station. However, due to symmetry, we can limit ourselves to only one cut. At section I-I:

$$M_{(x)} = \frac{P}{2}x.$$

The strain energy is:

$$U = \int \frac{M_{(x)}^2 dx}{2EI} = 2\int_{x=0}^{\frac{l}{2}} \frac{\frac{P^2x^2}{4}dx}{2EI} = \frac{P^2}{4EI}\int_{x=0}^{\frac{l}{2}} x^2dx = \frac{P^2}{4EI}\left(\frac{1}{3}\right)\left(\frac{l}{2}\right)^3 = \frac{P^2l^3}{96EI}.$$

Applying Castigliano's theorem, the vertical deflection under load P is:

$$\delta = \frac{\partial U}{\partial P} = \frac{Pl^3}{48EI} \qquad \downarrow \text{downward.}$$

EXAMPLE 7.3

For the simply supported beam shown in the figure below, compute the vertical deflection under load P. Use energy methods. Assume that the total strain energy is due to bending only. Assume EI to be constant throughout.

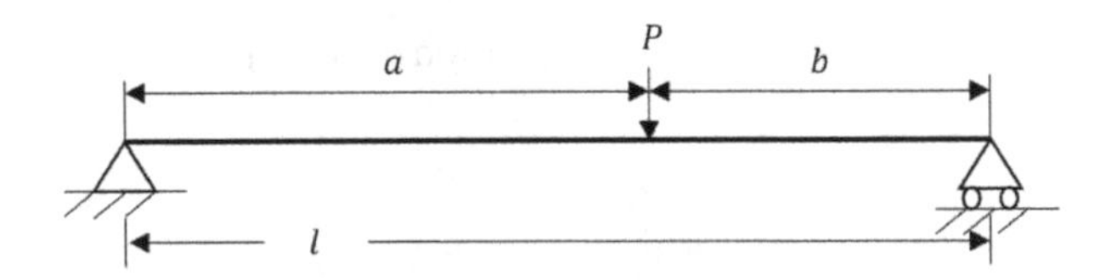

FIGURE 7.10

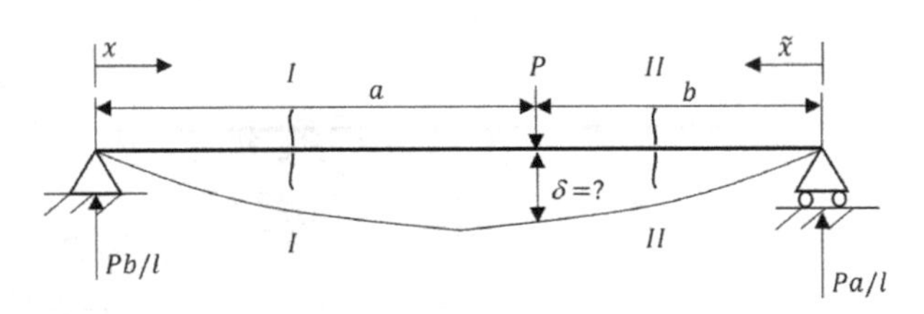

FIGURE 7.11

The problem is similar to the previous problem except that, here, symmetry was destroyed. The beam is still statically determinate. Therefore, the reactions can be easily computed from statics. We definitely need two cuts here in order to determine $M_{(x)}$ at each and every station.

$$U = \int \frac{M_{(x)}^2 dx}{2EI} = \int_{x=0}^{a} \frac{\left(\frac{Pbx}{l}\right)^2 dx}{2EI} + \int_{\tilde{x}=0}^{b} \frac{\left(\frac{Pa\tilde{x}}{l}\right)^2 d\tilde{x}}{2EI}$$

$$= \frac{P^2b^2}{2l^2EI} \int_{x=0}^{a} x^2 dx + \frac{P^2a^2}{2l^2EI} \int_{\tilde{x}=0}^{b} \tilde{x}^2 d\tilde{x}$$

$$= \frac{P^2b^2}{2l^2EI}\left(\frac{a^3}{3}\right) + \frac{P^2a^2}{2l^2EI}\left(\frac{b^3}{3}\right) = \frac{P^2a^2b^2}{6lEI}$$

Applying Castigliano's theorem, the vertical deflection under load *P* is:

$$\delta = \frac{\partial U}{\partial P} = \frac{Pa^2b^2}{3lEI} \qquad \downarrow\text{downward.}$$

Verification: For the special case when $a = b = l / 2$, we obtain

$$\delta = \frac{P\left(\frac{l}{2}\right)^2\left(\frac{l}{2}\right)^2}{3lEI} = \frac{Pl^3}{48EI} \qquad \downarrow\text{downward,}$$

which is exactly the same result obtained in example 7.2.

EXAMPLE 7.4

For the cantilevered beam shown in the figure below, compute the vertical deflection at the free end. Use energy methods. Assume that the total strain energy is due to bending only. Assume EI to be constant throughout.

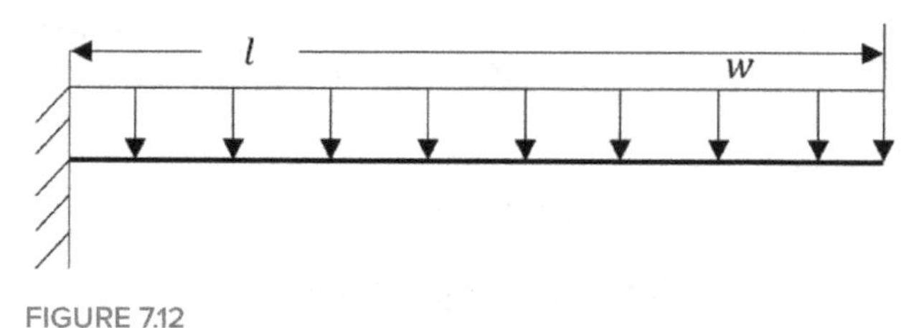

FIGURE 7.12

SOLUTION

We are asked to compute the vertical deflection at the free end. Do we have a concentrated vertical force acting at the free end? No! Therefore, we cannot apply Castigliao's theorem directly. We can overcome such an obstacle in two ways.

Method (1)

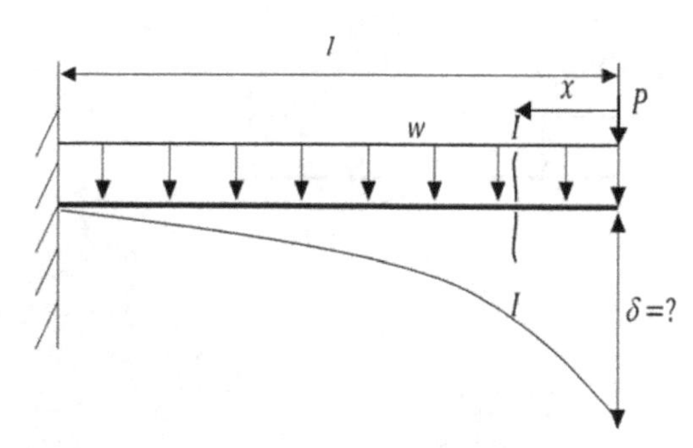

FIGURE 7.13

Since we want to evaluate the vertical displacement at the free end, we will introduce a fictitious vertical force *P* at the free end. Notice that such a vertical force *P* does not exist in the original problem. We are introducing it in order to be able to apply Castigliano's theorem. However, we need to dump P after using the theorem.

Choosing the origin at the free end (in order to avoid computing the reactions and to simplify calculus):

$$M_{(x)} = -Px - \frac{wx^2}{2},$$

The strain energy is:

$$U = \int \frac{M_{(x)}^2 dx}{2EI} = \int_{x=0}^{l} \frac{\left(Px + \frac{wx^2}{2}\right)^2 dx}{2EI}$$

$$\Rightarrow U = \frac{1}{2EI} \int_{x=0}^{l} \left(Px + \frac{wx^2}{2}\right)^2 dx.$$

We can expand the above expression using Newton's binomial formula and then perform the integration in order to obtain an expression of U as a function of P: $U_{(p)}$.

However, in Calculus, whether we do the integration first and then take the partial derivative or the other way around (i.e., take the partial derivative and then do the integration), the result should be the same. Applying Castigliano's theorem and using chain rule:

$$\delta = \frac{\partial U}{\partial P} = \frac{1}{2EI} \int_{x=0}^{l} 2\left(Px + \frac{wx^2}{2}\right)(x)dx.$$

Setting $P = 0$ (since P did not exist in the original problem):

$$\delta = \frac{1}{EI} \int_{x=0}^{l} \frac{wx^3}{2} dx = \frac{w}{2EI}\left(\frac{l^4}{4}\right) = \frac{wl^4}{8EI} \qquad \downarrow\text{downward.}$$

Method (2): (Unit-Load Method)

An alternative way (indeed, an equivalent way) to compute the vertical deflection at the free end is to use the unit-load method.

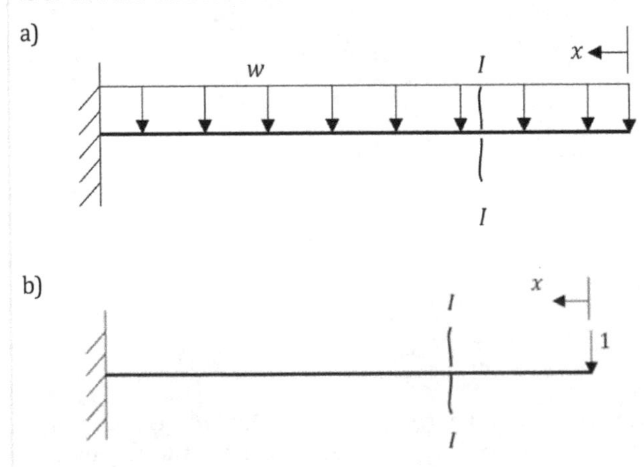

FIGURE 7.14

The beam is statically determinate, and we can determine the bending moment at each and every station. Only one cut is needed and for simplicity, we choose the origin at the free end in order to determine the bending moment at I-I in (a):

$$M_{(x)} = -\frac{wx^2}{2}.$$

Next, we unload the beam. Since we are asked to compute the vertical displacement at the free end, we introduce a unit load in the vertical direction at the free end (hence, we call it the unit-load method). The structure in (b) is also statically determinate, and we should be able to compute the bending moment at I-I:

$$m_{(x)} = -(1)(x) = -x.$$

The vertical displacement at the free end is given by the following formula:

$$\delta = \int \frac{M_{(x)} m_{(x)}}{EI} dx.$$

In our example:

$$\delta = \int_{x=0}^{l} \frac{\left(-\frac{wx^2}{2}\right)(-x)}{EI} dx$$

$$= \frac{w}{2EI} \int_{x=0}^{l} x^3 dx = \frac{w}{2EI}\left(\frac{l^4}{4}\right) = \frac{wl^4}{8EI} \downarrow \text{downward},$$

which is exactly the same result obtained in method (1).

The unit-load method is equivalent to applying Castigliano's theorem. Indeed, the strain energy due to bending in the beam is given by:

$$U = \int \frac{M_{(x)}^2 dx}{2EI}.$$

Applying Castigliano's theorem and using chain rule:

$$\delta = \frac{\partial U}{\partial P} = \int \frac{2M_{(x)} \frac{\partial M_{(x)}}{\partial P}}{2EI} dx$$

$$= \int \frac{M_{(x)} \frac{\partial M_{(x)}}{\partial P}}{EI} dx.$$

$\frac{\partial M_{(x)}}{\partial P}$ is in fact $m_{(x)}$. Thus,

$$\delta = \int \frac{M_{(x)} m_{(x)}}{EI} dx.$$

EXAMPLE 7.5

For the simply supported beam shown in the figure below, compute the vertical deflection at midspan point. Use energy methods. Assume that the total strain energy is due to bending only. Assume EI to be constant throughout.

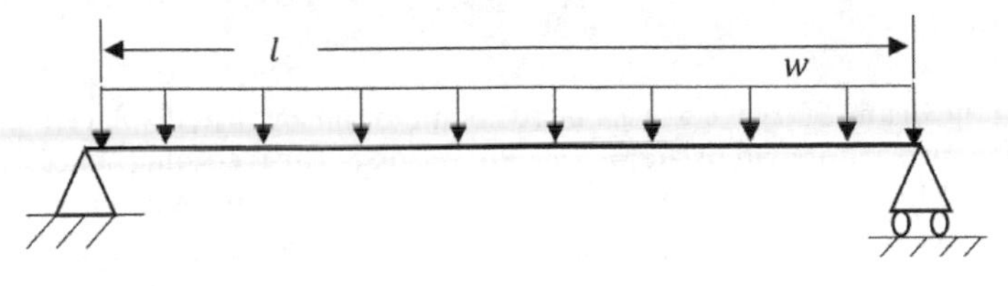

FIGURE 7.15

SOLUTION

Again, Castigliano's theorem cannot be applied directly to evaluate the vertical deflection at mid-span point. One of the following two methods can be used.

Method (1)

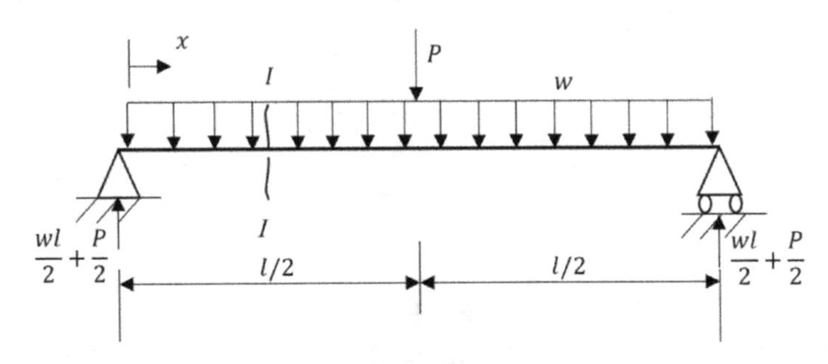

FIGURE 7.16

Since we want to compute the vertical displacement at midspan point, we will introduce a fictitious concentrated vertical load *P* at midspan point. Two cuts are required to determine the bending moment $M_{(x)}$. However, due to symmetry, we can focus only on one cut.

At section I-I:

$$M_{(x)} = \left(\frac{wl}{2} + \frac{P}{2}\right)x - \frac{wx^2}{2}.$$

Strain energy in the entire beam:

$$U = \int \frac{M_{(x)}^2}{2EI} dx$$

$$= 2\int_{x=0}^{l/2} \frac{\left[\left(\frac{wl}{2} + \frac{P}{2}\right)x - \frac{wx^2}{2}\right]^2}{2EI} dx$$

$$= \frac{1}{EI}\int_{x=0}^{l/2} \left[\left(\frac{wl}{2} + \frac{P}{2}\right)x - \frac{wx^2}{2}\right]^2 dx.$$

Instead of expanding the trinomial and then performing the integration, we can apply Castigliano's theorem at this stage:

$$\delta = \frac{\partial U}{\partial P} = \frac{1}{EI}\int_{x=0}^{l/2} 2\left(\frac{wlx}{2} + \frac{Px}{2} - \frac{wx^2}{2}\right)\left(\frac{x}{2}\right)dx$$

$$= \frac{1}{EI}\int_{x=0}^{l/2}\left(\frac{wlx^2}{2} + \frac{Px^2}{2} - \frac{wx^3}{2}\right)dx.$$

Setting $P = 0$:

$$\delta = \frac{1}{EI}\int_{x=0}^{l/2}\left(\frac{wl}{2}x^2 - \frac{wx^3}{2}\right)dx$$

$$= \frac{1}{EI}\left[\left(\frac{wl}{2}\right)\left(\frac{1}{3}\right)\left(\frac{l}{2}\right)^3 - \left(\frac{w}{2}\right)\left(\frac{1}{4}\right)\left(\frac{l}{2}\right)^4\right]$$

$$= \frac{1}{EI}\left(\frac{wl^4}{48} - \frac{wl^4}{128}\right)$$

$$= \frac{5wl^4}{384EI} \quad \downarrow \text{downward.}$$

Method (2)

Alternatively, we can use the unit-load method.

a)

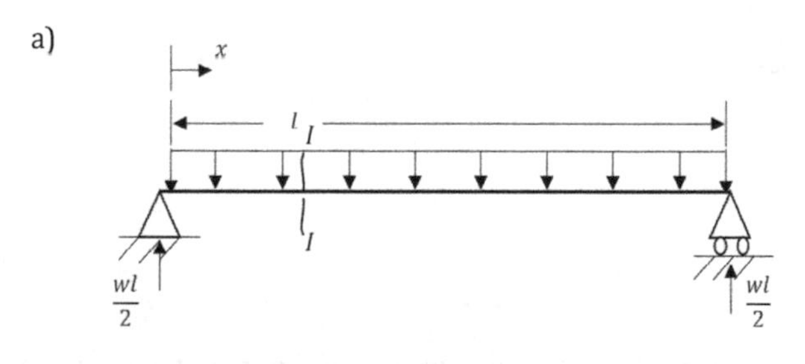

FIGURE 7.17

b)

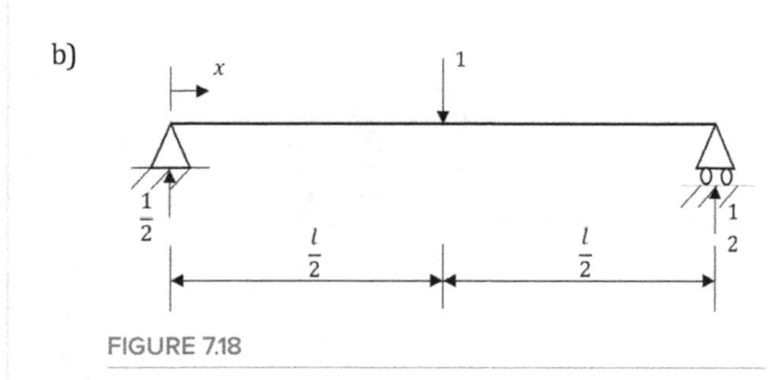

FIGURE 7.18

In figure (a):

$$M_{(x)} = \frac{wl}{2}x - \frac{wx^2}{2}.$$

In figure (b):

$$m_{(x)} = \frac{1}{2}x.$$

Therefore,

$$\begin{aligned}
\delta &= \int \frac{M_{(x)} m_{(x)}}{EI} dx \\
&= 2\int_{x=0}^{l/2} \frac{\left(\frac{wl}{2}x - \frac{wx^2}{2}\right)\left(\frac{x}{2}\right)}{EI} dx \\
&= \frac{1}{EI}\int_{x=0}^{l/2} \left(\frac{wl}{2}x^2 - \frac{w}{2}x^3\right) dx \\
&= \frac{1}{EI}\left[\left(\frac{wl}{2}\right)\left(\frac{1}{3}\right)\left(\frac{l}{2}\right)^3 - \left(\frac{w}{2}\right)\left(\frac{1}{4}\right)\left(\frac{l}{2}\right)^4\right] \\
&= \frac{1}{EI}\left(\frac{wl^4}{48} - \frac{wl^4}{128}\right) \\
&= \frac{5wl^4}{384EI} \qquad \downarrow \text{downward,}
\end{aligned}$$

which is exactly the same result obtained in method (1).

EXAMPLE 7.6

For the statically determinate cantilevered beam shown in the figure below, determine the vertical deflection at the free end. Use the energy method. Assume that the total strain energy is due to bending only. Assume EI to be constant throughout.

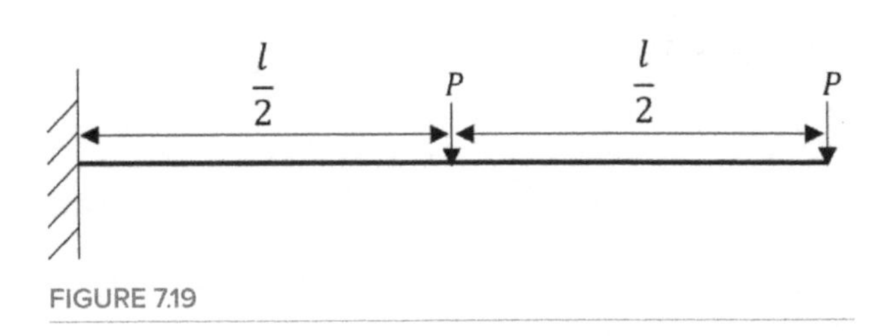

FIGURE 7.19

SOLUTION

Although there is a vertical concentrated load P at the free end, one must be careful applying Castigliano's theorem here, since there is another vertical concentrated load P acting at midspan point. In order to compute the vertical deflection at the free end, we can use one of the following two methods.

Method (1)

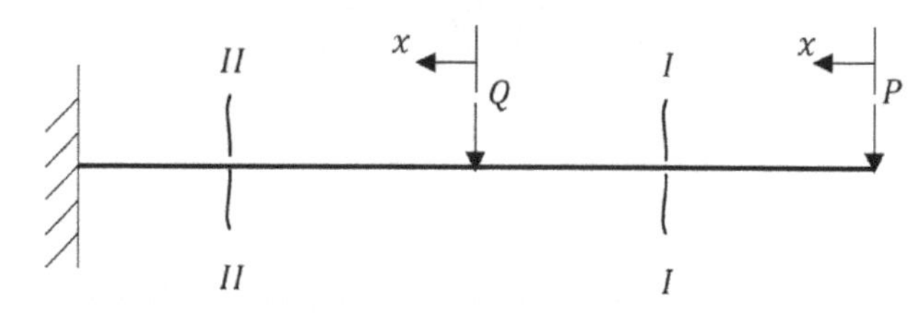

FIGURE 7.20

The beam is statically determinate. Two cuts are needed to establish the bending moment.

Strain energy in the entire beam:

$$U = \int \frac{M_{(x)}^2}{2EI} dx$$

$$= \int_{x=0}^{l/2} \frac{P^2x^2}{2EI} dx + \int_{x=0}^{l/2} \frac{\left(Qx + Px + \frac{Pl}{2}\right)^2}{2EI} dx$$

$$= \frac{1}{2EI}\left[\int_{x=0}^{l/2} P^2x^2 dx + \int_{x=0}^{l/2} \left(Qx + Px + \frac{Pl}{2}\right)^2 dx\right].$$

Applying Castigliano's theorem, vertical deflection at the free end is:

$$\delta = \frac{\partial U}{\partial P} = \frac{1}{2EI}\left[\int_{x=0}^{l/2} 2Px^2 dx + \int_{x=0}^{l/2} 2\left(Qx + Px + \frac{Pl}{2}\right)\left(x + \frac{l}{2}\right) dx\right]$$

$$= \frac{1}{EI}\left[\int_{x=0}^{l/2} Px^2 dx + \int_{x=0}^{l/2} \left(Qx + Px + \frac{Pl}{2}\right)\left(x + \frac{l}{2}\right) dx\right].$$

Setting $Q = P$:

$$\delta = \frac{7Pl^3}{16EI} \qquad \downarrow\text{downward.}$$

Method (2): (Unit-Load Method)

a)

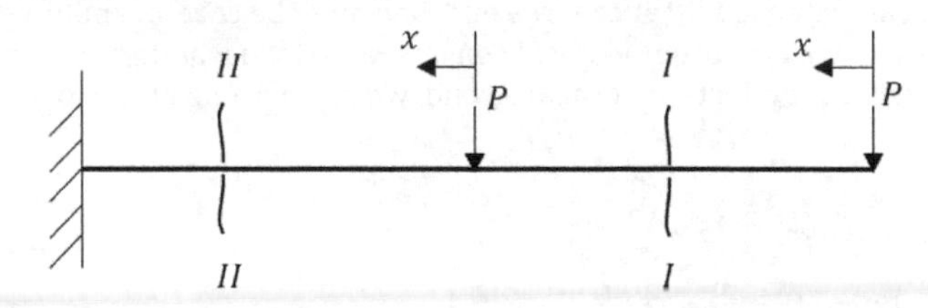

FIGURE 7.21

$$\text{I-I: } M_{(x)} = -Px$$

$$\text{II-II: } M_{(x)} = -2Px - \frac{Pl}{2}$$

b)

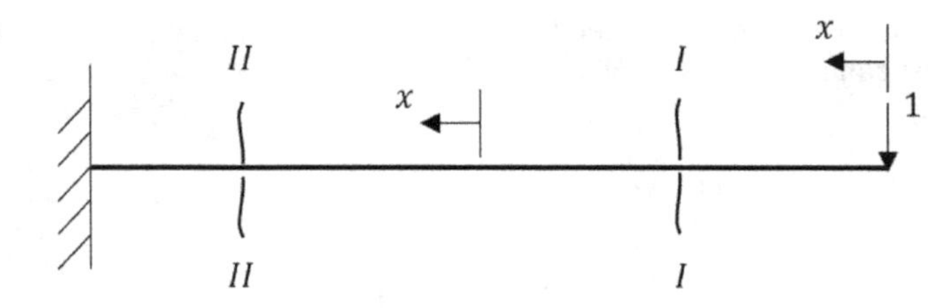

FIGURE 7.22

$$\text{I-I: } m_{(x)} = -x$$

$$\text{II-II: } m_{(x)} = -\left(x + \frac{l}{2}\right)$$

The vertical deflection at the free end:

$$\begin{aligned}
\delta &= \int \frac{M_{(x)} m_{(x)}}{EI} dx \\
&= \int_{x=0}^{l/2} \frac{Px^2}{EI} dx + \int_{x=0}^{l/2} \frac{\left(2Px + \frac{Pl}{2}\right)\left(x + \frac{l}{2}\right)}{EI} dx \\
&= \frac{1}{EI} \int_{x=0}^{l/2} \left[Px^2 + \left(2Px + \frac{Pl}{2}\right)\left(x + \frac{l}{2}\right)\right] dx \\
&= \frac{1}{EI} \int_{x=0}^{l/2} \left(3Px^2 + \frac{3}{2}plx + \frac{pl^2}{4}\right) dx \\
&= \frac{7Pl^3}{16EI} \quad \downarrow \text{downward,}
\end{aligned}$$

which is exactly the same result obtained in method (1).

7.4 Application of Energy Methods to Frames

A frame is a collection of beam elements. The following example illustrates how energy methods can be applied to a frame.

EXAMPLE 7.7

For the statically determinate plane frame shown in the figure below, compute the vertical deflection, the horizontal deflection, and the rotation at the free end. Use energy methods.

Do the problem:

i assuming that the total strain energy is due to bending only
ii taking into consideration, in addition to bending, the axial deformation effect

Assume EI and AE to be constant throughout.

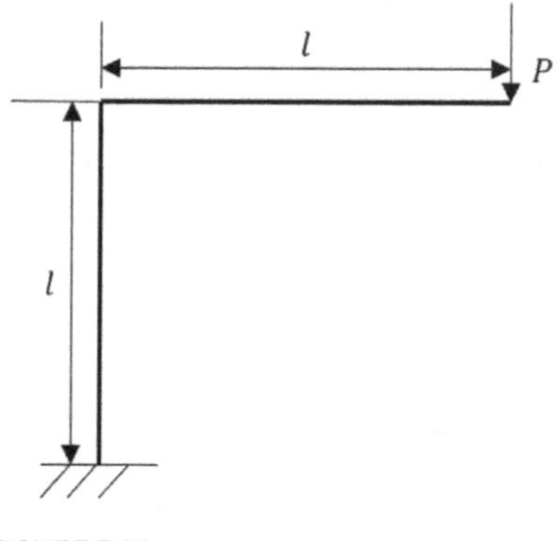

FIGURE 7.23

SOLUTION

We will assume that the total strain energy is due to bending only.

Vertical deflection at the free end:

Castigliano's theorem is shown in **figure 7.24**.

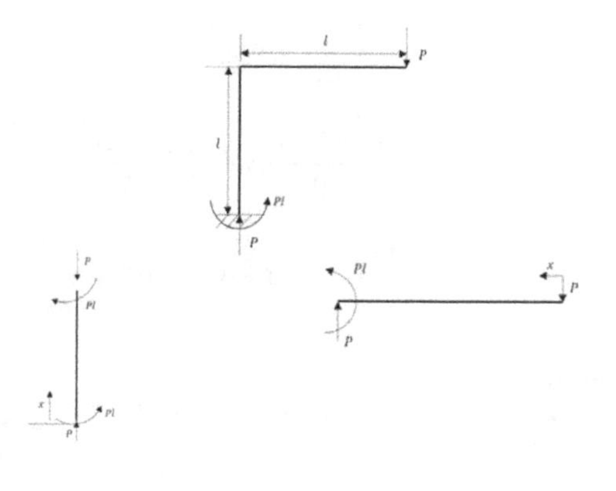

FIGURE 7.24

Strain energy is as follows:

$$U = \int \frac{M_{(x)}^2}{2EI} dx$$

$$= \int_{x=0}^{l} \frac{P^2x^2}{2EI} dx + \int_{x=0}^{l} \frac{P^2l^2}{2EI} dx$$

$$= \frac{2P^2l^3}{3EI}$$

$$\delta_V = \frac{\partial U}{\partial P} = \frac{4Pl^3}{3EI} \quad \downarrow \text{(downward).}$$

Unit-load method is shown in **figure 7.25**.

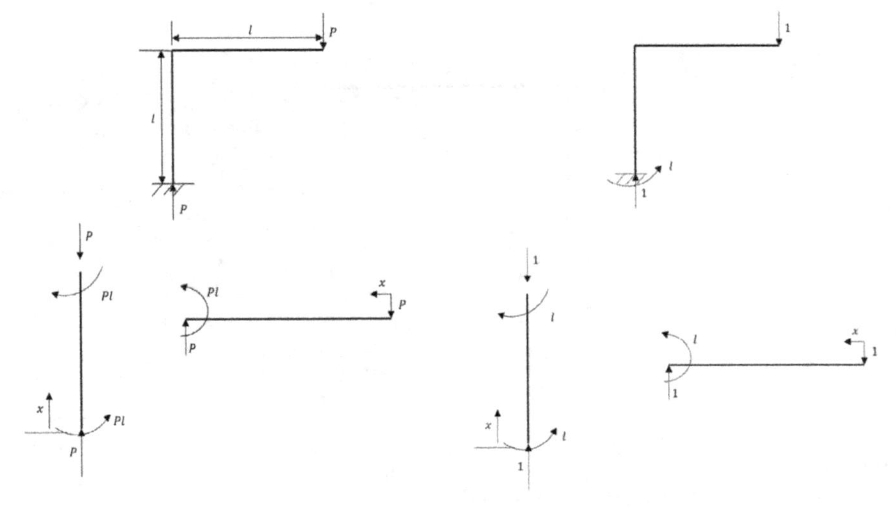

FIGURE 7.25

$$\delta_v = \int \frac{M_{(x)}m_{(x)}}{EI} dx$$

$$= \int_{x=0}^{l} \frac{(Px)(x)}{EI} dx + \int_{x=0}^{l} \frac{(Pl)(l)}{EI} dx$$

$$\Rightarrow \quad = \frac{4Pl^3}{3EI} \quad \downarrow \text{(downward),}$$

which is the same result obtained before.

Horizontal deflection at the free end is shown in **figure 7.26**.

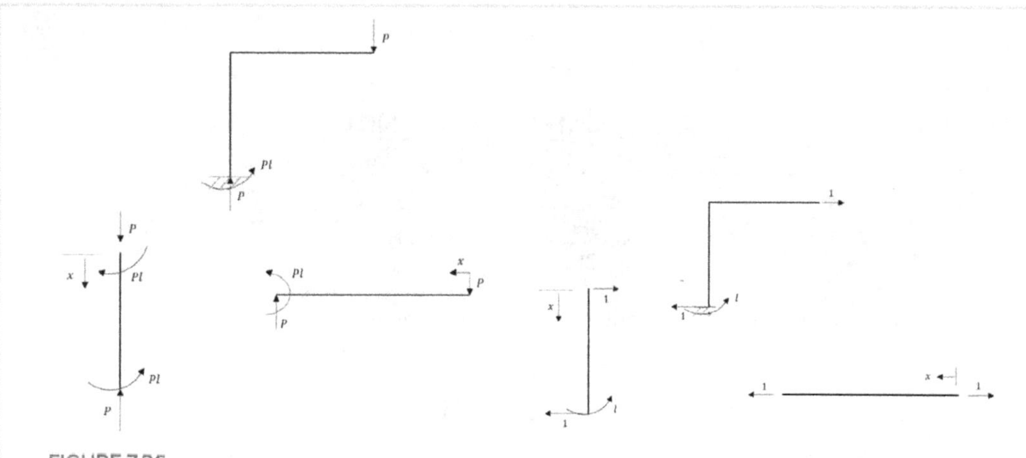

FIGURE 7.26

$$
\begin{aligned}
\delta_H &= \int \frac{M_{(x)} m_{(x)}}{EI} dx \\
&= \int_{x=0}^{l} \frac{(Pl)(x)}{EI} dx \\
&= \frac{Pl^3}{2EI} \quad \rightarrow \text{(to the right)}
\end{aligned}
$$

Rotation at the free end is shown in **figure 7.27**.

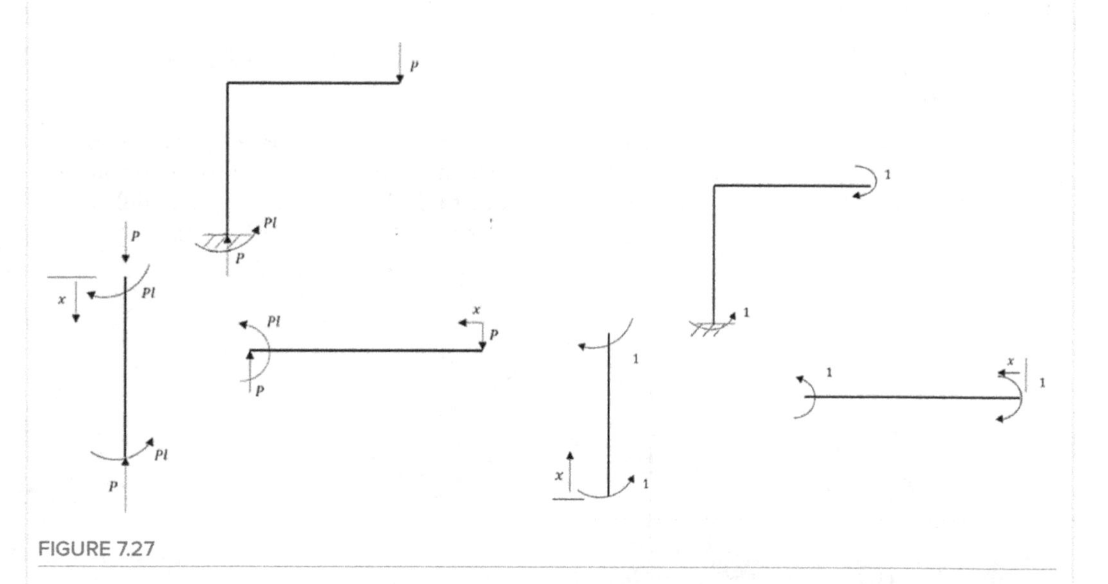

FIGURE 7.27

$$\delta = \int \frac{M_{(x)} m_{(x)}}{EI} dx$$

$$= \int_{x=0}^{l} \frac{(Px)(1)}{EI} dx + \int_{x=0}^{l} \frac{(Pl)(1)}{EI} dx$$

$$= \frac{3Pl^2}{2EI} \quad \circlearrowright \text{(clockwise)}$$

Taking under consideration the axial affect in addition to bending, the total strain energy U becomes:

$$U = \frac{2P^2 l^3}{3EI} + \frac{P^2 l}{2AE}.$$

Applying Castigliano's theorem:

$$\delta_V = \frac{\partial U}{\partial P} = \left(\frac{4Pl^3}{3EI} + \frac{Pl}{AE} \right) \quad \downarrow \text{(downward)}.$$

Notice that $\frac{Pl}{AE}$ is the correction term. For Euler–Bernoulli beams, such a correction term usually will be around 1%.

For the horizontal deflection at the free end and the rotation at the free end, δ_H and θ will not be affected for this problem.

7.5 Application of Energy Methods to Trusses

A truss is a collection of bar members or axial force members. The following example illustrates how energy methods can be used in solving truss problems.

EXAMPLE 7.8

For the statically determinate simply supported plane truss shown in the figure below, compute the vertical deflection and the horizontal deflection of joint C. Assume that all three truss members to be identical (i.e., same length l, same cross section area A, and same Young's modulus of elasticity E).

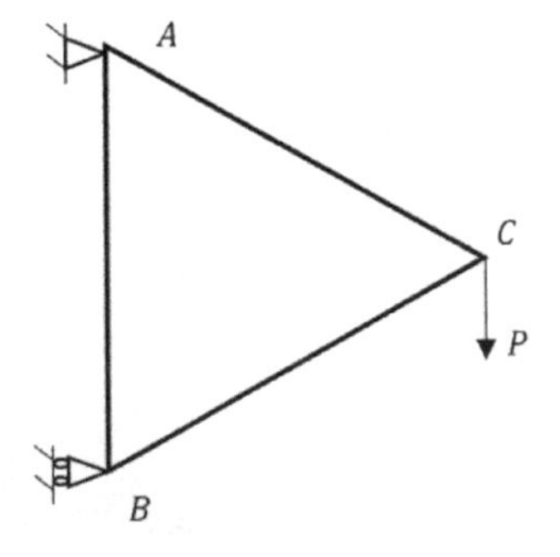

FIGURE 7.28

SOLUTION

To find the vertical deflection of joint C: Since there is a concentrated vertical load *P* acting at joint C, Castigliano's theorem can be applied directly. The truss is statically determinate. Therefore, we should be able to find the axial force in each member using the method of joints.

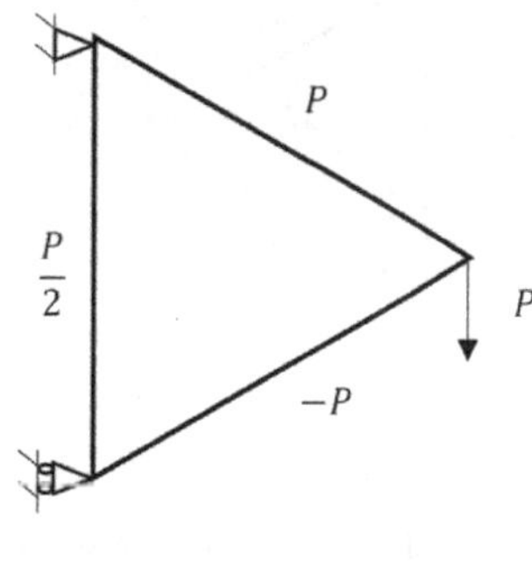

FIGURE 7.29

Total strain energy in the truss is as follows:

$$U = \frac{P^2 l}{2AE} + \frac{P^2 l}{2AE} + \frac{\left(\frac{P}{2}\right)^2 l}{2AE} = \frac{9P^2 l}{8AE}. \tag{7.6}$$

Applying Castigliano's theorem is as follows:

$$\delta_V = \frac{\partial U}{\partial P} = \frac{9Pl}{4AE} = 2.25\frac{Pl}{AE} \downarrow \text{downward.} \tag{7.7}$$

To find the horizontal deflection of joint C: Since there is no concentrated horizontal load acting at C in the original problem, we cannot apply Castigliano's theorem directly. In order to overcome such an obstacle, we will introduce a fictitious horizontal concentrated load H at joint C. Notice that such a force did not exist in the original problem. Therefore, we must dump it and set it equal to zero after using Castigliano's theorem.

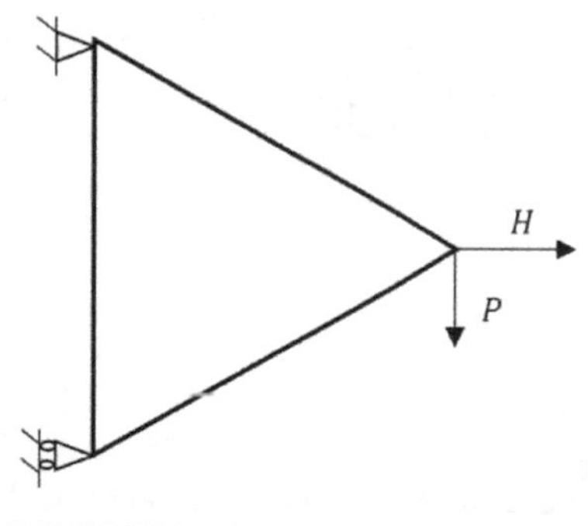

FIGURE 7.30

The truss above is still statically determinate, and the axial force in each and every member can be determined. For convenience, the principle of super position can be used, as shown in **figure 7.31**.

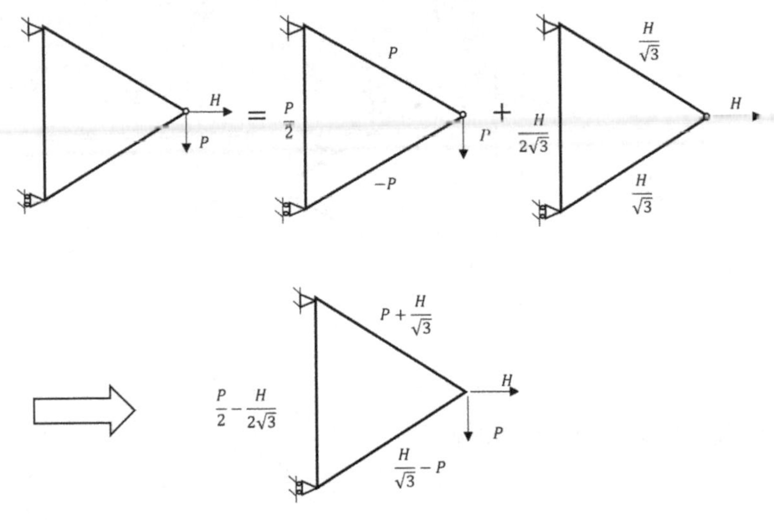

FIGURE 7.31

Total strain energy in the truss is as follows:

$$U = \frac{\left(P + \frac{H}{\sqrt{3}}\right)^2 l}{2AE} + \frac{\left(\frac{H}{\sqrt{3}} - P\right)^2 l}{2AE} + \frac{\left(\frac{P}{2} - \frac{H}{2\sqrt{3}}\right)^2 l}{2AE}$$

$$= \frac{l}{2AE}\left[\left(P + \frac{H}{\sqrt{3}}\right)^2 + \left(\frac{H}{\sqrt{3}} - P\right)^2 + \left(\frac{P}{2} - \frac{H}{2\sqrt{3}}\right)^2\right].$$

Applying Castigliano's theorem is shown as follows:

$$\delta_H = \frac{\partial U}{\partial H}$$

$$= \frac{l}{2AE}\left[2\left(P + \frac{H}{\sqrt{3}}\right)\left(\frac{1}{\sqrt{3}}\right) + 2\left(\frac{H}{\sqrt{3}} - P\right)\left(\frac{1}{\sqrt{3}}\right) + 2\left(\frac{P}{2} - \frac{H}{2\sqrt{3}}\right)\left(-\frac{1}{2\sqrt{3}}\right)\right].$$

Setting $H = 0$:

$$\delta_H = -\frac{Pl}{4\sqrt{3}AE}$$

$$\text{Therefore } \delta_H = \frac{Pl}{4\sqrt{3}AE} \quad \leftarrow \text{to the left.}$$

Notice also that the expression for $U_{(p,h)}$ can be used to determine the vertical deflection of joint C:

$$\delta_V = \frac{\partial U}{\partial P} = \frac{1}{2AE}\left[2\left(P + \frac{H}{\sqrt{3}}\right)(1) + 2\left(\frac{H}{\sqrt{3}} - P\right)(-1) + 2\left(\frac{P}{2} - \frac{H}{2\sqrt{3}}\right)\left(\frac{1}{2}\right)\right].$$

Setting H = 0:

$$\delta_V = \frac{9Pl}{4AE} = 2.25\frac{Pl}{AE} \quad \downarrow \text{downward},$$

which is exactly the same result obtained before.

Alternatively, the vertical displacement and the horizontal displacement of joint C can be computed using the unit-load method.

The following figures illustrate how the unit-load method can be used to obtain the same result.

Vertical displacement of joint C is shown in **figure 7.32**.

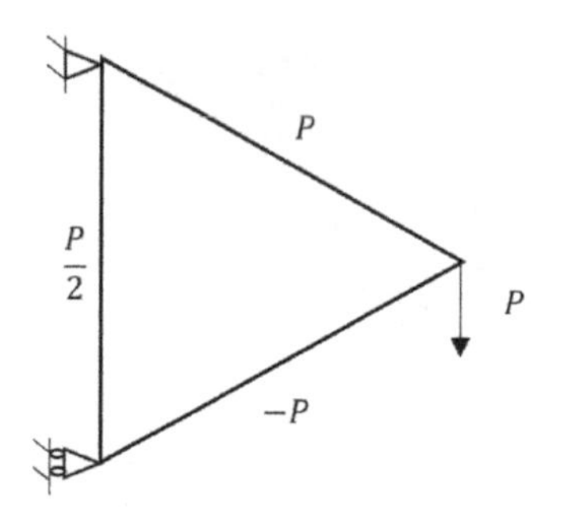

"Determine S"

1
1/2
1
−1

"Determine u"

FIGURE 7.32

$$\delta_V = \sum \frac{Sul}{AE}$$

$$= \frac{1}{AE}\sum Su$$

$$= \frac{1}{AE}\left[(P)(1) + (-P)(-1) + \left(\frac{P}{2}\right)\left(\frac{1}{2}\right)\right]$$

$$= 2.25\frac{Pl}{AE} \quad \downarrow \text{downward}$$

This is the same result obtained before.

Horizontal displacement of joint C is shown in **figure 7.33**.

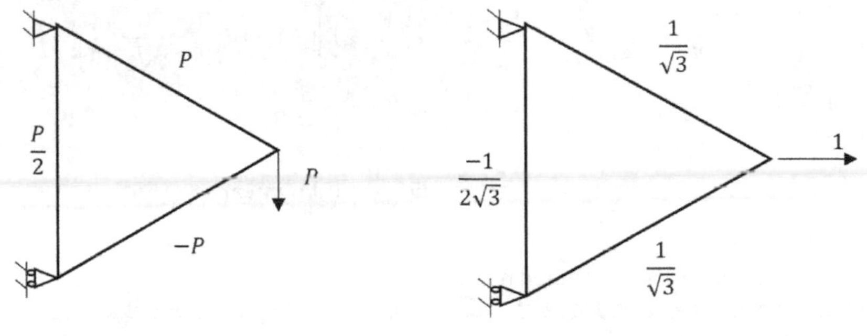

FIGURE 7.33

$$\delta_H = \sum \frac{Sul}{AE}$$

$$= \frac{1}{AE}\sum Su$$

$$= \frac{1}{AE}\left[(P)\left(\frac{1}{\sqrt{3}}\right) + (-P)\left(\frac{1}{\sqrt{3}}\right) + \left(\frac{P}{2}\right)\left(-\frac{1}{2\sqrt{3}}\right)\right]$$

$$= \frac{-Pl}{4\sqrt{3}AE}$$

Therefore, $\delta_H = \frac{Pl}{4\sqrt{3}AE}$ ←to the left.

This is the same result obtained before.

7.6 Application of Energy Methods to Curved Beams

Energy methods can be easily applied to curved beams as illustrated in the following example.

EXAMPLE 7.9

For the statically determinate quarter ring of mean radius R loaded by the vertical force *P* at the free end:

a) Assuming that the total strain energy is due to bending only, determine the vertical displacement, horizontal displacement and rotation at the free end.
b) Taking into consideration the axial force effect in addition to bending, compute the vertical displacement at the free end.

Assume EI to be constant throughout. Also, assume AE to be constant throughout.

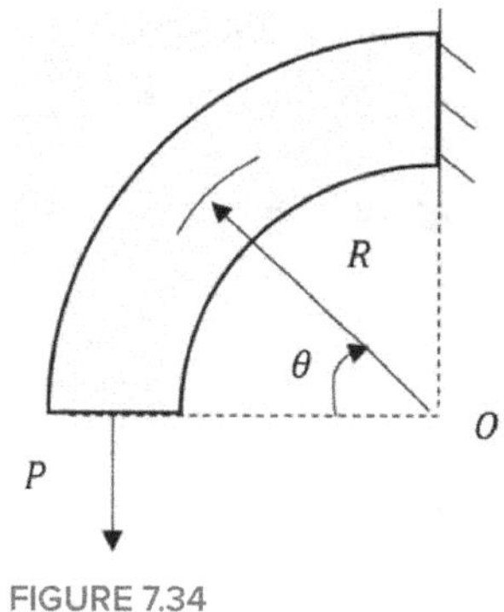

FIGURE 7.34

SOLUTION

a) Assuming that the total strain energy is due to bending only:

The vertical displacement is shown in **figure 7.35**.

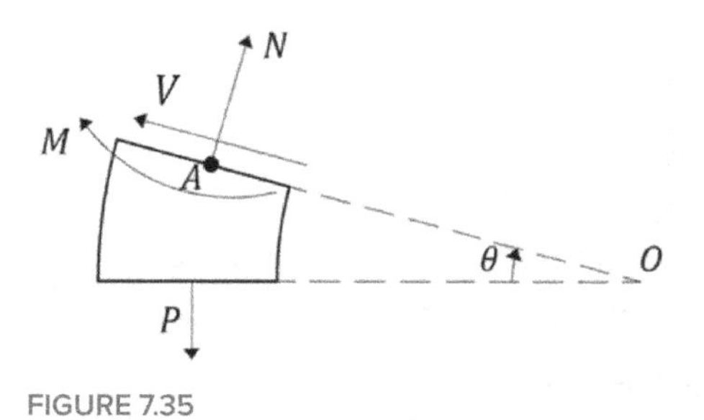

FIGURE 7.35

From statics, we use the following:

$$\sum M_A = 0 \Rightarrow P(R - R\cos\theta) - M = 0 \Rightarrow M_{(\theta)} = PR(1 - \cos\theta)$$

Strain energy is shown below:

$$U = \int \frac{M^2_{(\theta)} ds}{2EI} = \int_{\theta=0}^{\frac{\pi}{2}} \frac{P^2R^2(1 - \cos\theta)^2 R d\theta}{2EI}$$

$$U = \frac{P^2R^3}{2EI} \int_{\theta=0}^{\frac{\pi}{2}} (1 - \cos\theta)^2 d\theta$$

$$= \frac{P^2R^3}{2EI}\left(\frac{3\pi}{4} - 2\right)$$

Applying Castigliano's theorem is shown below:

$$\delta_V = \frac{\partial U}{\partial P} = \frac{PR^3}{EI}\left(\frac{3\pi}{4} - 2\right) \quad \downarrow \text{downward.}$$

Horizontal displacement is shown in **figure 7.36**.

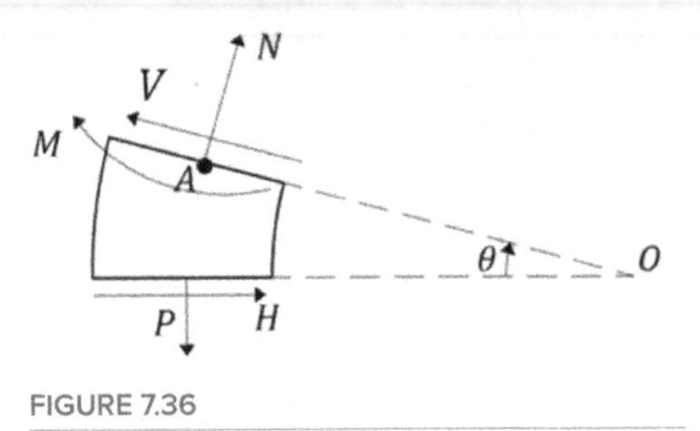

FIGURE 7.36

From statics, we use the following:

$$\sum M_A = 0 \Rightarrow P(R - R\cos\theta) + HR\sin\theta - M = 0 \Rightarrow M = PR - PR\cos\theta + HR\sin\theta.$$

Strain energy is shown below:

$$U = \int \frac{M^2_{(\theta)}ds}{2EI} = \int_{\theta=0}^{\frac{\pi}{2}} \frac{(PR - PR\cos\theta + HR\sin\theta)^2 Rd\theta}{2EI}.$$

Applying Castigliano's theorem, we get:

$$\delta_H = \frac{\partial U}{\partial H} = \int_{\theta=0}^{\frac{\pi}{2}} \frac{2(PR - PR\cos\theta + HR\sin\theta)(R\sin\theta)Rd\theta}{2EI}$$

$$= \frac{R^3}{EI}\int_{\theta=0}^{\frac{\pi}{2}} (P - P\cos\theta + H\sin\theta)\sin\theta d\theta.$$

Setting $H = 0$:

$$\delta_H = \frac{R^3}{EI}\int_{\theta=0}^{\frac{\pi}{2}} (P - P\cos\theta)\sin\theta d\theta$$

$$= \frac{PR^3}{2EI} \quad \rightarrow \text{ to the right.}$$

Rotation is shown in **figure 7.37**.

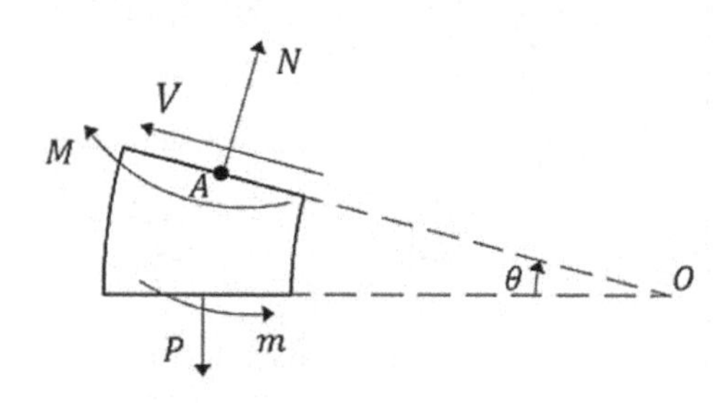

FIGURE 7.37

From statics:

$$\sum M_A = 0 \Rightarrow P(R - R\cos\theta) + m - M = 0 \Rightarrow M = PR(1 - \cos\theta) + m$$

Strain energy is shown below:

$$U = \int \frac{M^2_{(\theta)} ds}{2EI} = \int_{\theta=0}^{\frac{\pi}{2}} \frac{(PR - PR\cos\theta + m)^2 R d\theta}{2EI}.$$

Applying Castigliano's theorem, we get:

$$\theta = \left.\frac{\partial U}{\partial m}\right|_{m=0} = \frac{PR^2}{EI}\int_{\theta=0}^{\frac{\pi}{2}}(1 - \cos\theta)d\theta$$

$$= \frac{PR^2}{EI}\left(\frac{\pi}{2} - 1\right) \quad \circlearrowleft \text{ counterclockwise.}$$

b) Taking into consideration the axial force effect in addition to bending:

Vertical deflection is shown in **figure 7.38**.

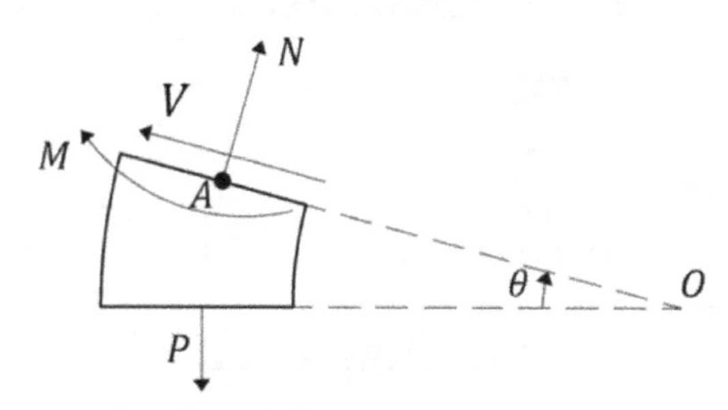

FIGURE 7.38

We evaluated M in part (a):

$$M = PR(1 - \cos\theta).$$

Also, from statics:

$$\sum F_x = 0 \quad \Rightarrow N\sin\theta - V\cos\theta = 0$$

$$\sum F_y = 0 \quad \Rightarrow V\sin\theta + N\cos\theta - P = 0.$$

Solving for N, we obtain:

$$N = P\cos\theta.$$

Strain energy is shown below:

$$U = \int_{\theta=0}^{\frac{\pi}{2}} \frac{P^2R^2(1-\cos\theta)^2 Rd\theta}{2EI} + \int_{\theta=0}^{\frac{\pi}{2}} \frac{P^2\cos^2\theta Rd\theta}{2AE}$$

$$\Rightarrow U = \frac{P^2R^3}{2EI}\left(\frac{3\pi}{4} - 2\right) + \frac{P^2R}{AE}\left(\frac{\pi}{8}\right).$$

Applying Castigliano's theorem, we get:

$$\delta_V = \frac{\partial U}{\partial P} = \left[\frac{PR^3}{EI}\left(\frac{3\pi}{4} - 2\right) + \frac{PR}{AE}\left(\frac{\pi}{4}\right)\right] \quad \downarrow \text{downward.}$$

Comparing the above result to the one we obtained in part (a), we notice that $\frac{PR}{AE}\left(\frac{\pi}{4}\right)$ is the correction term due to the axial force effect.

7.7 Application of Energy Methods to Statically Indeterminate Structures

EXAMPLE 7.10

For the statically indeterminate beam shown in **figure 7.39**, determine all the reactions. Also, draw the shear and bending moment diagrams. Assume EI to be constant throughout.

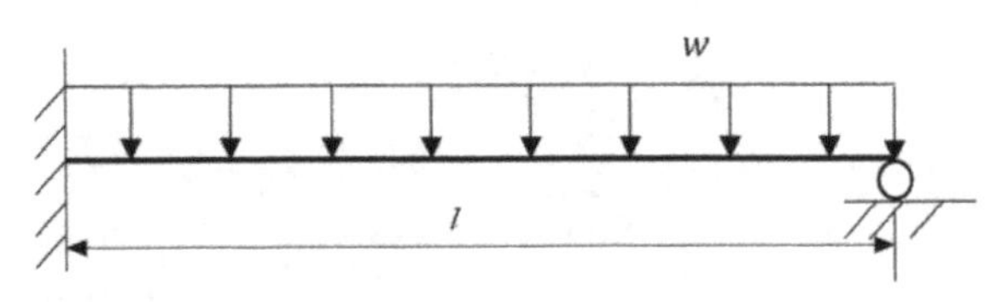

FIGURE 7.39

SOLUTION

The beam is statically indeterminate to the first degree. Denoting the vertical reaction at the roller by R and choosing the origin at the roller (see **figure 7.40**):

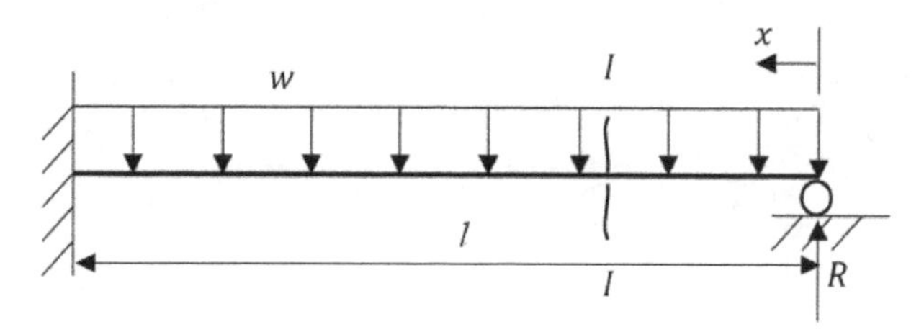

FIGURE 7.40

$$M_{(x)} = Rx - \frac{wx^2}{2}.$$

Strain energy is shown below:

$$U = \int \frac{M_{(x)}^2}{2EI} dx$$

$$= \int_{x=0}^{l} \frac{\left(Rx - \frac{wx^2}{2}\right)^2}{2EI} dx.$$

Since the vertical displacement at the roller is zero, applying Castigliano's theorem, we can write:

$$\frac{\partial U}{\partial R} = 0$$

$$\Rightarrow \frac{1}{2EI} \int_{x=0}^{l} 2\left(Rx - \frac{wx^2}{2}\right)(x)dx = 0$$

$$\Rightarrow \int_{x=0}^{l} \left(Rx^2 - \frac{wx^3}{2}\right) dx = 0$$

$$\Rightarrow R\frac{l^3}{3} - \frac{w}{2}\frac{l^4}{4} = 0$$

$$\Rightarrow R = \frac{3wl}{8}.$$

The remaining reactions can be determined from statics.

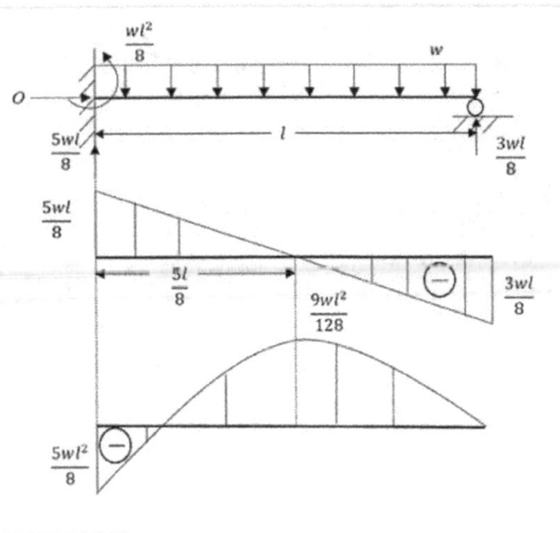

FIGURE 7.41

It is interesting that the same results could have been obtained using the method of consistent deformations. Choosing the vertical reaction at the roller to be the redundant (see **figure 7.42**):

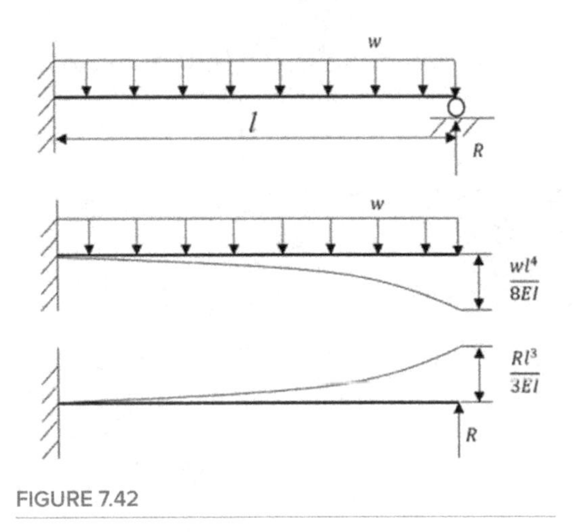

FIGURE 7.42

Compatibility equation is:

$$\frac{Rl^3}{3EI} = \frac{wl^4}{8EI}$$

$$\Rightarrow R = \frac{3wl}{8},$$

which is exactly the same result obtained using energy methods. Indeed $\frac{\partial U}{\partial R} = 0$ in energy methods will lead to the same compatibility equation in the method of consistent deformations.

EXAMPLE 7.12

For the statically indeterminate frame shown in the figure below, compute all the reactions. Assume EI to be constant throughout.

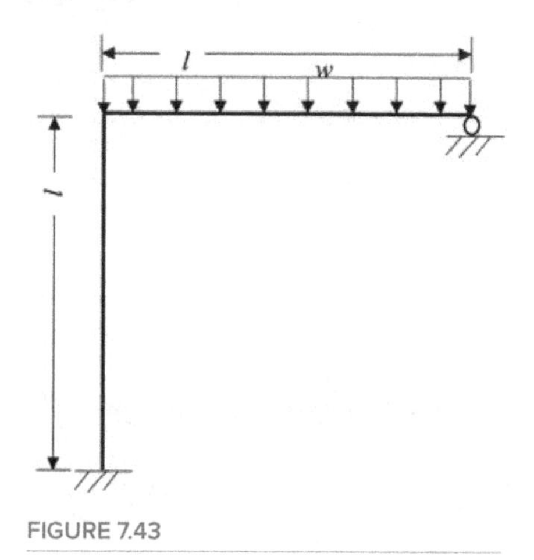

FIGURE 7.43

SOLUTION

The frame is statically indeterminate to the first degree (i.e., the degree of indeterminacy is one), denoting the vertical reaction at the roller by R.

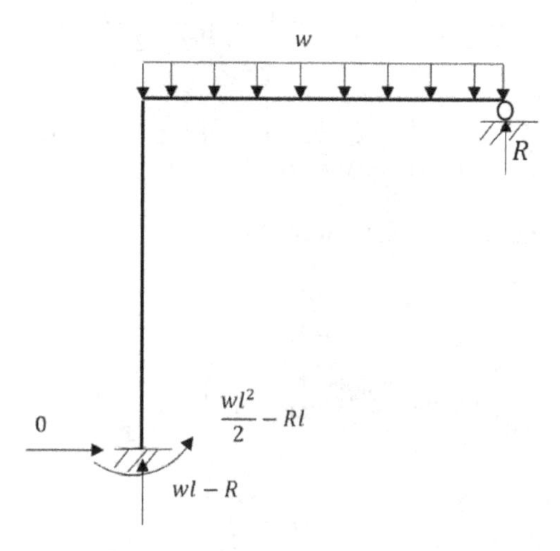

FIGURE 7.44

Splitting the frame into two beam element and drawing the FBDs (see **figure 7.45**):

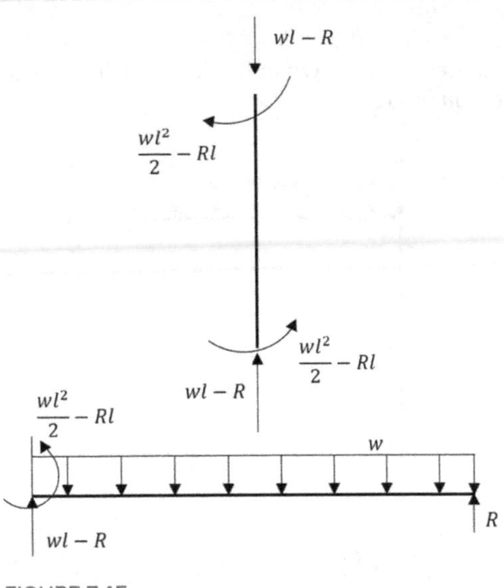

FIGURE 7.45

Strain energy is shown below:

$$U = \int_{x=0}^{l} \frac{\left(Rx - \frac{wx^2}{2}\right)^2}{2EI} dx + \int_{x=0}^{l} \frac{\left(\frac{wl^2}{2} - Rl\right)^2}{2EI} dx$$

$$= \frac{1}{2EI}\left[\int_{x=0}^{l}\left(Rx - \frac{wx^2}{2}\right)^2 dx + \int_{x=0}^{l}\left(\frac{wl^2}{2} - Rl\right)^2 dx\right].$$

The vertical deflection at the roller must be zero. Therefore,

$$\frac{\partial U}{\partial R} = 0$$

$$\Rightarrow \frac{1}{2EI}\left[\int_{x=0}^{l} 2\left(Rx - \frac{wx^2}{2}\right) x dx + \int_{x=0}^{l} 2\left(\frac{wl^2}{2} - Rl\right)(-l) dx\right] = 0$$

$$\Rightarrow R = \frac{15wl}{32}.$$

The remaining reactions can be determined using statics.

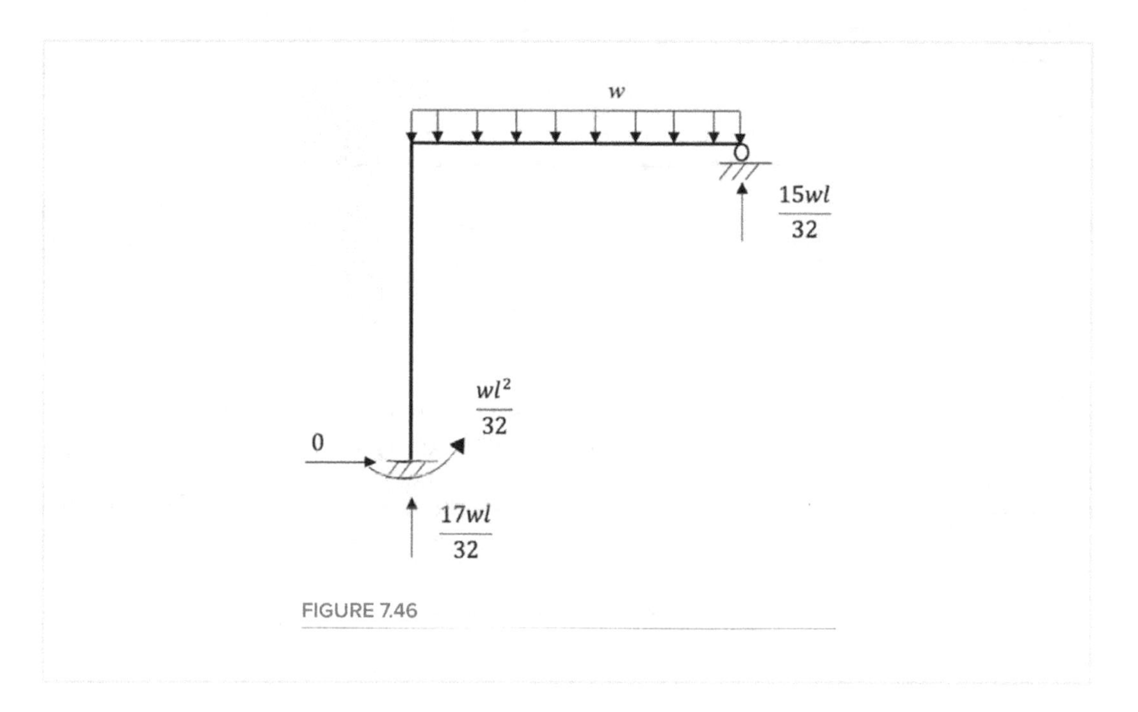

FIGURE 7.46

Problems

7.1. For the stepped cantilever beam of span l shown in the figure below, compute the vertical displacement at the free end. Assume that the total strain energy is due to bending only.

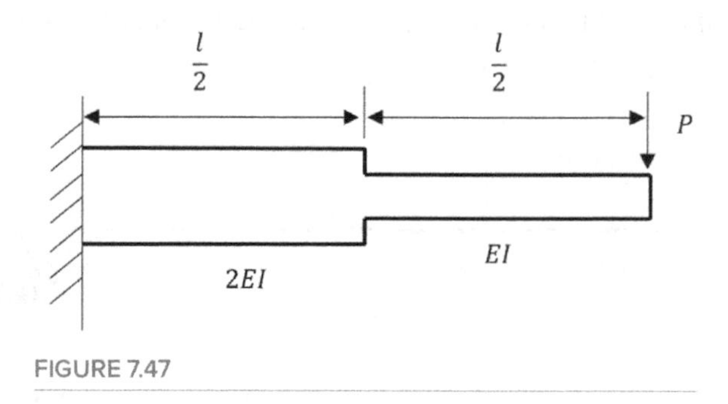

FIGURE 7.47

7.2. For the cantilevered beam shown in the figure below, compute the vertical displacement at the free end. Assume that the total strain energy is due to bending only. Assume *EI* to be constant throughout.

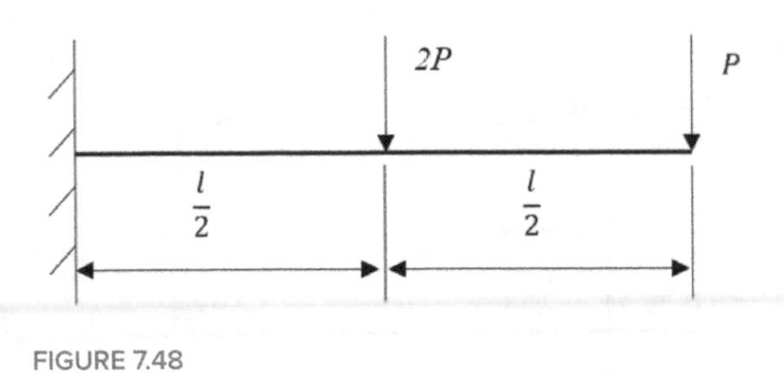

FIGURE 7.48

7.3. For the simply supported beam of span l shown in the figure below, compute the vertical displacement at the midspan point. Use energy methods. Assume that the total strain energy is due to bending only. Assume EI to be constant throughout.

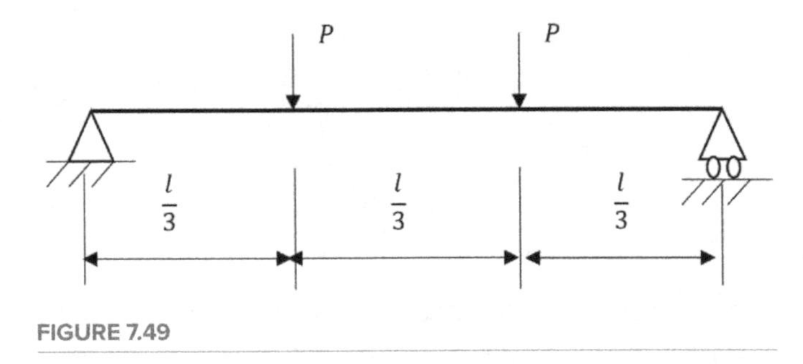

FIGURE 7.49

7.4. For the simply supported beam of span l shown in the figure below, compute the vertical displacement at the midspan point. Use energy methods. Assume that the total strain energy is due to bending only. Assume EI to be constant throughout.

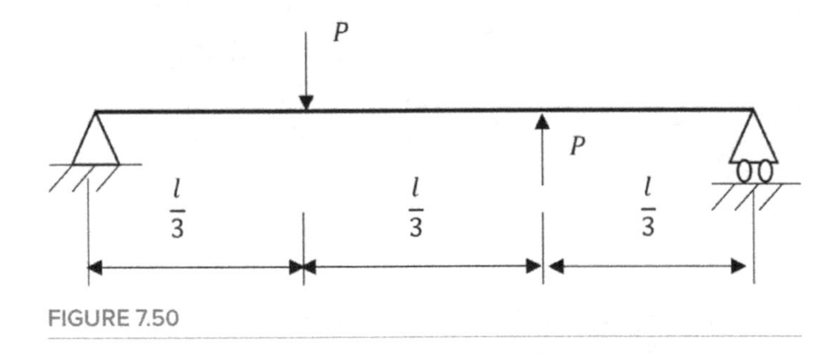

FIGURE 7.50

7.5. For the overhanging beam shown in the figure below, compute the vertical displacement at the free end. Use energy methods. Assume that the total strain energy is due to bending only. Assume EI to be constant throughout.

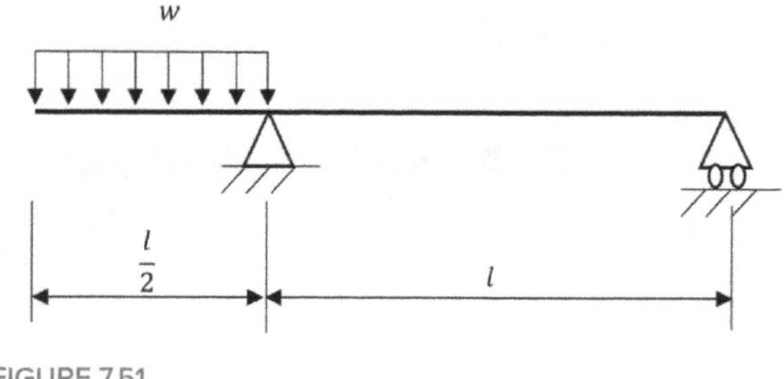

FIGURE 7.51

7.6. For the statically determinate frame shown in the figure below, compute the vertical displacement and the horizontal displacement at the free end:

i. first, by assuming that the total strain energy is due to bending only
ii. then, by taking into consideration the axial force effect in addition to bending

Assume AE to be constant throughout.

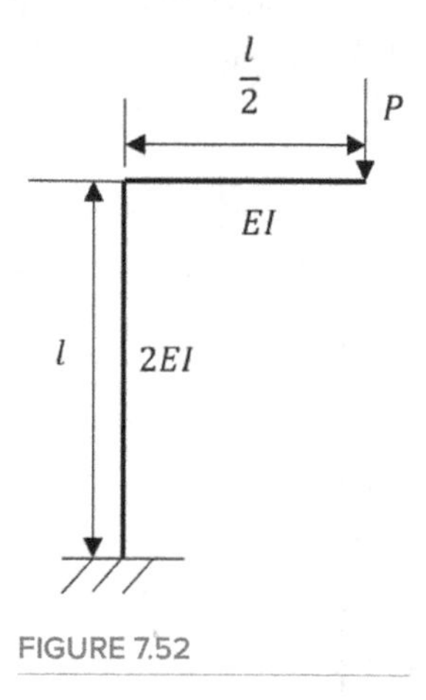

FIGURE 7.52

7.7. For the statically determinate frame shown in the figure below, compute the vertical displacement and the horizontal displacement at the free end:

i. first, by assuming that the total strain energy is due to bending only
ii. then, by taking into consideration the axial force effect in addition to bending

Assume AE and EI to be constant throughout.

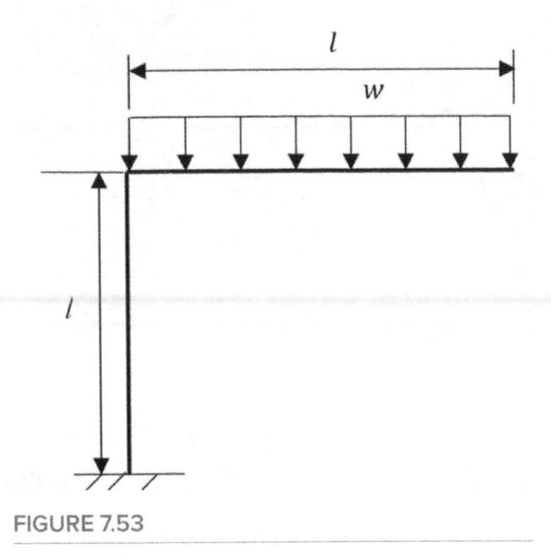

FIGURE 7.53

7.8. For the statically determinate frame shown in the figure below, compute the vertical displacement, horizontal displacement, and rotation at the free end. Use energy methods. Assume that the total strain energy is due to bending only. Assume EI to be constant throughout.

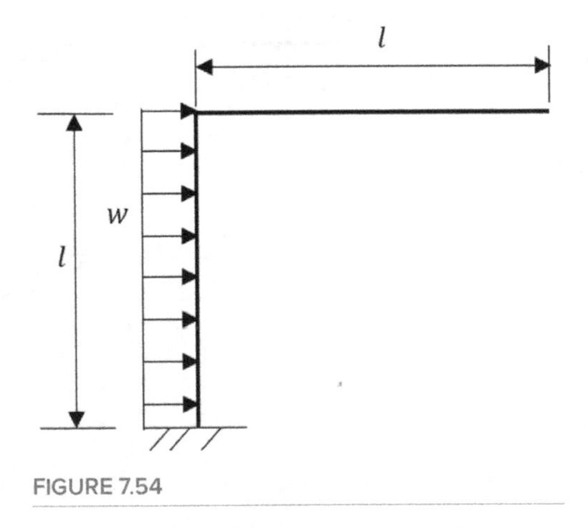

FIGURE 7.54

7.9. The frame shown in the figure below is statically indeterminate to the first degree. Determine all the reactions. Assume EI to be constant throughout.

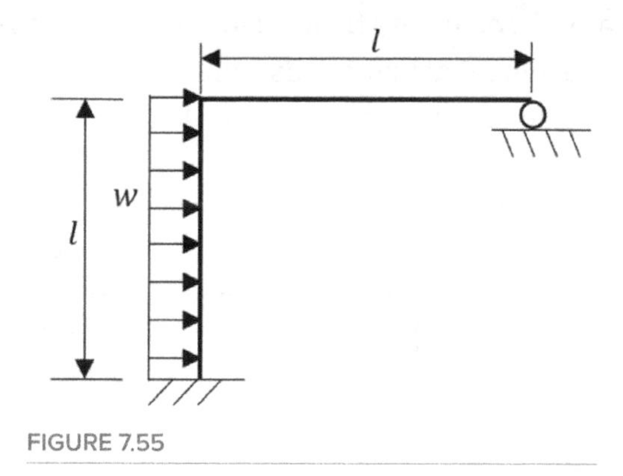

FIGURE 7.55

7.10. The frame shown in the figure below is statically indeterminate to the second degree. Compute all the reactions. Assume EI to be constant throughout.

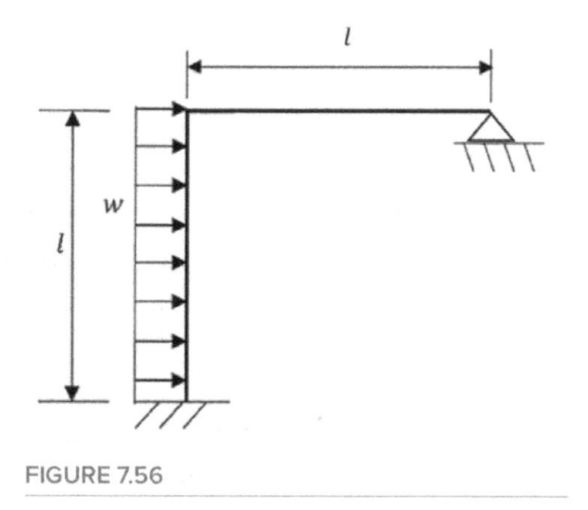

FIGURE 7.56

7.11. The frame shown in the figure below is statically indeterminate to the third degree. Determine all the reactions. Assume EI to be constant throughout.

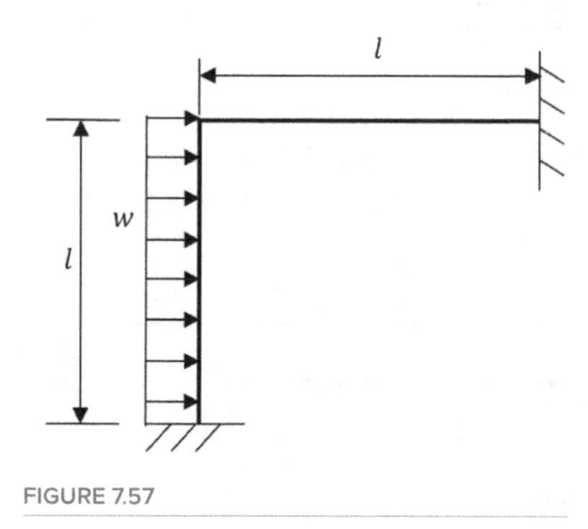

FIGURE 7.57

7.12. For the statically determinate frame shown in the figure below, compute the horizontal displacement at point A. Use energy methods. Assume that the total strain energy is due to bending only. Assume EI to be constant throughout.

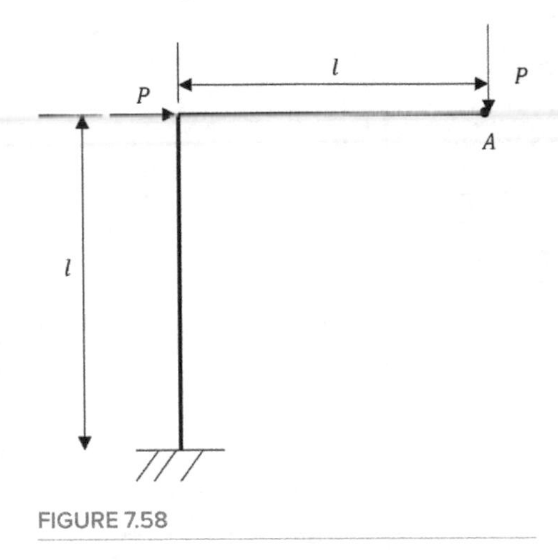

FIGURE 7.58

7.13. For the statically determinate frame shown in the figure below, compute the vertical displacement at the free end. Use energy methods. Assume that the total strain energy is due to bending only. Assume EI to be constant throughout.

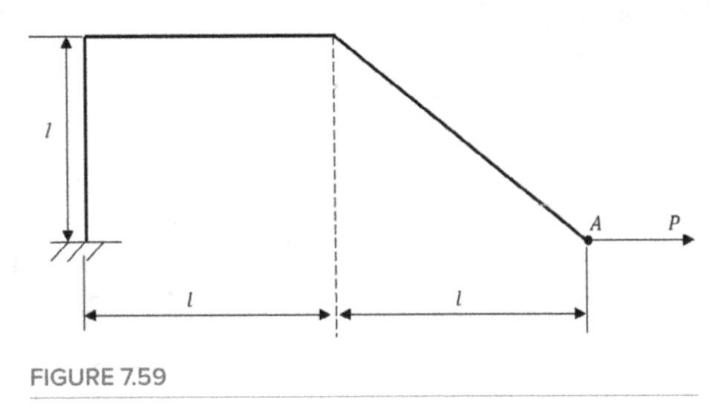

FIGURE 7.59

7.14. Determine the reactions in the statically indeterminate beam shown in the figure below. Assume EI to be constant throughout.

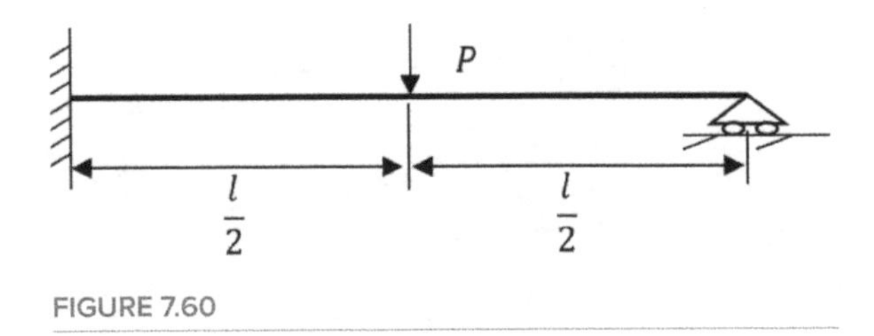

FIGURE 7.60

7.15. Determine the reactions in the statically indeterminate beam shown in the figure below. Assume EI to be constant throughout.

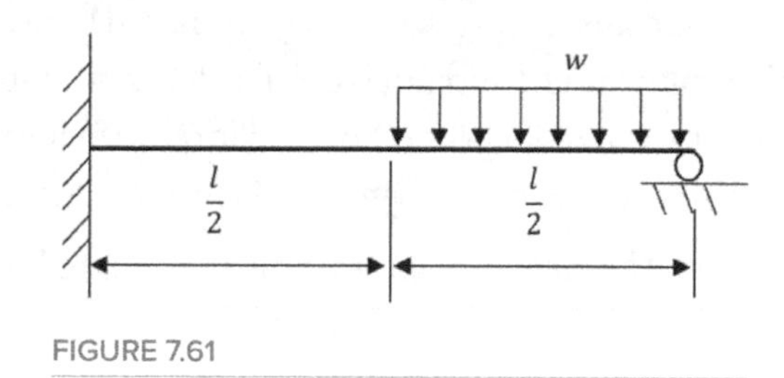

FIGURE 7.61

7.16. For the plane truss shown in the figure below, compute the horizontal displacement of joint A. Assume AE to be the same for all truss members.

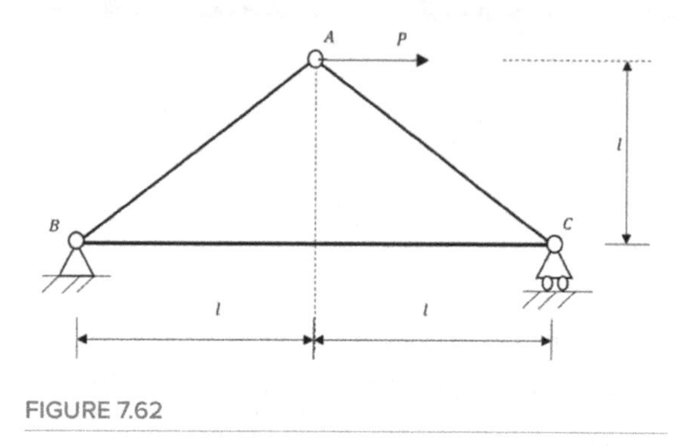

FIGURE 7.62

7.17. For the plane truss shown in the figure below, compute the vertical displacement and horizontal displacement of joint A. Assume AE to be the same for all truss members.

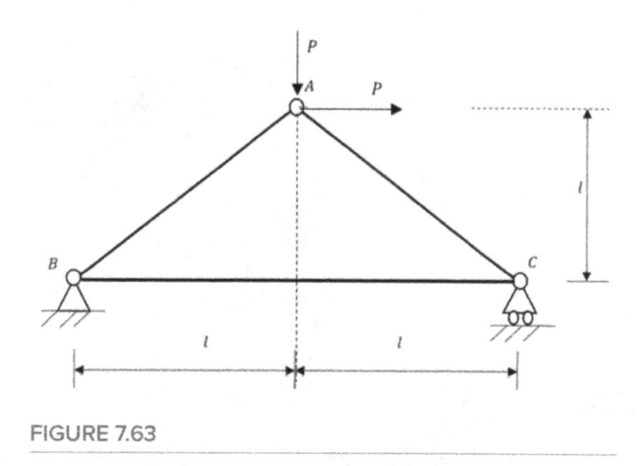

FIGURE 7.63

7.18. The curved beam shown in the figure below is subjected to load P at its free end.

i. Assuming that the total strain energy is due to bending only, compute the vertical displacement and horizontal displacement at the free end.

ii. By taking into consideration the axial force effect in addition to bending, compute the vertical displacement at the free end.

Assume EI to be constant throughout. Also, assume AE to be constant throughout.

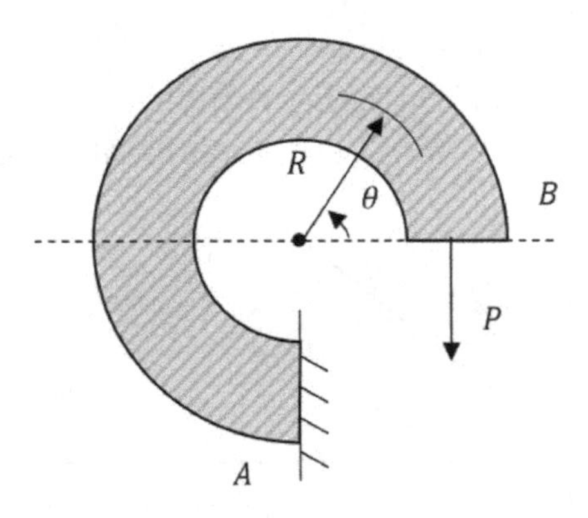

FIGURE 7.64

7.19. Determine all the reactions in the statically indeterminate frame shown in the figure below. Assume EI to be constant throughout.

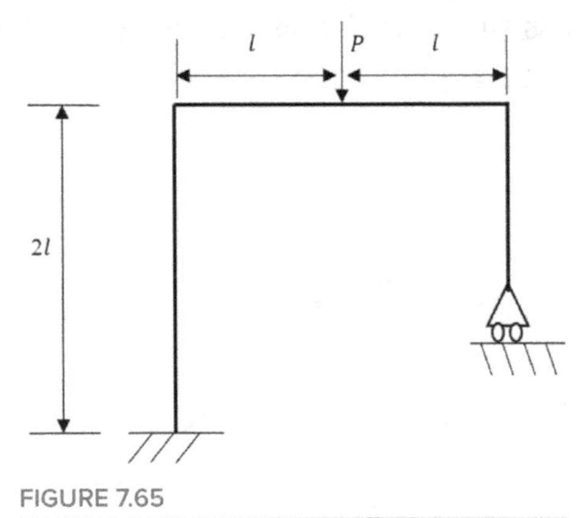

FIGURE 7.65

Further Reading

Beer, Ferdinand P., E. Russell Johnston, Jr., John T. DeWolf, and David. F. Mazurek. *Mechanics of Materials.* 7th ed. New York City: McGraw-Hill, 2015.

Budynas, Richard G. *Advanced Strength and Applied Stress Analysis.* New York City: McGraw-Hill, 1977.

Curtis, H. D. *Fundamentals of Aircraft Structural Analysis.* New York City: McGraw-Hill, 1997.

Donaldson, Bruce K. *Analysis of Aircraft Structures—An Introduction.* New York City: McGraw-Hill, 1993.

Roylance, David. *Mechanics of Materials.* Hoboken: Wiley, 1996.

Ugural, Ansel. C. *Mechanical Design: An Integrated Approach.* New York City: McGraw-Hill, 2004.

Ugural, Ansel C., and Saul K. Fenster. *Advanced Mechanics of Materials and Applied Elasticity.* 5th ed. Upper Saddle River: Prentice Hall, 2012.

CHAPTER 8

Structural Stability

8.1 Introduction

We studied failure by yielding in chapter 4. Consider a prismatic bar loaded axially with a load *P*. In chapter 1, we defined $\sigma = P/A$ to be the normal conventional stress, where A is the cross-sectional area of the prismatic bar.

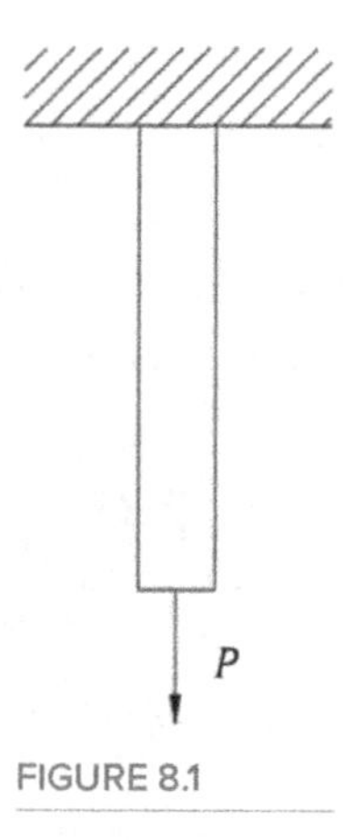

FIGURE 8.1

We also saw that each material has a tabulated yield stress σ_{yield}. It is a material property. If σ exceeds σ_{yield}, we say that failure by yielding occurs. For the most general case, when a body is subject to a system of forces as shown in the figure below.

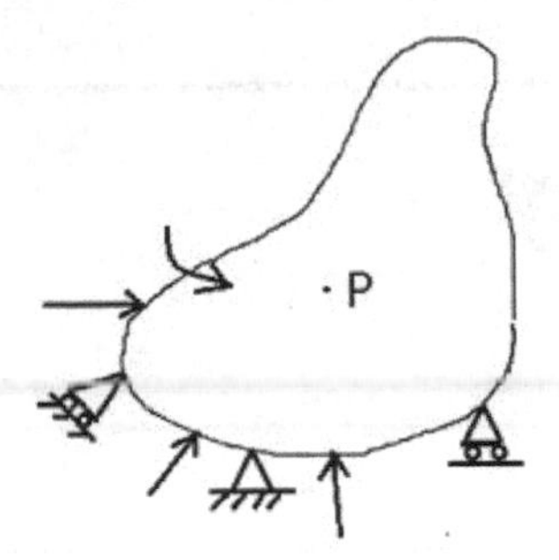

FIGURE 8.2

The stress matrix $[\sigma_{ij}]$ that defines the state of stress at a point becomes fully populated.

$$[\sigma_{ij}] = \begin{bmatrix} \sigma_x & \tau_{xy} & \tau_{xz} \\ \tau_{yx} & \sigma_y & \tau_{yz} \\ \tau_{zx} & \tau_{zy} & \sigma_z \end{bmatrix}$$

Chapter 4 discussed the most common failure by yielding theories, which addressed an important question: when does failure by yielding occur?

In this chapter, we will be covering another type of failure: failure by buckling or failure by structural instability. This type of failure is more serious and often more catastrophic than failure by yielding. We will see in this chapter that in some cases, when P is compressive and the bar is very thin, even though σ is way below σ_{yield}, buckling can still take place. Buckling or structural instability should be avoided by all means. This chapter is only an introduction to the topic. An entire graduate course, Stability of Structures, can be taken if needed.

8.2 Pinned-Pinned Column

Consider the simply supported column of length l subject to the compressive axial force P, as shown in the figure below.

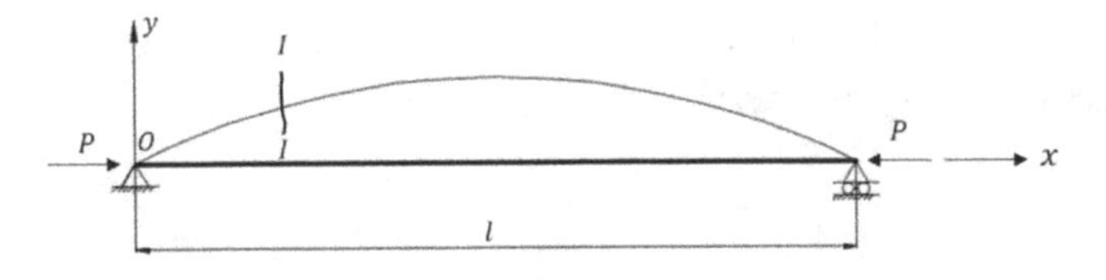

FIGURE 8.3 Pined-Pined Column

The differential equation describing the elastic curve of the column is:

$$EIy'' = M_{(x)}.$$

At I-I:

$$M_{(x)} = -Py$$

$$\Rightarrow \quad EIy'' = -Py$$

$$\Rightarrow \quad EIy'' + Py = 0.$$

Let us assume that EI is constant throughout, and let $\lambda = \sqrt{\frac{P}{EI}}$, then the above differential equation can be written as:

$$y'' + \lambda^2 y = 0. \tag{8.1}$$

Equation (8.1) is a homogeneous second order linear ordinary differential equation with constant coefficients.

It is interesting to notice that λ has the dimension of $(\text{length})^{-1}$ with units of m^{-1}, cm^{-1}, ft^{-1}, etc. Since, for instance, in the SI system of units:

$$\sqrt{\frac{N}{\frac{N}{m^2}m^4}} = \frac{1}{m}.$$

The general solution to (8.1) is

$$y = A\sin\lambda x + B\cos\lambda x,$$

where A and B are constants of integration to be determined from the boundary conditions. Notice that since λ has the dimension of $(\text{length})^{-1}$, λx is unitless, and that is what the argument of sine or cosine should be.

The boundary conditions for this problem are:

$$x = 0 \;\Rightarrow\; y = 0$$

$$x = l \;\Rightarrow\; y = 0$$

$$x = 0 \;\Rightarrow\; y = 0 \;\Rightarrow\; B = 0$$

$$x = l \;\Rightarrow\; y = 0 \;\rightarrow\; A\sin\lambda l = 0$$

$$\Rightarrow \text{Either } A = 0 \text{ (trivial solution)}$$

$$\Rightarrow \text{or } \sin\lambda l = 0 \text{ (nontrivial solution).}$$

$\text{Sin}\lambda l = 0$ is the characteristic equation for this case and leads to:

$$\lambda l = n\pi, \quad n = 1,2,3,4,\ldots$$

$$\Rightarrow \quad \lambda = \frac{n\pi}{l}$$

$$\Rightarrow \quad \frac{P}{EI} = \frac{n^2\pi^2}{l^2}$$

$$\Rightarrow \quad P = \frac{n^2\pi^2 EI}{l^2}; \; n = 1,2,3,\ldots,$$

The smallest value of *P* is obtained when n = 1:

$$P_{Cr} = \frac{\pi^2 EI}{l^2}. \tag{8.2}$$

(8.2) is called Euler's[1] formula.

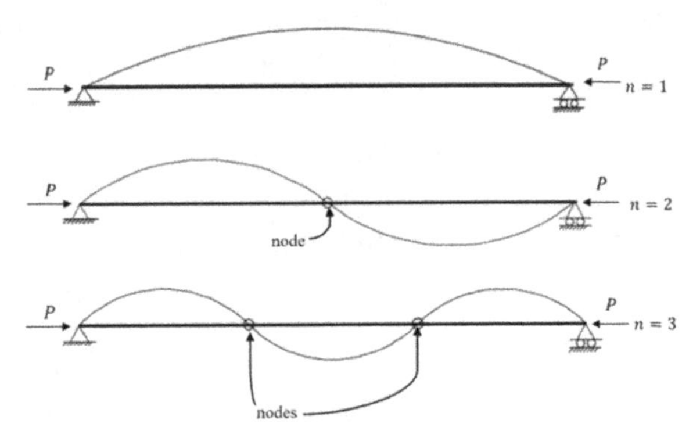

FIGURE 8.4 Buckling modes

(8.2) can be used to establish the critical stress σ_{Cr}

$$\sigma_{Cr} = \frac{P_{Cr}}{A} = \frac{\pi^2 EI}{l^2 A} = \frac{\pi^2 E r^2}{l^2}$$

$$\Rightarrow \quad \sigma_{Cr} = \frac{\pi^2 E}{\left(\frac{l}{r}\right)^2}, \tag{8.3}$$

1 Euler's formula is named after Leonard Euler, a Swiss mathematician who contributed a lot to applied mechanics. Euler was a student of one of the Bernoullis at Basel University in Switzerland.

where:

- σ_{Cr} is the critical stress;
- E is Young's modulus of elasticity;
- l is length of the column;
- r is radius of gyration; and
- l/r is the slenderness ratio.

Notice that l/r is unitless, and σ_{Cr} has the same dimension as E(Pa, lb_f/ft^2, *psi* etc.).

Gyration means rotation, and the term "radius of gyration" is borrowed from dynamics. $\vec{F} = m\vec{a}$ is Newton's second law or the fundamental equation in dynamics. It is used for a translational motion. For a rigid body that can spin about a fixed axis, as shown in **figure 8.5**.

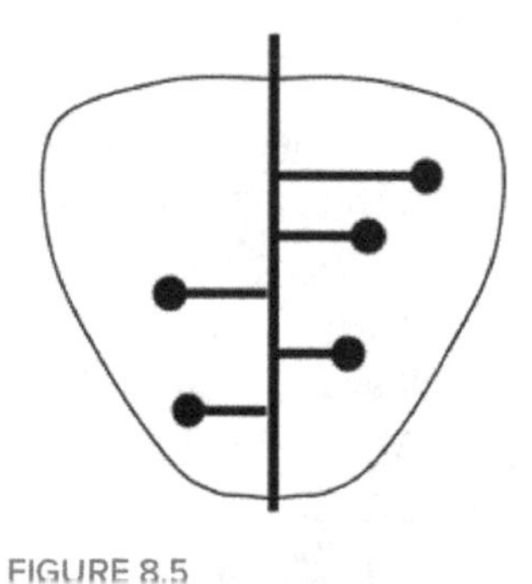

FIGURE 8.5

The rotational motion is described by $M = I\alpha$, where M is the moment, α is the angular acceleration, and I is called the mass moment of inertia about the fixed axis (unit in SI system is kgm^2):

$$I = \int \rho^2 dm.$$

The radius of gyration is defined to be:

$$r = \sqrt{\frac{I}{m}} \quad ; \quad \left[\sqrt{\frac{kgm^2}{kg}} = m \right].$$

If the entire mass m of the rigid body is to be concentrated at a point located at a distance r from the axis, it will produce precisely the same amount of mass moment of inertia and, thus, will have the same rotational effect.

Obviously, here we have area moment of inertia (m^4) instead of mass moment of inertia (kgm^2), and in this case, the radius of gyration is defined to be:

$$r = \sqrt{\frac{I}{A}} \quad ; \quad \left[\sqrt{\frac{m^4}{m^2}} = m\right].$$

8.3 Free-Fixed Column

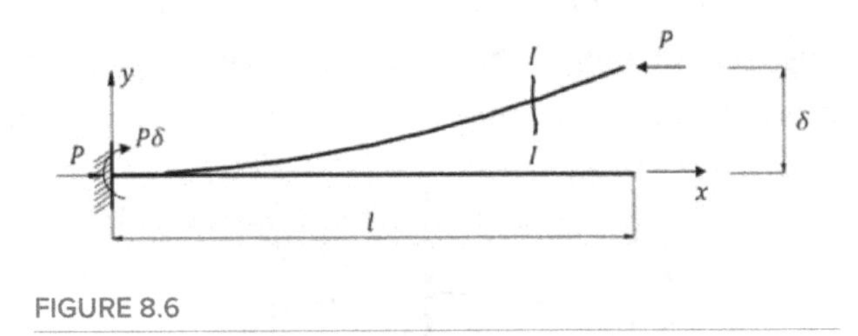

FIGURE 8.6

The differential equation describing the elastic curve of the column is:

$$EIy'' = M_{(x)}$$

$$M_{(x)} = P\delta - Py$$

$$\Rightarrow \quad EIy'' = P\delta - Py$$

$$\Rightarrow \quad EIy'' + Py = P\delta. \tag{8.4}$$

Again, assuming EI to be constant throughout, (8.4) is a nonhomogeneous second order linear ordinary differential equation with constant coefficients. The general solution to a nonhomogeneous linear ODE is equal to the general solution to the corresponding homogeneous equation plus a particular solution to the nonhomogeneous equation.

The corresponding homogeneous equation is:

$$EIy'' + Py = 0$$

$$\Rightarrow \quad y'' + \frac{P}{EI}y = 0.$$

Let:

$$\lambda = \sqrt{\frac{P}{EI}}.$$

Then,

$$y'' + \lambda^2 y = 0.$$

The general solution to the above corresponding homogeneous equation is:

$$y = A\sin\lambda x + B\cos\lambda x.$$

Also, it is very obvious to notice that

$$y = \delta$$

is a particular solution to the nonhomogeneous ODE.

Therefore, the general solution to the nonhomogeneous ODE is

$$y = A\sin\lambda x + B\cos\lambda x + \delta,$$

where A and B are arbitrary constants of integration to be determined from the boundary conditions of the problem.

Boundary conditions are as follows:

$$x = 0 \Rightarrow y = 0$$

$$x = 0 \Rightarrow y' = 0$$

$$x = l \Rightarrow y = \delta$$

$$y = A\sin\lambda x + B\cos\lambda x + \delta$$

$$\Rightarrow y' = A\lambda\cos\lambda x - B\lambda\sin\lambda x$$

$$x = 0 \Rightarrow y' = 0 \Rightarrow A = 0$$

$$x = 0 \Rightarrow y = 0 \Rightarrow B + \delta = 0 \Rightarrow B = -\delta.$$

Therefore,

$$y = \delta - \delta\cos\lambda x$$

$$x = l \Rightarrow y = \delta \Rightarrow \cos\lambda l = 0,$$

and the above trigonometric equation is the characteristic equation.

Therefore,

$$\lambda l = n\frac{\pi}{2}, \quad n = 1,3,5,7,\ldots$$

$$\Rightarrow \quad \lambda = \frac{n\pi}{2l}$$

$$\Rightarrow \quad \frac{P}{EI} = \frac{n^2\pi^2}{4l^2}$$

$$\Rightarrow \quad P = \frac{n^2\pi^2 EI}{4l^2} \quad ; n = 1,3,5,\ldots.$$

The smallest value of P can be obtained by letting $n = 1$:

$$P_{Cr} = \frac{\pi^2 EI}{4l^2}. \tag{8.5}$$

Alternatively, (8.5) can be written as:

$$P_{Cr} = \frac{\pi^2 EI}{(2l)^2} = \frac{\pi^2 EI}{l_e^2},$$

where $l_e = 2l$ is called the effective length.

Notice that it is easier for a free-fixed column to buckle compared to a pinned-pinned column.

8.4 Pinned-Fixed Column

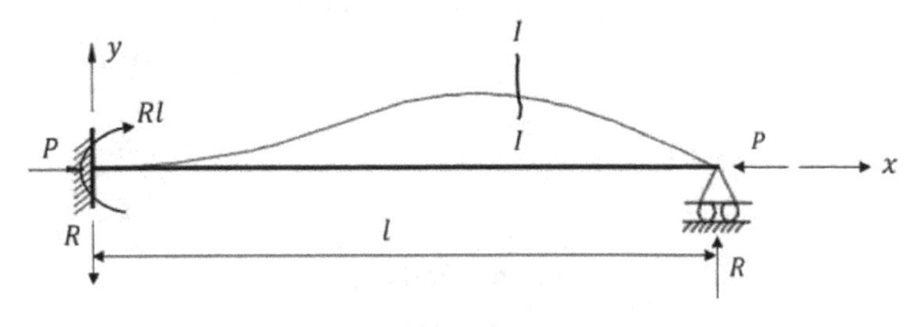

FIGURE 8.7

The differential equation describing the elastic curve of the column is:

$$EIy'' = M_{(x)}.$$

At I-I:

$$M_{(x)} = Rl - Rx - Py$$

$$\Rightarrow \quad EIy'' = Rl - Rx - Py$$

$$\Rightarrow \quad EIy'' + Py = Rl - Rx$$

$$\Rightarrow \qquad y'' + \frac{P}{EI}y = \frac{Rl}{EI} - \frac{Rx}{EI}. \qquad (8.6)$$

The above equation is a nonhomogeneous second order linear ordinary differential equation with constant coefficients (assuming that EI is constant throughout).

The corresponding homogeneous equation is:

$$y'' + \frac{P}{EI}y = 0,$$

or (letting $\lambda = \sqrt{\frac{P}{EI}}$):

$$y'' + \lambda^2 y = 0,$$

and the general solution to the above corresponding homogeneous equation is:

$$y = A\sin\lambda x + B\cos\lambda x.$$

In order to find a particular solution to the nonhomogeneous ODE, assume a particular solution of the form:

$$y = c_1 + c_2 x,$$

where c_1 and c_2 are coefficients yet to be determined.

$$y = c_1 + c_2 x$$

$$\Rightarrow \quad y' = c_2$$

$$\Rightarrow \quad y'' = 0$$

Plugging in equation (8.6):

$$\frac{P}{EI}(c_1 + c_2x) = \frac{Rl}{EI} - \frac{Rx}{EI}$$

$$\Rightarrow \frac{Pc_1}{EI} + c_2\frac{Px}{EI} = \frac{Rl}{EI} - \frac{Rx}{EI}.$$

Therefore,

$$\frac{Pc_1}{EI} = \frac{Rl}{EI} \text{ and } \frac{Pc_2}{EI} = -\frac{R}{EI},$$

which leads to

$$c_1 = \frac{Rl}{P}$$

$$\text{and } \quad c_2 = -\frac{R}{P}.$$

Thus,

$$y = \frac{Rl}{P} - \frac{R}{P}x$$

is a particular solution to the nonhomogeneous ODE.

We conclude that the general solution to the nonhomogeneous ODE is

$$y = A\sin\lambda x + B\cos\lambda x + \frac{Rl}{P} - \frac{R}{P}x,$$

where A and B are arbitrary constants of integration that need to be determined from the boundary conditions.

Boundary conditions are as follows:

$$x = 0 \quad \Rightarrow \quad y = 0$$

$$x = 0 \quad \Rightarrow \quad y' = 0$$

$$x = l \quad \Rightarrow \quad y = 0$$

$$y = A\sin\lambda x + B\cos\lambda x + \frac{Rl}{P} - \frac{R}{P}x$$

$$\Rightarrow \; y' = A\lambda\cos\lambda x - B\lambda\sin\lambda x - \frac{R}{P}$$

$$x = 0 \;\Rightarrow\; y = 0 \;\Rightarrow B + \frac{Rl}{P} = 0 \;\Rightarrow\; B = -\frac{Rl}{P}$$

$$x = 0 \;\Rightarrow\; y' = 0 \;\Rightarrow A\lambda - \frac{R}{P} = 0 \;\Rightarrow\; A = \frac{R}{P\lambda}$$

$$x = l \;\Rightarrow\; y = 0 \;\Rightarrow A\sin\lambda l + B\cos\lambda l + \frac{Rl}{P} - \frac{Rl}{P} = 0$$

$$\Rightarrow A\sin\lambda l + B\cos\lambda l = 0.$$

Therefore, we conclude that:

$$B = -\frac{Rl}{P}$$

$$A = \frac{R}{P\lambda} \tag{8.7}$$

$$A\sin\lambda l + B\cos\lambda l = 0.$$

From the first two relationships in (8.7), we can write:

$$\frac{B}{A} = -\lambda l.$$

The third relationship in (8.7) can be written as:

$$\frac{B}{A} = -tan\lambda l$$

$$\Rightarrow \qquad \tan\lambda l = \lambda l, \tag{8.8}$$

and the above equation is the characteristic equation for this case. It is a transcendental equation that resists analytic solution. It can be solved numerically. Keep in mind that λl is dimensionless (or unitless), since λ has dimension of $(\text{length})^{-1}$.

8.5 Critical Loading for a Pinned-Fixed Column

In order to determine P_{cr} for a pinned-fixed column, we need to solve equation (8.8). We will use Newton's iteration technique encountered in an elementary class of mathematics (Calculus I). We will briefly review the method.

Mathematicians have been fascinated by solving algebraic equations since the birth of algebra.

Algebraic equations can be polynomial, such as

$$ax^4 + bx^3 + cx^2 + dx + e; \quad a \neq 0$$

or transcendental, such as

$$e^{x^2} - x + \sin x + x^9 - \ln(1 + x^2) - 25 = 0.$$

Any algebraic equation, whether polynomial or transcendental, and no matter how difficult it is, can be reduced into the following form:

$$f(x) = 0.$$

The method outlined below illustrates how to solve an algebraic equation numerically. The method is called Newton's iteration technique or the Newton-Raphson method. We recall from elementary Calculus I that:

$$f'(x) = \frac{df}{dx} = \lim_{\Delta x \to 0} \frac{\Delta f}{\Delta x}$$

$$= \lim_{\Delta x \to 0} \frac{f(x + \Delta x) - f(x)}{\Delta x}$$

$$\approx \frac{f(x + \Delta x) - f(x)}{\Delta x}.$$

Therefore,

$$f'(x) \approx \frac{f(x + \Delta x) - f(x)}{\Delta x}.$$

We start with an initial guessing x. We evaluate f(x). If $f(x) = 0$, then our guessing was correct, and x is a root to the equation. However, unless we are extremely lucky, our initial guessing, most likely, will not give us the exact root. Assuming the exact root to be $x + \Delta x$, where Δx is yet to be determined and since $x + \Delta x$ is an exact root, then $f(x + \Delta x) = 0$.

Therefore,

$$f'(x) = -\frac{f(x)}{\Delta x}$$

or

$$\Delta x = -\frac{f(x)}{f'(x)}. \tag{8.9}$$

The algorithm goes as follows:

- Start with a "smart initial" guessing x.
- Evaluate f(x).
- If $f(x) = 0$, stop. x is an exact root.
- If $f(x) \neq 0$, compute Δ from (8.9).
- Your new trial will be $x + \Delta x$.

If you start with a proper smart initial guessing, the method converges rapidly after few iterations. If you start with a wrong initial guessing, the method can diverge, and in this case, you need to abort the process and change your guessing. For instance, if $f'(x)$ is too small, it can be an indication that the technique will diverge rather than converge, and it means you need to abort the process.

Newton's iteration technique will be now used to solve the transcendental equation:

$$\tan x = x$$

$$\Rightarrow \tan x - x = 0$$

$$f(x) = \tan x - x$$

$$f'(x) = \sec^2 x - 1$$

How can we come up with smart initial guessing?

Plot $y = x$ and $y = \tan x$:

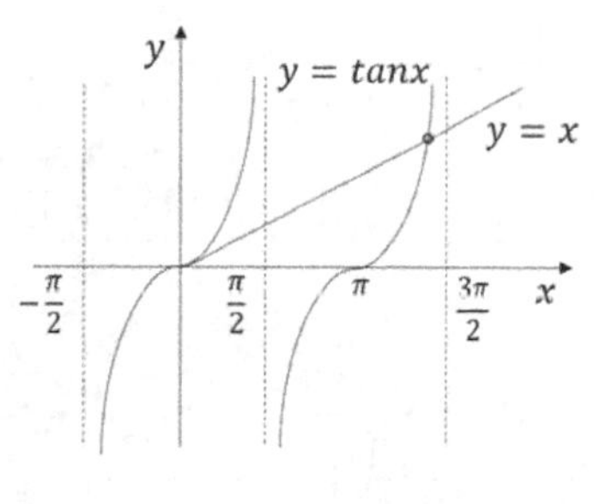

FIGURE 8.8

The roots of the transcendental equation should be the points of intersection of the two curves. The origin O is a point of intersection of these curves. The smallest nontrivial root is seen to be slightly less than $\frac{3\pi}{2}$.

Start with $x = 4.5$:

$$f(x) = \tan x - x = 0.1373$$

$$f'(x) = \sec^2 x - 1 = 21.50485$$

$$\Delta x = -\frac{0.1373}{21.50485} = -0.006385$$

$$\Rightarrow x = 4.5 - 0.006385 = 4.494.$$

Now, $x = 4.494$:

$$f(x) = \tan x - x = 0.01196$$

$$f'(x) = \sec^2 x - 1 = 20.30365$$

$$\Delta x = -\frac{0.01196}{20.30365} = -0.000589$$

$$\Rightarrow x = 4.493.$$

Now, $x = 4.493$:

$$f(x) = -0.00825.$$

Although f(x) is not exactly zero, we can stop here. The precise root should be between 4.493 and 4.494.

Let:

$$\lambda l = 4.493$$

$$\Rightarrow \quad \lambda = \frac{4.493}{l}$$

$$\Rightarrow \quad \frac{P}{EI} = \left(\frac{4.493}{l}\right)^2 = \frac{20.187}{l^2}$$

$$P_{Cr} = \frac{20.187EI}{l^2} = \frac{20.187\pi^2 EI}{\pi^2 l^2}$$

or

$$P_{Cr} = \frac{\pi^2 EI}{(0.699l)^2} = \frac{\pi^2 EI}{l_e^2}, \tag{8.10}$$

where $l_e = 0.699l$ is the effective length.

8.6 "Fixed-Fixed" Column

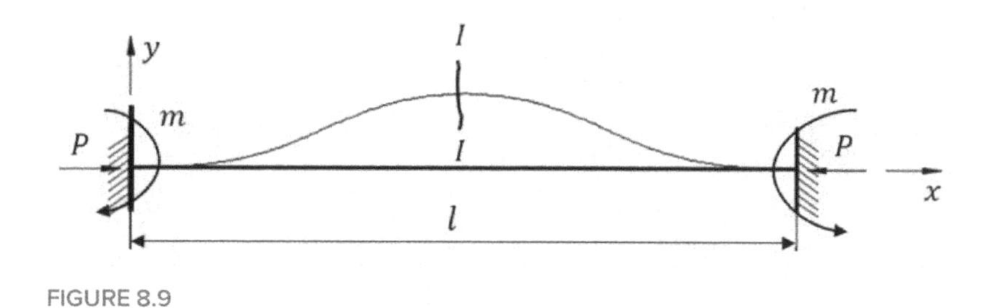

FIGURE 8.9

The differential equation describing the elastic curve:

$$EIy'' = M_{(x)}$$

$$EIy'' = m - Py \Rightarrow y'' + \frac{P}{EI}y = \frac{m}{EI}.$$

Let $\lambda = \sqrt{\frac{P}{EI}}$

$$\Rightarrow y'' + \lambda^2 y = \frac{m}{EI}.$$

The above equation is a second-order nonhomogeneous linear ordinary differential equation with constant coefficients.

Corresponding homogeneous equation:

$$y'' + \lambda^2 y = 0.$$

⇒ The general solution to the corresponding homogeneous equation is:

$$y = A\sin\lambda x + B\cos\lambda x.$$

A particular solution to the nonhomogeneous equation is:

$$y = \frac{m}{P}.$$

⇒ The general solution to the nonhomogeneous ODE:

$$y = A\sin\lambda x + B\cos\lambda x + \frac{m}{P}$$

$$\Rightarrow y' = A\lambda\cos\lambda x - B\lambda\sin\lambda x.$$

Boundary conditions are as follows:

$$x = 0 \Rightarrow y = 0$$

$$x = 0 \Rightarrow y' = 0$$

$$x = l \Rightarrow y = 0$$

$$x = l \Rightarrow y' = 0$$

$$x = 0 \Rightarrow y = 0 \Rightarrow B + \frac{m}{P} = 0 \Rightarrow B = -\frac{m}{P}$$

$$x = 0 \Rightarrow y' = 0 \Rightarrow A\lambda = 0 \Rightarrow A = 0$$

$$\Rightarrow y = \frac{m}{P}(1 - \cos\lambda x)$$

$$x = l \Rightarrow y = 0 \Rightarrow \cos\lambda l = 1$$

$$\Rightarrow \lambda l = 2n\pi, \quad n = 1, 2, 3, \ldots$$

$$\lambda = \frac{2n\pi}{l}$$

$$\Rightarrow \lambda^2 = \frac{4n^2\pi^2}{l^2} \quad \Rightarrow \quad \frac{P}{EI} = \frac{4n^2\pi^2}{l^2}$$

$$\Rightarrow P = \frac{4n^2\pi^2 EI}{l^2}$$

$$n = 1 \Rightarrow P_{Cr} = \frac{4\pi^2 EI}{l^2}$$

$$\text{or } P_{Cr} = \frac{\pi^2 EI}{\left(\frac{l}{2}\right)^2} = \frac{\pi^2 EI}{l_e^2}, \quad \text{where } l_e = \frac{l}{2}.$$

8.7 Summary of P_{cr} for Different End Conditions

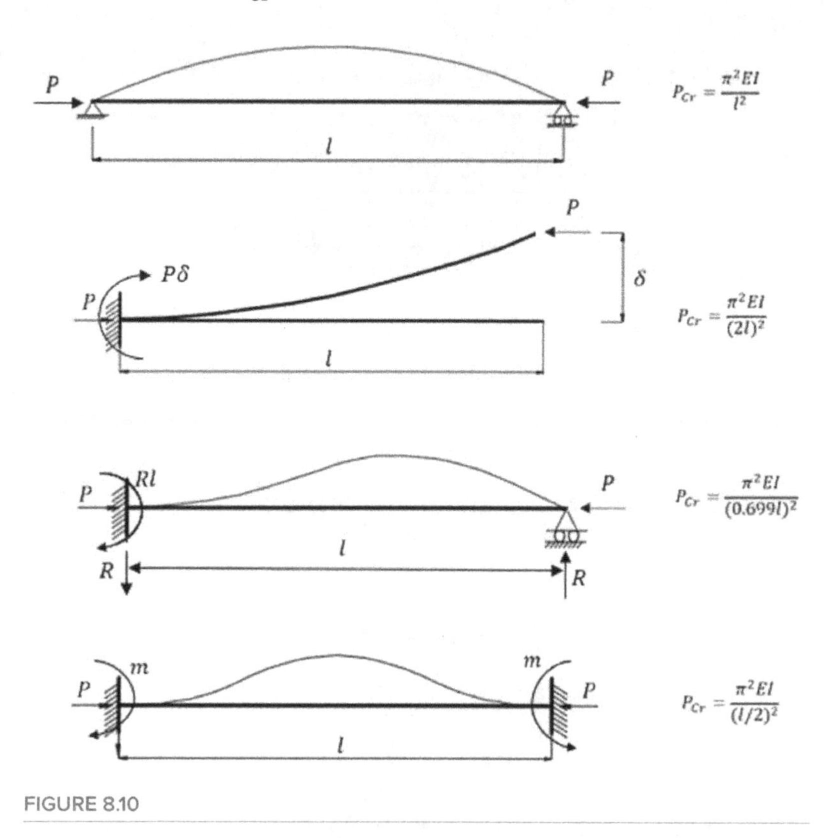

FIGURE 8.10

$$P_{Cr} = \frac{\pi^2 EI}{l_e^2}, \text{ where } l_e \text{ is the effective length.}$$

Practice Problem

By solving two second-order ordinary differential equations, determine the buckling load P_{cr} for the pinned-pinned, stepped column shown in the figure below:

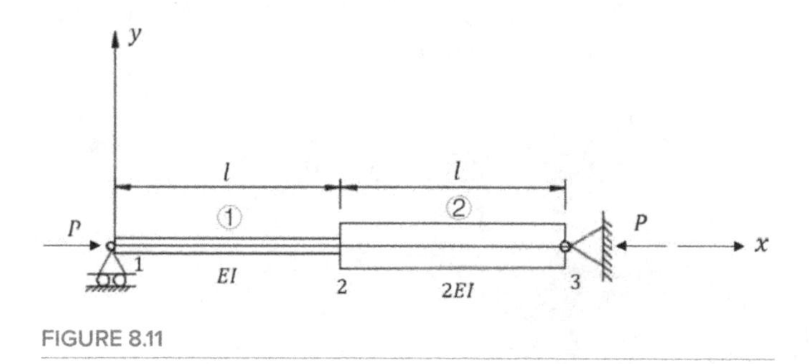

FIGURE 8.11

Solution

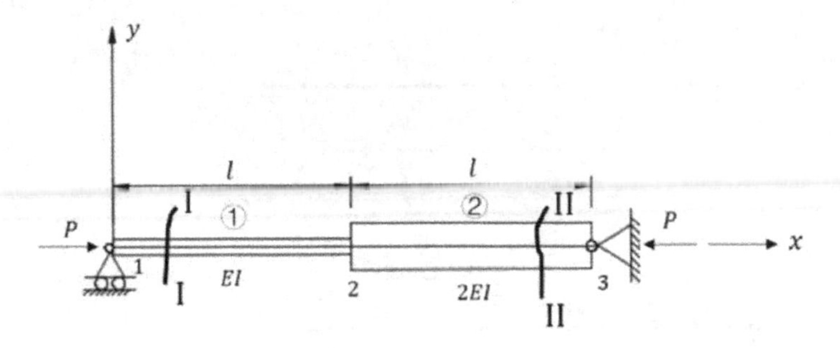

FIGURE 8.12

Section I-I

The differential equation describing the elastic curve is:

$$EIy'' = M_{(x)}$$

$$EIy'' = -Py$$

$$\Rightarrow \quad y'' + \frac{P}{EI}y = 0. \qquad \text{(I–I)}$$

Section II-II

The differential equation describing the elastic curve is:

$$2EIy'' = M_{(x)}$$

$$2EIy'' = -Py$$

$$\Rightarrow \quad y'' + \frac{P}{2EI}y = 0 \qquad \text{(II–II)}$$

Let $\lambda = \sqrt{\frac{P}{EI}}$.

Notice that λ has the dimension of length^{-1}.

Then,

$$y'' + \lambda^2 y = 0 \qquad \text{(I–I)}$$

$$y'' + \frac{1}{2}\lambda^2 y = 0 \qquad \text{(II–II)}$$

I-I: $$y'' + \lambda^2 y = 0.$$

The general solution to the above homogeneous second-order linear ordinary differential equation is:

$$y = A\sin\lambda x + B\cos\lambda x$$

II-II:

$$y'' + \frac{1}{2}\lambda^2 y = 0.$$

The general solution to the above homogeneous second-order linear ordinary differential equation is:

$$y = C\sin\frac{\lambda}{\sqrt{2}}x + D\cos\frac{\lambda}{\sqrt{2}}x.$$

We have four constants of integration.

Therefore, we need four boundary conditions:

$$x = 0 \Rightarrow y = 0$$

$$x = 2l \Rightarrow y = 0$$

$$x = l \Rightarrow y_{I-I} = y_{II-II},$$

and

$$x = l \Rightarrow \frac{dy}{dx}\Big|_{I-I} = \frac{dy}{dx}\Big|_{II-II}.$$

I-I:

$$x = 0 \Rightarrow y = A\sin\lambda x + B\cos\lambda x = 0$$

$$\Rightarrow B = 0$$

II-II:

$$x = 2l \Rightarrow y = C\sin\frac{\lambda}{\sqrt{2}}x + D\cos\frac{\lambda}{\sqrt{2}}x = 0$$

$$\Rightarrow C\sin\left[\frac{\lambda}{\sqrt{2}}(2l)\right] + D\cos\left[\frac{\lambda}{\sqrt{2}}(2l)\right] = 0$$

$$\Rightarrow C\sin\sqrt{2}\lambda l + D\cos\sqrt{2}\lambda l = 0$$

At $x = l, y_{I-I} = y_{II-II}$

$$\Rightarrow A\sin\lambda l = C\sin\frac{\lambda l}{\sqrt{2}} + D\cos\frac{\lambda l}{\sqrt{2}}$$

$$\Rightarrow A\sin\lambda l - C\sin\frac{\lambda l}{\sqrt{2}} - D\cos\frac{\lambda l}{\sqrt{2}} = 0$$

I-I: $$x = 0 \Rightarrow y = A\sin\lambda x + B\cos\lambda x = 0$$

II-II: $$y' = C\frac{\lambda}{\sqrt{2}}\cos\frac{\lambda}{\sqrt{2}}x - D\frac{\lambda}{\sqrt{2}}\sin\frac{\lambda}{\sqrt{2}}x$$

$$x = l \Rightarrow y'_{I-I} = y'_{II-II}$$

$$\Rightarrow A\lambda\cos\lambda l = C\frac{\lambda}{\sqrt{2}}\cos\frac{\lambda}{\sqrt{2}}l - D\frac{\lambda}{\sqrt{2}}\sin\frac{\lambda}{\sqrt{2}}l$$

$$\Rightarrow A\lambda\cos\lambda l - C\frac{\lambda}{\sqrt{2}}\cos\frac{\lambda l}{\sqrt{2}} + D\frac{\lambda}{\sqrt{2}}\sin\frac{\lambda l}{\sqrt{2}} = 0$$

Therefore,

$$\begin{bmatrix} \sin\lambda l & -\sin\frac{\lambda l}{\sqrt{2}} & -\cos\frac{\lambda l}{\sqrt{2}} \\ \cos\lambda l & -\frac{1}{\sqrt{2}}\cos\frac{\lambda l}{\sqrt{2}} & \frac{1}{\sqrt{2}}\sin\frac{\lambda l}{\sqrt{2}} \\ 0 & \sin\sqrt{2}\lambda l & \cos\sqrt{2}\lambda l \end{bmatrix} \begin{pmatrix} A \\ C \\ D \end{pmatrix} = \begin{pmatrix} 0 \\ 0 \\ 0 \end{pmatrix}.$$

For a non-trivial solution, we must have:

$$\begin{vmatrix} \sin\lambda l & -\sin\frac{\lambda l}{\sqrt{2}} & -\cos\frac{\lambda l}{\sqrt{2}} \\ \cos\lambda l & -\frac{1}{\sqrt{2}}\cos\frac{\lambda l}{\sqrt{2}} & \frac{1}{\sqrt{2}}\sin\frac{\lambda l}{\sqrt{2}} \\ 0 & \sin\sqrt{2}\lambda l & \cos\sqrt{2}\lambda l \end{vmatrix} = 0.$$

Using mathematica, we obtain:

$$\lambda l = 1.78993$$

$$\Rightarrow \lambda = \frac{1.78993}{l}$$

$$\Rightarrow \frac{P}{EI} = \left(\frac{1.78993}{l}\right)^2 = \frac{3.2038}{l^2}$$

$$\Rightarrow P_{cr} = \frac{3.2038EI}{l^2}.$$

For verification, if the entire column were uniform with EI cross section, then

$$P_{cr} = \frac{\pi^2 EI}{(2l)^2} = \frac{\pi^2 EI}{4l^2} = \frac{2.4674EI}{l^2}.$$

If the entire column were uniform with 2EI cross section, then

$$P_{cr} = \frac{\pi^2(2EI)}{(2l)^2} = \frac{2\pi^2 EI}{4l^2} = \frac{\pi^2 EI}{2l^2} = \frac{4.9348EI}{l^2}.$$

Our answer $P_{cr} = \frac{3.2038EI}{l^2}$ is between $\frac{2.4674EI}{l^2}$ and $\frac{4.9348EI}{l^2}$.

8.8 Energy Methods

In the previous sections, we used the differential equation method in order to determine P_{cr}. Solving the ODE analytically is usually simple when the column is uniform. However, such an approach can become very cumbersome if we want to apply it, say for the stepped column shown in **figure 8.13**.

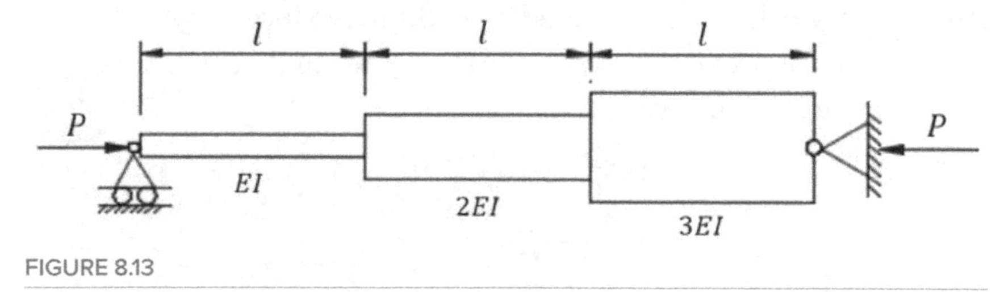

FIGURE 8.13

The differential equation might even resist any analytic solution when EI is not constant throughout, such as the case of the column shown in **figure 8.14**.

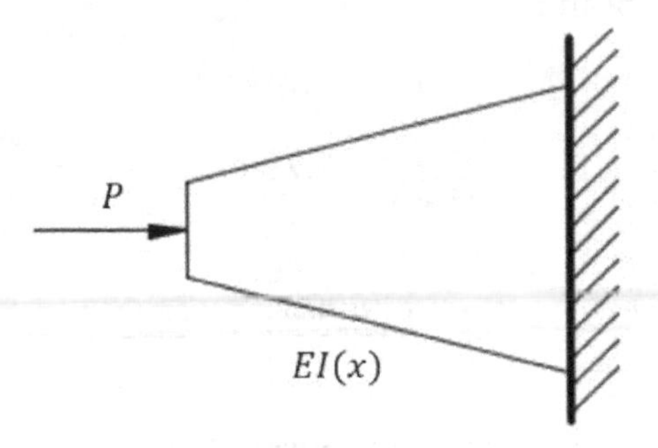

FIGURE 8.14

We will be discussing, in the remainder of this chapter, approximate methods that are called energy methods, which can be used in order to determine the critical load P_{cr}.

8.9 Derivation of Rayleigh–Ritz Formula

Below is a non-rigorous way to derive an approximate formula that will enable us to determine P_{cr}. Prior to buckling, the column was straight and undeformed (zero strain energy). When it buckles, the column undergoes deformation, and thus, we should be able to compute the strain energy stored in it after deformation, and this strain energy must be equal to the work done by the compressive force *P*.

Strain energy in the column is:

$$U = \int_{x=0}^{l} \frac{M_{(x)}^2 dx}{2EI} = \int_{x=0}^{l} \frac{(EIy'')^2 dx}{2EI} = \int_{x=0}^{l} \frac{EI}{2}\left(\frac{d^2y}{d^2x}\right)^2 dx$$

$$\Rightarrow \qquad U = \frac{1}{2}\int_{x=0}^{l} EI\left(\frac{d^2y}{d^2x}\right)^2 dx.$$

On the other hand, work can be obtained by multiplying force by displacement. Such displacement can be approximated to be the change in length of the straight column.

From elementary calculus, we obtain:

$$(ds)^2 = (dx)^2 + (dy)^2$$

$$\Rightarrow ds = \sqrt{(dx)^2 + (dy)^2}$$

$$= \sqrt{1 + \left(\frac{dy}{dx}\right)^2}\ dx.$$

When $\frac{dy}{dx} \ll 1$,

$$ds = \left[1 + \frac{1}{2}\left(\frac{dy}{dx}\right)^2\right] dx.$$

Therefore, work done by the compressive force *P* is:

$$P \int_{x=0}^{l} \frac{1}{2}\left(\frac{dy}{dx}\right)^2 dx.$$

Thus,

$$P \int_{x=0}^{l} \frac{1}{2}\left(\frac{dy}{dx}\right)^2 dx = \frac{1}{2} \int_{x=0}^{l} EI\left(\frac{d^2y}{dx^2}\right)^2 dx.$$

We conclude that

$$P_{cr} = \frac{\int_{x=0}^{l} EI\left(\frac{d^2y}{dx^2}\right)^2 dx}{\int_{x=0}^{l} \left(\frac{dy}{dx}\right)^2 dx},$$

and the above formula is called the Rayleigh–Ritz formula. Notice that everything we write down should be dimensionally homogeneous. The right-hand side and the left-hand side of the above formula have the same dimension, which is the dimension of force (Newtons in the SI system: $\frac{\frac{N}{m^2} m^4 \left(\frac{1}{m}\right)^2 m}{m} = N$).

The Rayleigh–Ritz method, referred to as the R–R method, is an approximate method very popular in applied mechanics. It was named after Rayleigh, an English physicist credited as discovering Argon. He won the Nobel Prize in Physics in 1904. He wrote a classical book *The Theory of Sound*. Ritz was a Swiss theoretical physicist who died in 1909 at a very young age (he was only 31 years old!). He is most famous for the Rydberg–Ritz combination principle in atomic physics used to interpret the electromagnetic spectrum of the atom of hydrogen.

8.10 Computing P_{cr} Using the Rayleigh–Ritz Formula

Let us revisit the pinned-pinned column as shown in **figure 8.15**.

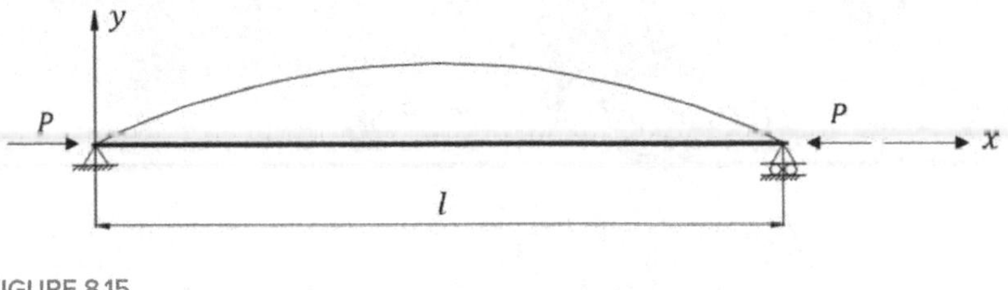

FIGURE 8.15

Let us assume that EI is constant throughout (although the practical application of energy methods is when EI is not constant throughout).

Assume a deflection function:

$$y = a\sin\frac{\pi x}{l}$$

$$y' = \frac{a\pi}{l}\cos\frac{\pi x}{l}$$

$$y'' = -\frac{a\pi^2}{l^2}\sin\frac{\pi x}{l}.$$

Notice, to begin with, that the above deflection function does indeed satisfy the boundary conditions for this problem, namely:

At $x = 0 : y = 0$

$y'' = 0$

At $x = l : y = 0$

$y'' = 0.$

Next, let us compute:

$$\int_{x=0}^{l} EI\left(\frac{d^2y}{d^2x}\right)^2 dx = \int_{x=0}^{l} EIa^2\frac{\pi^4}{l^4}\sin^2\frac{\pi x}{l}dx$$

$$= \frac{EIa^2\pi^4}{l^4}\int_{x=0}^{l}\sin^2\frac{\pi x}{l}dx$$

$$= \frac{EIa^2\pi^4}{l^4}\left(\frac{l}{2}\right)$$

$$= \frac{a^2\pi^4 EI}{2l^3}.$$

Let us also evaluate:

$$\int_{x=0}^{l}\left(\frac{dy}{dx}\right)^2 dx = \int_{x=0}^{l}\frac{a^2\pi^2}{l^2}\cos^2\frac{\pi x}{l}dx$$

$$= \frac{a^2\pi^2}{l^2}\int_{x=0}^{l}\cos^2\frac{\pi x}{l}dx$$

$$= \frac{a^2\pi^2}{l^2}\left(\frac{l}{2}\right)$$

$$= \frac{a^2\pi^2}{2l}.$$

Therefore,

$$P_{cr} = \frac{\int_{x=0}^{l} EI\left(\frac{d^2y}{d^2x}\right)^2 dx}{\int_{x=0}^{l}\left(\frac{dy}{dx}\right)^2 dx}$$

$$= \frac{\frac{a^2\pi^4 EI}{2l^3}}{\frac{a^2\pi^2}{2l}}$$

$$= \frac{\pi^2 EI}{l^2},$$

and the above result is exactly the same result we obtained earlier using the previous method (i.e., by solving the differential equation). Indeed, we obtained precisely Euler's formula! That should not be surprising to us at all. We obtained exactly the same result because we started assuming a deflection function

$$y = a\sin\frac{\pi x}{l},$$

which happened to be the exact solution.

Let us now redo the same problem starting with another (not exact) shape function.

Assume a polynomial shape function of the form:

$$y = a + bx + cx^2 + dx^3 + ex^4$$

$$\Rightarrow \quad y' = b + 2cx + 3dx^2 + 4ex^3$$

$$\Rightarrow \quad y'' = 2c + 6dx + 12ex^2.$$

The boundary conditions for this column are:

$$x = 0 \Rightarrow y = 0$$

$$x = 0 \Rightarrow y'' = 0$$

$$x = l \Rightarrow y = 0$$

$$x = l \Rightarrow y'' = 0$$

$$x = 0 \Rightarrow y = 0 \Rightarrow a = 0$$

$$x = 0 \Rightarrow y'' = 0 \Rightarrow c = 0$$

$$x = l \Rightarrow y = 0 \Rightarrow bl + dl^3 + el^4 = 0$$

$$\Rightarrow b + dl^2 + el^3 = 0$$

$$x = l \Rightarrow y'' = 0 \Rightarrow 6dl + 12el^2 = 0$$

$$\Rightarrow d + 2el = 0.$$

Therefore, we conclude that:

$$b = el^3 \;;\; d = -2el.$$

Thus, the shape function becomes:

$$y = el^3x - 2elx^3 + ex^4$$

$$= e(l^3x - 2lx^3 + x^4).$$

Therefore, assume a shape function:

$$y = A(l^3x - 2lx^3 + x^4)$$

$$y' = A(l^3 - 6lx^2 + 4x^3)$$

$$y'' = A(-12lx + 12x^2).$$

It can be easily verified that such a shape function, indeed, does satisfy the boundary conditions for this problem.

Next, let us compute

$$\int_{x=0}^{l}\left(\frac{dy}{dx}\right)^2 dx = \int_{x=0}^{l} A^2(l^3 - 6lx^2 + 4x^3)^2 dx$$

$$= A^2\int_{x=0}^{l}(l^3 - 6lx^2 + 4x^3)^2 dx$$

$$= A^2\int_{x=0}^{l}(l^6 + 36l^2x^4 + 16x^6 - 12l^4x^2 - 48lx^5 + 8l^3x^3)dx$$

$$= A^2\left[(l^6)(l) + (36l^2)\left(\frac{1}{5}l^5\right) + (16)\left(\frac{1}{7}l^7\right) - 12l^4\left(\frac{1}{3}l^3\right) - 48l\left(\frac{1}{6}l^6\right) + 8l^3\left(\frac{1}{4}l^4\right)\right]$$

$$= \frac{17}{35}A^2l^7.$$

Let us also evaluate:

$$\int_{x=0}^{l} EI\left(\frac{d^2y}{dx^2}\right)^2 dx$$

$$= \int_{x=0}^{l} EIA^2(12x^2 - 12lx)^2 dx$$

$$= 144EIA^2\int_{x=0}^{l}(x^2 - lx)^2 dx$$

$$= 144EIA^2\int_{x=0}^{l}(x^4 + l^2x^2 - 2lx^3)dx$$

$$= 144EIA^2\left[\frac{1}{5}l^5 + (l^2)\left(\frac{1}{3}l^3\right) - (2l)\left(\frac{1}{4}l^4\right)\right]$$

$$= \frac{24}{5}EIA^2l^5.$$

Therefore,

$$P_{cr} = \frac{\int_{x=0}^{l} EI\left(\frac{d^2y}{d^2x}\right)^2 dx}{\int_{x=0}^{l}\left(\frac{dy}{dx}\right)^2 dx}$$

$$= \frac{\frac{24}{5}EIA^2l^5}{\frac{17}{35}A^2l^7}$$

$$= \frac{9.88EI}{l^2}.$$

Comparing the above approximate value to the exact value $P_{cr} = \frac{\pi^2 EI}{l^2} \approx \frac{9.87EI}{l^2}$ obtained by solving the ordinary differential equation, we notice that such an approximation is excellent and very impressive.

The Rayleigh–Ritz formula will always lead to excellent results. However, we need to start with a shape function that does satisfy the boundary conditions for the problem.

EXAMPLE

Use the Rayleigh–Ritz formula in order to estimate the critical buckling load P_{cr} for a fixed-fixed column of length l and uniform EI throughout.

SOLUTION

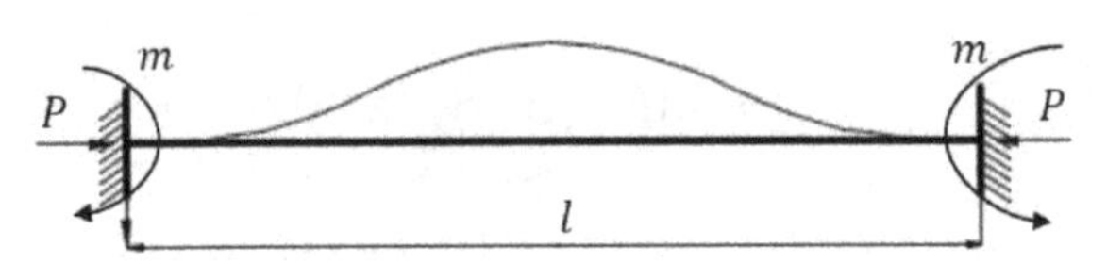

FIGURE 8.16

First, we need to assume a shape function that does satisfy the boundary conditions.

Start with:

$$y = a + bx + cx^2 + dx^3 + ex^4$$

$$\Rightarrow \quad y' = b + 2cx + 3dx^2 + 4ex^3$$

$$\Rightarrow \quad y'' = 2c + 6dx + 12ex^2.$$

The boundary conditions for this problem:

$$x = 0 \Rightarrow y = 0$$
$$y' = 0$$
$$x = l \Rightarrow y = 0$$
$$y' = 0$$

$$x = 0 \Rightarrow y = 0 \Rightarrow a = 0$$
$$x = 0 \Rightarrow y' = 0 \Rightarrow b = 0$$
$$x = l \Rightarrow y = 0 \Rightarrow cl^2 + dl^3 + el^4 = 0$$
$$\Rightarrow c + dl + el^2 = 0$$
$$x = l \Rightarrow y' = 0 \Rightarrow 2cl + 3dl^2 + 4el^3 = 0$$
$$\Rightarrow 2c + 3dl + 4el^2 = 0.$$

Therefore, we conclude that:

$$d = -2el; \quad c = el^2.$$

Thus,

$$y = el^2x^2 - 2elx^3 + ex^4$$
$$= e(l^2x^2 - 2lx^3 + x^4).$$

Therefore, choose a shape function:

$$y = A(l^2x^2 - 2lx^3 + x^4)$$
$$y' = A(2l^2x - 6lx^2 + 4x^3)$$
$$y'' = A(2l^2 - 12lx + 12x^2).$$

It is clear that such a shape function, indeed, does satisfy the boundary conditions for this problem:

$$\int_{x=0}^{l} \left(\frac{dy}{dx}\right)^2 dx = \int_{x=0}^{l} A^2(2l^2x - 6lx^2 + 4x^3)^2 dx$$

$$= 4A^2 \int_{x=0}^{l} (l^2x - 3lx^2 + 2x^3)^2 dx$$

$$= 4A^2 \int_{x=0}^{l} (l^4x^2 + 9l^2x^4 + 4x^6 - 6l^3x^3 + 4l^2x^4 - 12lx^5)dx$$

$$= 4A^2\left[l^4\left(\frac{1}{3}l^3\right) + 9l^2\left(\frac{1}{5}l^5\right) + (4)\left(\frac{1}{7}l^7\right) - 6l^3\left(\frac{1}{4}l^4\right) + 4l^2\left(\frac{1}{5}l^5\right) - 12l\left(\frac{1}{6}l^6\right)\right]$$

$$= \frac{2A^2l^7}{105}.$$

On the other hand,

$$\int_{x=0}^{l} EI\left(\frac{d^2y}{d^2x}\right)^2 dx$$

$$= \int_{x=0}^{l} EIA^2(2l^2 - 12lx + 12x^2)^2 dx$$

$$= 4EIA^2 \int_{x=0}^{l} (l^2 - 6lx + 6x^2)^2 dx$$

$$= 4EIA^2 \int_{x=0}^{l} (l^4 + 36l^2x^2 + 36x^4 - 12l^3x + 12l^2x^2 - 72lx^3)dx$$

$$= 4EIA^2\left[(l^4)(l) + 36l^2\left(\frac{1}{3}l^3\right) + 36\left(\frac{1}{5}l^5\right) - 12l^3\left(\frac{1}{2}l^2\right) + 12l^2\left(\frac{1}{3}l^3\right) - 72l\left(\frac{1}{4}l^4\right)\right]$$

$$= \frac{4EIA^2l^5}{5}.$$

Thus,

$$P_{cr} = \frac{\int_{x=0}^{l} EI\left(\frac{d^2y}{d^2x}\right)^2 dx}{\int_{x=0}^{l}\left(\frac{dy}{dx}\right)^2 dx}$$

$$= \frac{\frac{4}{5}EIA^2l^5}{\frac{2}{105}A^2l^7}$$

$$= \frac{42EI}{l^2}.$$

Comparing the above approximate value to the exact value $P_{cr} = \frac{42EI}{l^2} \approx \frac{39.478EI}{l^2}$, we observe that the error does not exceed 6.4%.

Problems

8.1. A 3.5 m long pinned-pinned column is made of bronze ($E = 110$ GPa) and has a solid circular cross section with a diameter $D = 40$ mm. In order to reduce the weight of the column, the solid circular cross section is replaced by a hollow circular one as shown in **figure 8.17**.

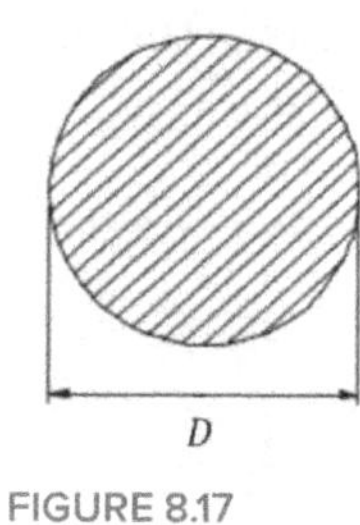

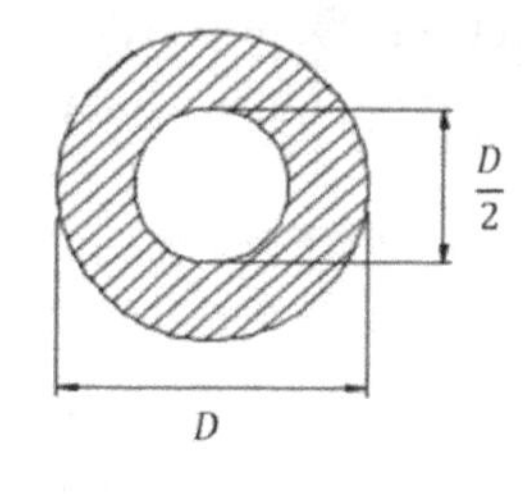

FIGURE 8.17

Compute (a) the percent reduction in the weight; (b) the percent reduction in the critical load; (c) the critical load P_{cr} for the solid rod; and (d) the critical load P_{cr} for the hollow rod.

8.2. A 1.5 m long pin-ended column of square cross section is to be constructed of timber for which $E = 11$ GPa and $\sigma_{allowable} = 15\ MPa$ for compression parallel to the grain. Using a factor of safety of 2 in computing Euler's buckling load, determine the size of the cross section if the column is to safely support (a) a 200 kN load and (b) a 300 kN load.

8.3. An unstressed aluminum rod of solid circular cross section is clamped between two walls. What increase in temperature (°C) will cause the rod to buckle? $E = 70$ GPa and $\alpha = 22 \times 10^{-6}$°$C^{-1}$.

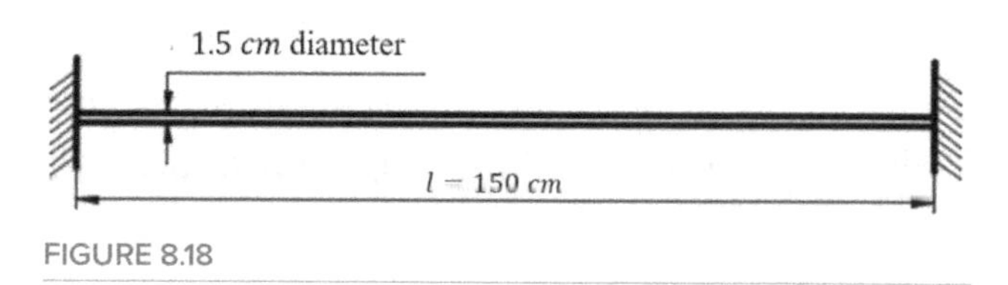

FIGURE 8.18

8.4. Knowing that $P = 7$ kN, determine the factor of safety for the structure shown in the figure below. Use $E = 200$ GPa, and consider only buckling in the plane of the simply supported truss.

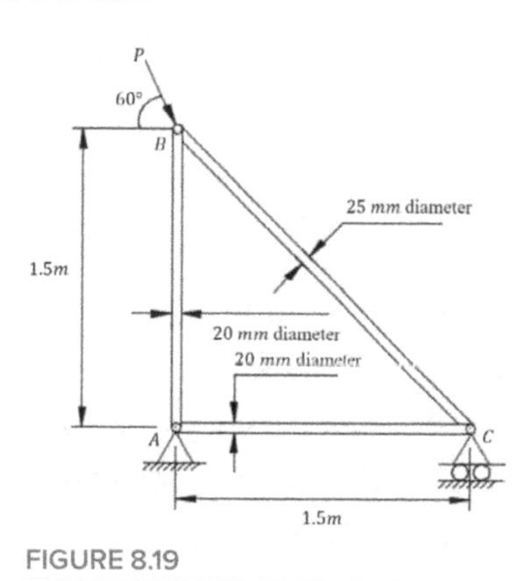

FIGURE 8.19

8.5. The cross section of a pin-ended column varies as in the figure below. Determine the critical load P_{cr}, using the Rayleigh–Ritz formula.

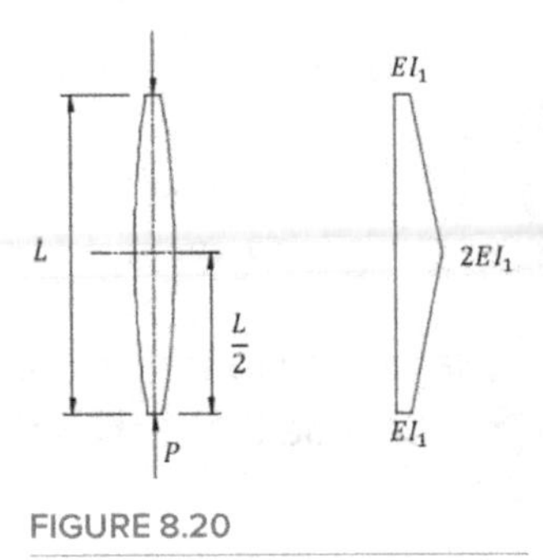

FIGURE 8.20

8.6. For the uniform beam shown in the figure below, determine the shape of the elastic curve if $P_0 < P_{cr}$. Assume EI to be uniform throughout.

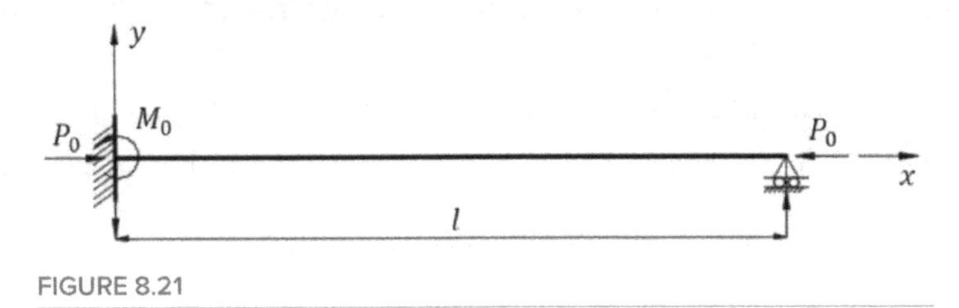

FIGURE 8.21

8.7. By solving three second-order ordinary differential equations, determine the buckling load P_{cr} for the pinned-pinned, stepped column shown in **figure 8.22**.

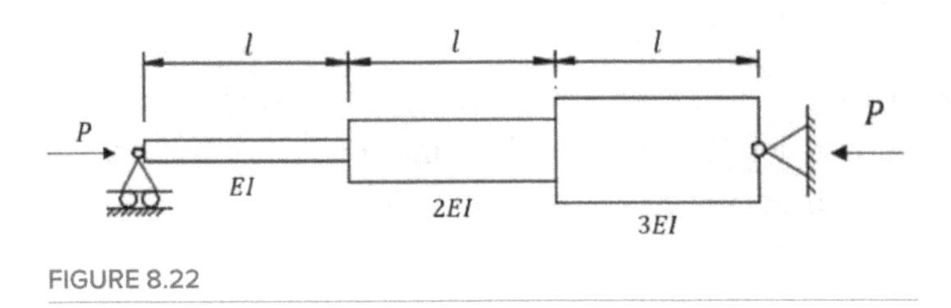

FIGURE 8.22

Further Reading

Beer, Ferdinand P., E. Russell Johnston, Jr., John T. DeWolf, and David. F. Mazurek. *Mechanics of Materials.* 7th ed. New York City: McGraw-Hill, 2015.

Curtis, H. D. *Fundamentals of Aircraft Structural Analysis.* New York City: McGraw-Hill, 1997.

Ugural, Ansel C., and Saul K. Fenster. *Advanced Mechanics of Materials and Applied Elasticity.* 5th ed. Upper Saddle River: Prentice Hall, 2012.

CHAPTER 9

Introduction to Theory of Plates

9.1 Historical Background

Many prominent mathematicians and scientists contributed to the theory of plates and shells. Leonard Euler, a Swiss mathematician born in 1707 and who studied in Basel, Switzerland, was among the first to study thin plates. In 1776, he worked on the free vibration of a thin plate. That work was continued by one of his students, Jacob II Bernoulli. Euler was a student of one of the Bernoullis and later became a teacher of another Bernoulli. Lagrange, a student of Euler, also contributed to the theory of thin plates. Lagrange taught at École Polytechnique in Paris. Simeon Poisson, who also taught at the same famous school in Paris, was another French mathematician who contributed to the theory of thin plates. Navier, a student of the famous mathematician Fourier, also contributed to the theory.

Later, Gustav Kirchhoff, a German physicist and scientist, contributed to the theory. In the 20th century, Stephen Timoshenko contributed to the theory and became an authority on the topic. Timoshenko was originally from Ukraine. He came to the United States and became affiliated with Stanford University. Indeed, two prominent names contributed largely to mechanics last century. Stephen Timoshenko was a major contributor to solid mechanics, while Theodore Von Karman, a Hungarian, was a major contributor to fluid mechanics. Von Karman also migrated to the United States and became affiliated with California Institute of Technology.

9.2 Brief Review of Euler–Bernoulli Beam Theory

In chapter 5, we discussed Euler–Bernoulli beams—long straight beams in which the cross section is very small compared to the span. Indeed, the ratio between the largest dimension of the cross section and the span of the beam should be less than $\frac{1}{20}$ for the beam to be called Euler–Bernoulli.

The reader is urged to study (or review) chapter 5 before reading chapter 9. In a Euler–Bernoulli beam and for pure symmetric bending, we found that

$$\sigma = -\frac{My}{I}.$$

Implicitly, in the above formula, we have:

$$\sigma_x = -\frac{M_z}{I_z} y,$$

while $\sigma_y = \sigma_z = \tau_{xy} = \tau_{xz} = \tau_{yz} = 0$.
Also, the differential equation describing the elastic curve of the beam can be written as a second-order ODE:

$$EIy'' = M_{(x)}.$$

Alternatively, we can write the above equation as a fourth-order ODE,

$$EI\frac{d^4y}{dx^4} = -\omega,$$

where ω is the linear intensity of the load, and the load per unit of length unit will be ($\frac{N}{m}$, $\frac{lb_f}{ft}$, $\frac{Kip}{in}$, etc.):

$$\left(\frac{N}{m^2}\right)(m^4)\left(\frac{1}{m^3}\right) = \frac{N}{m}.$$

9.3 Theory of Thin Plates

A plate is initially (prior to deformation) a flat structural element with small thickness compared to the remaining dimensions. We usually divide the thickness h of the plate into two equal halves by a plane parallel to the faces. This plane is called the mid-surface of the plate. A plate is said to be thin when the ratio of the thickness to the smaller span length is less than $\frac{1}{20}$ (compare that with Euler–Bernoulli beam).

This chapter is a brief introduction to theory of thin plates, and we will limit ourselves to the small deflection of homogeneous isotropic uniform thin plates. (The deflection of the mid-surface of the plate is small compared to the thickness h, and the slope of the deflected surface is much less than unity.)

Structural elements resembling curved plates are referred to as shells. We will skip discussion of shells in this brief introduction.

9.4 Stress Tensor and Moments

Our objective is to define the state of stress (i.e., to establish:

$$[\sigma_{ij}] = \begin{bmatrix} \sigma_x & \tau_{xy} & \tau_{xz} \\ \tau_{yx} & \sigma_y & \tau_{yz} \\ \tau_{zx} & \tau_{zy} & \sigma_z \end{bmatrix}_{3\times 3}$$

at each point of the plate.

In chapter 5, we used the so-called semi-inverse method in Euler–Bernoulli beam theory. Similarly, we will be using, in this chapter, the same semi-inverse method.

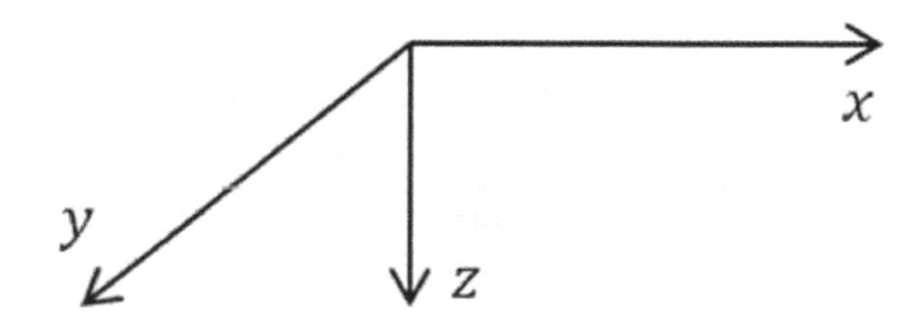

FIGURE 9.1 Right-handed coordinate system

The xy plane coincides with the mid-surface of the thin plate. The vertical deflection (in the z-direction) of such midsurface is w. We will assume that $\varepsilon_z = \gamma_{xz} = \gamma_{yz} = 0$, and furthermore, we will assume that σ_z can be neglected, thus $\sigma_z = 0$. Recall the six kinematic relationships that we encountered in chapter 3 (in the theory of elasticity):

$$\varepsilon_x = \frac{\partial u}{\partial x} \quad ; \quad \gamma_{xy} = \frac{\partial u}{\partial y} + \frac{\partial v}{\partial x}$$

$$\varepsilon_y = \frac{\partial v}{\partial y} \quad ; \quad \gamma_{xz} = \frac{\partial u}{\partial z} + \frac{\partial w}{\partial x}$$

$$\varepsilon_z = \frac{\partial w}{\partial z} \quad ; \quad \gamma_{yz} = \frac{\partial v}{\partial z} + \frac{\partial w}{\partial y}.$$

The above kinematic relationships relate strain tensor to the displacement field.

$$\varepsilon_z = 0 \;\Rightarrow\; \frac{\partial w}{\partial z} = 0 \;\Rightarrow\; \omega = f_1(x,y),$$

indicating that the lateral deflection does not vary throughout the plate thickness.

$$\gamma_{xz} = 0 \;\Rightarrow\; \frac{\partial u}{\partial z} + \frac{\partial w}{\partial x} = 0$$

$$\Rightarrow\; \frac{\partial u}{\partial z} = -\frac{\partial w}{\partial x}$$

$$\Rightarrow\; u = f_2(x,y) - z\frac{\partial w}{\partial x}$$

$$\gamma_{yz} = 0 \;\Rightarrow\; \frac{\partial v}{\partial z} + \frac{\partial w}{\partial y} = 0$$

$$\Rightarrow\; \frac{\partial v}{\partial z} = -\frac{\partial w}{\partial y}$$

$$\Rightarrow\; v = f_3(x,y) - z\frac{\partial w}{\partial y}$$

$$z = 0 \;\Rightarrow\; u = v = 0 \;\Rightarrow\; f_2(x,y) = f_3(x,y) = 0$$

because no mid-surface straining or in-plane straining, stretching, or contracting occurs as a result of bending.

Therefore,

$$u = -z\frac{\partial w}{\partial x}$$

$$v = -z\frac{\partial w}{\partial y}.$$

Thus,

$$\varepsilon_x = \frac{\partial u}{\partial x} = -z\frac{\partial^2 w}{\partial x^2}$$

$$\varepsilon_y = \frac{\partial v}{\partial y} = -z\frac{\partial^2 w}{\partial y^2}$$

$$\gamma_{xy} = \frac{\partial u}{\partial y} + \frac{\partial v}{\partial x} = -z\frac{\partial^2 w}{\partial x \partial y} - z\frac{\partial^2 w}{\partial x \partial y} = -2z\frac{\partial^2 w}{\partial x \partial y}.$$

Thus, we have established the state of strain:

$$\varepsilon_x = -z\frac{\partial^2 w}{\partial x^2}$$

$$\varepsilon_y = -z\frac{\partial^2 w}{\partial y^2}$$

$$\gamma_{xy} = -2z\frac{\partial^2 w}{\partial x \partial y}$$

$$\varepsilon_z = \gamma_{xz} = \gamma_{yz} = 0.$$

Next, we will use Hooke's generalized laws to establish the state of stress.

$$\varepsilon_x = \frac{\sigma_x}{E} - \frac{\nu}{E}\sigma_y$$

$$\varepsilon_y = \frac{\sigma_y}{E} - \frac{\nu}{E}\sigma_x$$

Solving the above equations simultaneously, we conclude that:

$$\sigma_x = \frac{E(\varepsilon_x + \nu\varepsilon_y)}{1-\nu^2}$$

$$\sigma_y = \frac{E(\varepsilon_y + \nu\varepsilon_x)}{1-\nu^2}.$$

Therefore,

$$\sigma_x = \frac{E}{1-\nu^2}\left(-z\frac{\partial^2 w}{\partial x^2} - z\nu\frac{\partial^2 w}{\partial y^2}\right)$$

$$= -\frac{Ez}{1-\nu^2}\left(\frac{\partial^2 w}{\partial x^2} + \nu\frac{\partial^2 w}{\partial y^2}\right)$$

$$\sigma_y = \frac{E}{1-\nu^2}\left(-z\frac{\partial^2 w}{\partial y^2} - z\nu\frac{\partial^2 w}{\partial x^2}\right)$$

$$= -\frac{Ez}{1-\nu^2}\left(\frac{\partial^2 w}{\partial y^2} + \nu\frac{\partial^2 w}{\partial x^2}\right)$$

$$\tau_{xy} = G\gamma_{xy} = -2Gz\frac{\partial^2 w}{\partial x \partial y}.$$

Thus, we have established the state of stress:

$$\sigma_x = -\frac{Ez}{1-\nu^2}\left(\frac{\partial^2 w}{\partial x^2} + \nu\frac{\partial^2 w}{\partial y^2}\right)$$

$$\sigma_y = -\frac{Ez}{1-\nu^2}\left(\frac{\partial^2 w}{\partial y^2} + \nu\frac{\partial^2 w}{\partial x^2}\right)$$

$$\tau_{xy} = -\frac{Ez}{1+\nu}\left(\frac{\partial^2 w}{\partial x\,\partial y}\right)$$

$$\sigma_z = \tau_{xz} = \tau_{yz} = 0.$$

The above expressions demonstrate clearly that the stresses vanish at the mid-surface and vary linearly over the thickness of the plate (compare this with Euler–Bernoulli beam theory).

Now, let us evaluate

$$\int_{-\frac{h}{2}}^{\frac{h}{2}} z\sigma_x dydz = dy\int_{-\frac{h}{2}}^{\frac{h}{2}} z\sigma_x dz = (dy)(M_x),$$

where

$$M_x = \int_{-\frac{h}{2}}^{\frac{h}{2}} z\sigma_x dz.$$

Obviously, M_x has the dimension of moment per unit length ($\frac{Nm}{m} = N$) that is the dimension of a force. M_x is a bending moment per unit length.

Using the expression for σ_x obtained earlier, the above can be rewritten as:

$$M_x = \int_{-\frac{h}{2}}^{\frac{h}{2}} z\left(-\frac{Ez}{1-\nu^2}\right)\left(\frac{\partial^2 w}{\partial x^2} + \nu\frac{\partial^2 w}{\partial y^2}\right)dz$$

$$= \int_{-\frac{h}{2}}^{\frac{h}{2}} -\frac{E}{1-\nu^2}z^2\left(\frac{\partial^2 w}{\partial x^2} + \nu\frac{\partial^2 w}{\partial y^2}\right)dz.$$

However,

$$\int_{-\frac{h}{2}}^{\frac{h}{2}} z^2 dz = \left[\frac{1}{3}z^3\right]_{-\frac{h}{2}}^{\frac{h}{2}}$$

$$= \frac{1}{3}\left(\frac{h^3}{8} + \frac{h^3}{8}\right) = \frac{1}{12}h^3$$

$$\Rightarrow \quad M_x = -\frac{Eh^3}{12(1-\nu^2)}\left(\frac{\partial^2 w}{\partial x^2} + \nu\frac{\partial^2 w}{\partial y^2}\right).$$

Similarly, we can get:

$$M_y = -\frac{Eh^3}{12(1-\nu^2)}\left(\frac{\partial^2 w}{\partial y^2} + \nu\frac{\partial^2 w}{\partial x^2}\right).$$

Also, we can define

$$M_{xy} = -\int_{-\frac{h}{2}}^{\frac{h}{2}} z\tau_{xy} dz$$

$$= \int_{-\frac{h}{2}}^{\frac{h}{2}} \frac{Ez^2}{1+\nu}\frac{\partial^2 w}{\partial x \partial y} dz$$

$$= -\frac{Eh^3}{12(1+\nu)}\frac{\partial^2 w}{\partial x \partial y}$$

$$= -\frac{Eh^3(1-\nu)}{12(1+\nu)(1-\nu)}\frac{\partial^2 w}{\partial x \partial y}$$

$$= -\frac{Eh^3}{12(1-\nu^2)}(1-\nu)\frac{\partial^2 w}{\partial x \partial y},$$

introducing

$$D = \frac{Eh^3}{12(1-\nu^2)}.$$

D is called flexural rigidity of a thin plate. Notice that D has the unit in the SI system of $\frac{N}{m^2}m^3 = Nm$ (dimension of a moment).

We can thus obtain the following relationships:

$$M_x = -D\left(\frac{\partial^2 w}{\partial x^2} + \nu\frac{\partial^2 w}{\partial y^2}\right)$$

$$M_y = -D\left(\frac{\partial^2 w}{\partial y^2} + \nu\frac{\partial^2 w}{\partial x^2}\right)$$

$$M_{xy} = -D(1-\nu)\frac{\partial^2 w}{\partial x\,\partial y}.$$

The above are the bending and twisting moments per unit of length.

Let us conclude this section by comparing the results obtained in it with the well-known results in Euler–Bernoulli beam theory:

Euler–Bernoulli Beam Theory	**Theory of Thin Plates**
$EI\frac{d^2y}{dx^2} = M$	$M_x = -D\left(\frac{\partial^2 w}{\partial x^2} + \nu\frac{\partial^2 w}{\partial y^2}\right)$
	$M_y = -D\left(\frac{\partial^2 w}{\partial y^2} + \nu\frac{\partial^2 w}{\partial x^2}\right)$
	$M_{xy} = -D(1-\nu)\frac{\partial^2 w}{\partial x\,\partial y}$

It is clear that the expressions in the theory of thin plates are much more complex than the one in Euler–Bernoulli Beam Theory.

D in the theory of thin plates plays the same role as *EI* in beam theory. Indeed, *EI* is called the flexural rigidity of a Euler–Bernoulli beam. However, it is important to keep in mind that *EI* has the unit in the SI system of $\frac{N}{m^2}m^4 = Nm^2$, whereas the unit of D in the SI system is Nm. Also, M in beam theory has the unit of moment (Nm), whereas M_x, M_y, and M_{xy} have the unit of moment per unit of length ($\frac{Nm}{m} = N$).

9.5 A Comparison of Euler–Bernoulli Beam Theory and Thin Plate Theory

a) The differential equation describing the elastic curve of a Euler–Bernoulli beam is

$$EI\frac{d^2y}{dx^2} = M$$

$$\left(\frac{N}{m^2}\right)(m^4)\left(\frac{1}{m}\right) = Nm,$$

where M is the bending moment (Nm). The above second-order ordinary differential equation can be rewritten for a beam (one-dimensional structure) as a fourth order ODE

$$EI\frac{d^4y}{dx^4} = -\omega$$

$$\left(\frac{N}{m^2}\right)(m^4)\left(\frac{1}{m^3}\right) = \frac{N}{m},$$

where ω is the linear intensity of loading $(\frac{N}{m})$.

It can be shown that the differential equation describing the elastic deflection of the mid-surface of a thin plate is

$$\frac{\partial^4 \omega}{\partial x^4} + 2\frac{\partial^4 \omega}{\partial x^2 \partial y^2} + \frac{\partial^4 \omega}{\partial y^4} = \frac{p}{D}$$

$$\text{or } \nabla^4 \omega = \frac{p}{D},$$

where $\omega_{(x,y)}$ is the deflection of the mid-surface.

$\nabla^2 \equiv \frac{\partial^2}{\partial x^2} + \frac{\partial^2}{\partial y^2}$ is the two-dimensional Laplacian operator.

$\nabla^4 \equiv \nabla^2(\nabla^2) = \frac{\partial^4}{\partial x^4} + 2\frac{\partial^4}{\partial x^2 \partial y^2} + \frac{\partial^4}{\partial y^4}$ is the biharmonic operator.

p here is the loading $(\frac{N}{m^2})$.

Thus, the differential equation describing the elastic deflection of a thin plate (two-dimensional structure) is a fourth-order partial differential equation.

Euler–Bernoulli Beam Theory

$$EI\frac{d^4y}{dx^4} = -\omega$$

$$\left(\frac{N}{m^2}\right)(m^4)\left(\frac{1}{m^3}\right) = \frac{N}{m}$$

Theory of Thin Plates

$$D\,\nabla^4\omega = p_{(x,y)}$$

$$\left(\frac{N}{m^2}\right)(m^3)\left(\frac{1}{m^3}\right) = \frac{N}{m^2}$$

It is important to emphasize here that EI, called the flexural rigidity of a Euler–Bernoulli beam, has the unit in SI system of Nm^2 and ω in beam theory has the unit of N/m.

Whereas D, called the flexural rigidity of a thin plate, has the unit in the SI system of Nm and $P_{(x,y)}$, in the plate theory it has the unit of $\frac{N}{m^2}$ (same as pressure).

b) The ratio of the largest dimension of the cross section of a Euler–Bernoulli beam to the span of the beam should be less than $\frac{1}{20}$.

Also, the ratio of the thickness of a thin plate to the smaller span length should be less than $\frac{1}{20}$.

Consider a thin rectangular plate of dimensions a and b and thickness h. Let us treat this thin plate as a Euler–Bernoulli beam of a span a and rectangular cross section $b \times h$, as shown in **figure 9.2**.

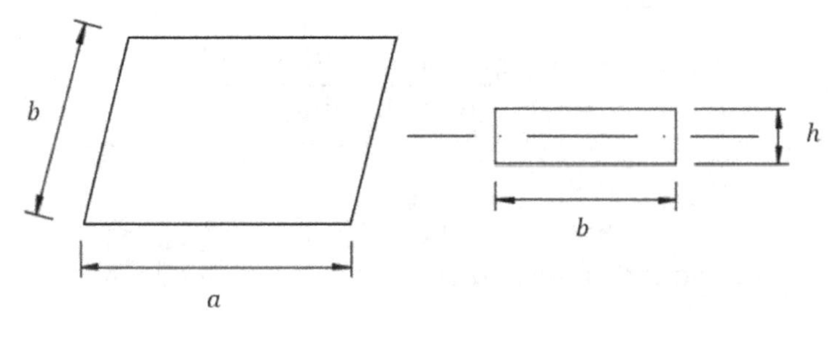

FIGURE 9.2

$$EI = (E)\left(\frac{1}{12}bh^3\right) = \frac{Ebh^3}{12}$$

$$\Rightarrow \qquad \frac{EI}{b} = \frac{Ebh^3}{12b} = \frac{Eh^3}{12}$$

Thus, the flexural rigidity of the beam per unit length is $\frac{Eh^3}{12}$.

Compare the above flexural rigidity of the beam per unit length to $D = \frac{Eh^3}{12(1-\nu^2)}$.

9.6 Deflection of a Fixed-Fixed Beam Subject to a Uniformly Distributed Load

Let us determine the deflection of a statically indeterminate fixed-fixed beam of span l subject to a uniformly distributed load $\omega(\frac{N}{m})$, as shown in **figure 9.3**.

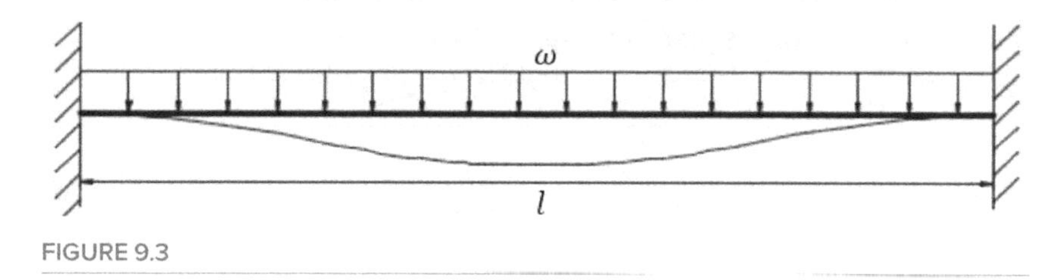

FIGURE 9.3

It is an elementary mechanics of materials problem and can be approached either by solving a second-order ordinary differential equation or a fourth-order ODE.

The problem is statically indeterminate, and we should be able to compute the reactions at the built-in supports.

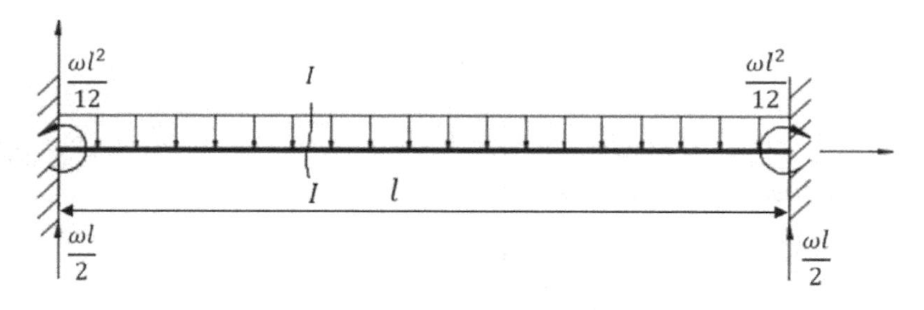

FIGURE 9.4

The differential equation describing the elastic curve is the second order ODE:

$$EIy'' = M_{(x)}$$

$$M_{(x)} = \frac{\omega l}{2}x - \frac{\omega l^2}{12} - \frac{\omega x^2}{2}.$$

Thus,

$$EIy'' = \frac{\omega l}{2}x - \frac{\omega l^2}{12} - \frac{\omega x^2}{2}.$$

At $x = 0$, $y = 0$ and $y' = 0$

$$\Rightarrow \quad EIy' = \frac{\omega l}{2}\frac{x^2}{2} - \frac{\omega l^2}{12}x - \frac{\omega}{2}\frac{x^3}{3}$$

$$\Rightarrow \quad EIy = \frac{\omega l}{4}\frac{x^3}{3} - \frac{\omega l^2}{12}\frac{x^2}{2} - \frac{\omega}{6}\frac{x^4}{4}.$$

Therefore,

$$y = \frac{1}{EI}\left(\frac{\omega l}{12}x^3 - \frac{\omega l^2}{24}x^2 - \frac{\omega}{24}x^4\right),$$

and the above should give us the deflection of the beam at each and every station.

Maximum deflection takes place midspan.

At $x = \frac{l}{2}$:

$$y = \frac{1}{EI}\left(\frac{\omega l}{12}\frac{l^3}{8} - \frac{\omega l^2}{24}\frac{l^2}{4} - \frac{\omega}{24}\frac{l^4}{16}\right)$$

$$= \frac{1}{EI}\left(\frac{\omega l^4}{96} - \frac{\omega l^4}{96} - \frac{\omega l^4}{384}\right) = -\frac{\omega l^4}{384EI}.$$

Thus,

$$\delta_{max} = \frac{\omega l^4}{384EI} \downarrow.$$

Alternatively, the above elementary mechanics of materials problem can be approached by solving the following fourth-order ODE:

$$EI\frac{d^4y}{dx^4} = -\omega.$$

Four boundary conditions are needed to solve the above fourth-order ODE. These are:

$$x = 0 \quad \Rightarrow \quad y = 0$$

$$x = 0 \quad \Rightarrow \quad y' = 0$$

$$x = l \quad \Rightarrow \quad y = 0$$

$$x = l \quad \Rightarrow \quad y' = 0$$

$$EI\frac{d^4y}{dx^4} = -\omega$$

$$\Rightarrow \quad EI\frac{d^3y}{dx^3} = C - \omega x$$

$$\Rightarrow \quad EI\frac{d^2y}{dx^2} = Cx - \omega\frac{x^2}{2} + D$$

$$\Rightarrow \quad EI\frac{dy}{dx} = C\frac{x^2}{2} - \frac{\omega}{2}\frac{x^3}{3} + Dx + F$$

$$\Rightarrow \quad EIy = \frac{C}{2}\frac{x^3}{3} - \frac{\omega}{6}\frac{x^4}{4} + D\frac{x^2}{2} + Fx + G$$

$$x = 0 \;\Rightarrow\; y = 0 \;\Rightarrow\; G = 0$$

$$x = 0 \;\Rightarrow\; y' = 0 \;\Rightarrow\; F = 0$$

$$x = l \;\Rightarrow\; y' = 0 \;\Rightarrow\; \frac{C}{2}l^2 - \frac{\omega}{6}l^3 + Dl = 0$$

$$x = l \;\Rightarrow\; y = 0 \;\Rightarrow\; \frac{C}{6}l^3 - \frac{\omega}{24}l^4 + \frac{D}{2}l^2 = 0.$$

Therefore,

$$\frac{C}{2}l - \frac{\omega}{6}l^2 + D = 0$$

$$\frac{C}{6}l - \frac{\omega}{24}l^2 + \frac{D}{2} = 0.$$

Solving the above equations simultaneously, we obtain:

$$C = \frac{\omega l}{2} \quad \text{and} \quad D = -\frac{\omega l^2}{12}.$$

Thus,

$$EIy = \frac{\omega l}{12}x^3 - \frac{\omega}{24}x^4 - \frac{\omega l^2}{24}x^2$$

$$\Rightarrow \quad y = \frac{1}{EI}\left(\frac{\omega l}{12}x^3 - \frac{\omega}{24}x^4 - \frac{\omega l^2}{24}x^2\right),$$

which is exactly the same result obtained by solving the second order ODE.

$$x = \frac{l}{2} \quad \Rightarrow \quad y = \frac{1}{EI}\left(\frac{\omega l}{12}\frac{l^3}{8} - \frac{\omega}{24}\frac{l^4}{16} - \frac{\omega l^2}{24}\frac{l^2}{4}\right) = -\frac{\omega l^4}{384EI}$$

$$\Rightarrow \quad \delta_{max} = \frac{\omega l^4}{384EI} \downarrow$$

$$\left(\frac{N}{m}\frac{m^4}{\frac{N}{m^2}m^4}=m\right)$$

This is exactly the same result obtained before.

9.7 Deflection of a Built-in Circular Plate Subject to a Uniformly Distributed Load

Our objective is to determine the deflection for a built-in circular plate of a radius subject to a uniformly distributed load $p_0\left(\frac{N}{m^2}\right)$.

The fourth-order partial differential equation describing the deflection of the mid-surface of the above thin circular plate is:

$$D\nabla^4\omega = p_{(x,y)},$$

where
$$\nabla^2 \equiv \frac{\partial^2}{\partial x^2}+\frac{\partial^2}{\partial y^2}.$$

The geometry of the problem dictates the type of coordinates used. We will be using polar coordinates. In polar coordinates:

$$\left(\frac{\partial^2}{\partial r^2}+\frac{1}{r}\frac{\partial}{\partial r}+\frac{1}{r^2}\frac{\partial^2}{\partial\theta^2}\right)\left(\frac{\partial^2\omega}{\partial r^2}+\frac{1}{r}\frac{\partial\omega}{\partial r}+\frac{1}{r^2}\frac{\partial^2\omega}{\partial\theta^2}\right)=\frac{p_0}{D}$$

$$\Rightarrow \frac{\partial^4\omega}{\partial r^4}+\frac{2}{r}\frac{\partial^3\omega}{\partial r^3}-\frac{1}{r^2}\frac{\partial^2\omega}{\partial r^2}+\frac{1}{r^3}\frac{\partial\omega}{\partial r}+\frac{1}{r^4}\frac{\partial^4\omega}{\partial\theta^4}+\frac{4}{r^4}\frac{\partial^2\omega}{\partial\theta^2}+\frac{2}{r^2}\frac{\partial^4\omega}{\partial r^2\,\partial\theta^2}-\frac{2}{r^3}\frac{\partial^3\omega}{\partial\theta^2\,\partial r}=\frac{p_0}{D}.$$

Because of circular symmetry, we should expect $\omega=\omega(r)$ (θ independent)

$$\Rightarrow \frac{d^4\omega}{dr^4}+\frac{2}{r}\frac{d^3\omega}{dr^3}-\frac{1}{r^2}\frac{d^2\omega}{dr^2}+\frac{1}{r^3}\frac{d\omega}{dr}=\frac{p_0}{D},$$

and the above equation is a fourth-order linear ordinary differential equation with variable coefficients. However, it is Euler's equation.

Let $t=\ln r$. Thus,

$$\frac{d\omega}{dr}=\frac{d\omega}{dt}\frac{dt}{dr}=\frac{1}{r}\frac{d\omega}{dt}$$

$$\frac{d^2\omega}{dr^2}=\frac{d}{dr}\left(\frac{d\omega}{dr}\right)=\frac{d}{dr}\left(\frac{1}{r}\frac{d\omega}{dt}\right)$$

$$= \frac{1}{r}\frac{d}{dr}\left(\frac{d\omega}{dt}\right) - \frac{1}{r^2}\frac{d\omega}{dt}$$

$$= \frac{1}{r^2}\frac{d^2\omega}{dt^2} - \frac{1}{r^2}\frac{d\omega}{dt}$$

$$\frac{d^3\omega}{dr^3} = \frac{d}{dr}\left(\frac{d^2\omega}{dr^2}\right) = \frac{d}{dr}\left(\frac{1}{r^2}\frac{d^2\omega}{dt^2} - \frac{1}{r^2}\frac{d\omega}{dt}\right)$$

$$= \left(\frac{1}{r^2}\right)\left(\frac{1}{r}\right)\frac{d^3\omega}{dt^3} - \frac{2}{r^3}\frac{d^2\omega}{dt^2} - \frac{1}{r^3}\frac{d^2\omega}{dt^2} + \frac{2}{r^3}\frac{d\omega}{dt}$$

$$= \frac{1}{r^3}\frac{d^3\omega}{dt^3} - \frac{3}{r^3}\frac{d^2\omega}{dt^2} + \frac{2}{r^3}\frac{d\omega}{dt}$$

$$\frac{d^4\omega}{dr^4} = \frac{d}{dr}\left(\frac{d^3\omega}{dr^3}\right) = \frac{d}{dr}\left(\frac{1}{r^3}\frac{d^3\omega}{dt^3} - \frac{3}{r^3}\frac{d^2\omega}{dt^2} + \frac{2}{r^3}\frac{d\omega}{dt}\right)$$

$$= \frac{1}{r^4}\frac{d^4\omega}{dt^4} - \frac{3}{r^4}\frac{d^3\omega}{dt^3} - \frac{3}{r^4}\frac{d^3\omega}{dt^3} + \frac{9}{r^4}\frac{d^2\omega}{dt^2} + \frac{2}{r^4}\frac{d^2\omega}{dt^2} - \frac{6}{r^4}\frac{d\omega}{dt}$$

$$= \frac{1}{r^4}\frac{d^4\omega}{dt^4} - \frac{6}{r^4}\frac{d^3\omega}{dt^3} + \frac{11}{r^4}\frac{d^2\omega}{dt^2} - \frac{6}{r^4}\frac{d\omega}{dt}$$

$$\Rightarrow \frac{1}{r^4}\frac{d^4\omega}{dt^4} - \frac{6}{r^4}\frac{d^3\omega}{dt^3} + \frac{11}{r^4}\frac{d^2\omega}{dt^2} - \frac{6}{r^4}\frac{d\omega}{dt} + \frac{2}{r^4}\frac{d^3\omega}{dt^3} - \frac{6}{r^4}\frac{d^2\omega}{dt^2} + \frac{4}{r^4}\frac{d\omega}{dt} - \frac{1}{r^4}\frac{d^2\omega}{dt^2} + \frac{1}{r^4}\frac{d\omega}{dt} + \frac{1}{r^4}\frac{d\omega}{dt} = \frac{p_0}{D}$$

$$\Rightarrow \frac{1}{r^4}\frac{d^4\omega}{dt^4} - \frac{4}{r^4}\frac{d^3\omega}{dt^3} + \frac{4}{r^4}\frac{d^2\omega}{dt^2} = \frac{p_0}{D}$$

$$\Rightarrow \frac{d^4\omega}{dt^4} - 4\frac{d^3\omega}{dt^3} + 4\frac{d^2\omega}{dt^2} = \frac{p_0}{D}r^4 = \frac{p_0}{D}e^{4t},$$

and the above equation is a nonhomogeneous fourth-order linear ordinary differential equation with constant coefficient.

The general solution to a nonhomogeneous linear ODE is equal to the general solution to the corresponding homogeneous equation plus a particular solution to the nonhomogeneous ODE.

The corresponding homogeneous ODE is:

$$\frac{d^4\omega}{dt^4} - 4\frac{d^3\omega}{dt^3} + 4\frac{d^2\omega}{dt^2} = 0.$$

The characteristic equation is:

$$\lambda^4 - 4\lambda^3 + 4\lambda^2 = 0$$

$$\Rightarrow \quad \lambda^2(\lambda^2 - 4\lambda + 4) = 0$$

$$\Rightarrow \quad \lambda^2(\lambda - 2)^2 = 0$$

$$\Rightarrow \quad \text{either } \lambda = 0 \text{ (double real root)}$$

$$\text{or } \lambda = 2 \text{ (double real root).}$$

Thus, the general solution to the corresponding homogeneous ordinary differential equation is:

$$\omega = \omega(t) = C_1 + C_2 t + (C_3 + C_4 t)e^{2t}.$$

In order to find a particular solution to the nonhomogeneous ODE, try a particular solution of the form:

$$\omega = Ae^{4t},$$

where A is a coefficient yet to be determined.

$$\omega = Ae^{4t}$$

$$\Rightarrow \quad \frac{d\omega}{dt} = 4Ae^{4t}$$

$$\Rightarrow \quad \frac{d^2\omega}{dt^2} = 16Ae^{4t}$$

$$\Rightarrow \quad \frac{d^3\omega}{dt^3} = 64Ae^{4t}$$

$$\Rightarrow \quad \frac{d^4\omega}{dt^4} = 256Ae^{4t}$$

$$\Rightarrow \quad 256Ae^{4t} - 256Ae^{4t} + 64Ae^{4t} = \frac{p_0}{D}e^{4t}$$

$$\Rightarrow \quad 64Ae^{4t} = \frac{p_0}{D}e^{4t}$$

$$\Rightarrow \quad A = \frac{P_0}{64D}$$

Thus, a particular solution to the nonhomogeneous ODE is:

$$\omega = \frac{p_0}{64D}e^{4t}.$$

Therefore, the general solution to the nonhomogeneous ODE is

$$\omega = \omega(t) = C_1 + C_2 t + (C_3 + C_4 t)e^{2t} + \frac{p_0}{64D}e^{4t}$$

or

$$\omega = \omega(r) = C_1 + C_2 \ln r + (C_3 + C_4 \ln r)r^2 + \frac{p_0}{64D}r^4$$

$$\Rightarrow \quad \frac{d\omega}{dr} = \frac{C_2}{r} + 2rC_3 + rC_4 + (2r\ln r)C_4 + \frac{p_0}{16D}r^3.$$

Inspecting ω and $\frac{d\omega}{dr}$, we conclude that we must have:

$$C_2 = 0 \quad \text{and} \quad C_4 = 0.$$

Therefore,

$$\omega = \omega(r) = C_1 + C_3 r^2 + \frac{p_0}{64D}r^4$$

$$\frac{d\omega}{dr} = 2C_3 r + \frac{p_0}{16D}r^3.$$

The boundary conditions for the problem are:

$$\text{At} \quad r = a: \qquad \omega = \frac{d\omega}{dr} = 0$$

$$r = a \quad \Rightarrow \quad \frac{d\omega}{dr} = 2aC_3 + \frac{p_0}{16D}a^3 = 0$$

$$\Rightarrow \quad C_3 = -\frac{p_0 a^2}{32D}$$

$$r = a \quad \Rightarrow \quad \omega = C_1 - \frac{p_0 a^2}{32D}a^2 + \frac{p_0}{64D}a^4 = 0$$

$$\Rightarrow \quad C_1 = \frac{p_0 a^4}{64D}.$$

Thus,

$$\omega = \omega(r) = \frac{p_0 a^4}{64D} - \frac{p_0 a^2}{32D} r^2 + \frac{p_0}{64D} r^4$$

$$= \frac{p_0}{64D}(a^4 - 2a^2 r^2 + r^4).$$

We conclude that:

$$\omega = \omega(r) = \frac{p_0}{64D}(a^2 - r^2)^2.$$

It is clear that the maximum deflection of the mid-surface takes place at $r = 0$ (center of the circular plate):

$$\omega_{max} = \frac{p_0 a^4}{64D}.$$

Notice that in the SI system the unit of P_o is $\frac{N}{m^2}$, the unit of a is m, and the unit of D is Nm. Thus, the unit of ω_{max} is $\frac{N}{m^2}\frac{m^4}{Nm} = m$.

PRACTICE PROBLEM

Our objective in this problem is to determine the deflection for a built-in circular plate of radius a subjected to uniformly distributed loading P_0 (force/area) using an alternative method to the one used earlier in this section. The differential equation describing the surface deflection ω is:

$$\left(\frac{d^2}{dr^2} + \frac{1}{r}\frac{d}{dr}\right)\left(\frac{d^2\omega}{dr^2} + \frac{1}{r}\frac{d\omega}{dr}\right) = \frac{d^4\omega}{dr^4} + \frac{2}{r}\frac{d^3\omega}{dr^3} - \frac{1}{r^2}\frac{d^2\omega}{dr^2} + \frac{1}{r^3}\frac{d\omega}{dr} = \frac{p_0}{D}. \tag{9.1}$$

Show that the above fourth-order linear ODE can be equivalently written in the form:

$$\frac{1}{r}\frac{d}{dr}\left\{r\frac{d}{dr}\left[\frac{1}{r}\frac{d}{dr}\left(r\frac{d\omega}{dr}\right)\right]\right\} = \frac{p_0}{D}. \tag{9.2}$$

Then, use equation (9.2) to solve for the deflection $\omega(r)$ for a built-in circular plate of radius a subjected to uniformly distributed P_0. What is ω_{max}?

SOLUTION

$$\frac{1}{r}\frac{d}{dr}\left\{r\frac{d}{dr}\left[\frac{1}{r}\frac{d}{dr}\left(r\frac{d\omega}{dr}\right)\right]\right\} = \frac{d^4\omega}{dr^4} + \frac{2}{r}\frac{d^3\omega}{dr^3} - \frac{1}{r^2}\frac{d^2\omega}{dr^2} + \frac{1}{r^3}\frac{d\omega}{dr}$$

We start with:

$$\frac{d}{dr}\left(r\frac{d\omega}{dr}\right) = r\frac{d^2\omega}{dr^2} + \frac{d\omega}{dr}$$

$$\Rightarrow \quad \frac{1}{r}\frac{d}{dr}\left(r\frac{d\omega}{dr}\right) = \frac{d^2\omega}{dr^2} + \frac{1}{r}\frac{d\omega}{dr}$$

$$\Rightarrow \quad \frac{d}{dr}\left[\frac{1}{r}\frac{d}{dr}\left(r\frac{d\omega}{dr}\right)\right] = \frac{d}{dr}\left[\frac{d^2\omega}{dr^2} + \frac{1}{r}\frac{d\omega}{dr}\right]$$

$$= \frac{d^3\omega}{dr^3} + \frac{1}{r}\frac{d^2\omega}{dr^2} - \frac{1}{r^2}\frac{d\omega}{dr}$$

$$\Rightarrow \quad r\frac{d}{dr}\left[\frac{1}{r}\frac{d}{dr}\left(r\frac{d\omega}{dr}\right)\right] = r\frac{d^3\omega}{dr^3} + \frac{d^2\omega}{dr^2} - \frac{1}{r}\frac{d\omega}{dr}$$

$$\Rightarrow \quad \frac{d}{dr}\left\{r\frac{d}{dr}\left[\frac{1}{r}\frac{d}{dr}\left(r\frac{d\omega}{dr}\right)\right]\right\} = \frac{d}{dr}\left(r\frac{d^3\omega}{dr^3} + \frac{d^2\omega}{dr^2} - \frac{1}{r}\frac{d\omega}{dr}\right)$$

$$= r\frac{d^4\omega}{dr^4} + \frac{d^3\omega}{dr^3} + \frac{d^3\omega}{dr^3} + \frac{1}{r^2}\frac{d\omega}{dr} - \frac{1}{r}\frac{d^2\omega}{dr^2}$$

$$\Rightarrow \quad \frac{1}{r}\frac{d}{dr}\left\{r\frac{d}{dr}\left[\frac{1}{r}\frac{d}{dr}\left(r\frac{d\omega}{dr}\right)\right]\right\} = \frac{d^4\omega}{dr^4} + \frac{2}{r}\frac{d^3\omega}{dr^3} - \frac{1}{r^2}\frac{d^2\omega}{dr^2} + \frac{1}{r^3}\frac{d\omega}{dr}.$$

Thus, equations (9.1) and (9.2) are equivalent.

Now, starting with equation (9.2):

$$\frac{1}{r}\frac{d}{dr}\left\{r\frac{d}{dr}\left[\frac{1}{r}\frac{d}{dr}\left(r\frac{d\omega}{dr}\right)\right]\right\} = \frac{p_0}{D}$$

$$\Rightarrow \quad \frac{d}{dr}\left\{r\frac{d}{dr}\left[\frac{1}{r}\frac{d}{dr}\left(r\frac{d\omega}{dr}\right)\right]\right\} = \frac{p_0 r}{D}$$

$$\Rightarrow \quad r\frac{d}{dr}\left[\frac{1}{r}\frac{d}{dr}\left(r\frac{d\omega}{dr}\right)\right] = \frac{p_0 r^2}{2D} + C_1$$

$$\Rightarrow \quad \frac{d}{dr}\left[\frac{1}{r}\frac{d}{dr}\left(r\frac{d\omega}{dr}\right)\right] = \frac{p_0 r}{2D} + \frac{C_1}{r}$$

$$\Rightarrow \quad \frac{1}{r}\frac{d}{dr}\left(r\frac{d\omega}{dr}\right) = \frac{p_0 r^2}{4D} + C_1 \ln r + C_2$$

$$\Rightarrow \quad \frac{d}{dr}\left(r\frac{d\omega}{dr}\right) = \frac{p_0 r^3}{4D} + C_1 r \ln r + C_2 r$$

$$\Rightarrow \quad r\frac{d\omega}{dr} = \frac{p_0 r^4}{16D} + C_1\left(\frac{r^2}{2}\ln r - \frac{r^2}{4}\right) + C_2\frac{r^2}{2} + C_3$$

$$\Rightarrow \quad \frac{d\omega}{dr} = \frac{p_0 r^3}{16D} + C_1\left(\frac{r}{2}\ln r - \frac{r}{4}\right) + C_2\frac{r}{2} + \frac{C_3}{r}.$$

At this state, we need to set

$$C_1 = 0 \text{ and } C_3 = 0$$

$$\Rightarrow \frac{d\omega}{dr} = \frac{p_0 r^3}{16D} + C_2\frac{r}{2}$$

$$\Rightarrow \omega = \frac{p_0 r^4}{64D} + C_2\frac{r^2}{4} + C_4,$$

using the boundary conditions:

$$r = a \Rightarrow \omega = \frac{d\omega}{dr} = 0.$$

We can write

$$r = a \Rightarrow \frac{d\omega}{dr} = 0 \Rightarrow C_2\left(\frac{a}{2}\right) + \frac{p_0 a^3}{16D} = 0$$

$$\Rightarrow C_2 = -\frac{p_0 a^2}{8D}$$

$$r = a \Rightarrow \omega = 0 \Rightarrow \frac{p_0 a^4}{64D} - \frac{p_0 a^4}{32D} + C_4 = 0$$

$$\Rightarrow C_4 = \frac{p_0 a^4}{64D}$$

$$\Rightarrow \omega = \omega(r) = \frac{p_0 a^4}{64D} - \frac{p_0 a^2}{32D}r^2 + \frac{p_0}{64D}r^4$$

$$\Rightarrow \omega = \omega(r) = \frac{p_0}{64D}(a^2 - r^2)^2,$$

which is exactly the same result obtained earlier by solving the fourth-order linear ODE. ω_{max} takes place at $r = 0$ (center of the circular plate):

$$\omega_{max} = \frac{p_0 a^4}{64D}.$$

9.8 Solution to a Simply Supported Rectangular Plate Problem

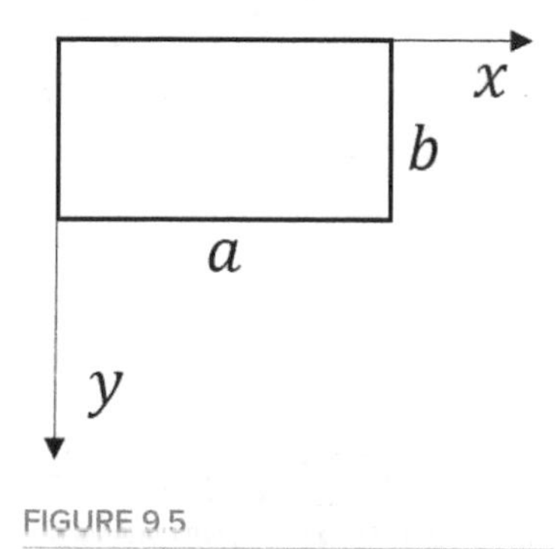

FIGURE 9.5

Our objective in this section is to determine the deflection $\omega_{(x,y)}$ of the mid-surface of a simply supported thin rectangular plate subject to loading $p_{(x,y)}$ $\left(\frac{\text{force}}{\text{area}}\right)$. The dimensions of the plate are a and b. The geometry of the problem dictates the types of coordinates to be used. Obviously, rectangular coordinates will be used here.

We need to solve the following fourth-order PDE:

$$\nabla^4 \omega = \frac{p}{D}$$

$$\text{or} \quad \frac{\partial^4 \omega}{\partial x^4} + 2\frac{\partial^4 \omega}{\partial x^2\, \partial y^2} + \frac{\partial^4 \omega}{\partial y^4} = \frac{p}{D}$$

subject to the following boundary conditions:

$$\omega = 0, \ \frac{\partial^2 \omega}{\partial x^2} = 0 \text{ for } x = 0 \ and \ x = a$$

$$\omega = 0, \ \frac{\partial^2 \omega}{\partial x^2} = 0 \text{ for } x = 0 \ and \ x = b.$$

The following solution was introduced by Navier in 1820. Claude Navier was a student of Joseph Fourier at École Polytechnique in Paris.

Assume:

$$p_{(x,y)} = \sum_{m=1}^{\infty}\sum_{n=1}^{\infty} p_{mn} \sin\frac{m\pi x}{a} \sin\frac{n\pi y}{b}$$

$$\text{and } \omega_{(x,y)} = \sum_{m=1}^{\infty}\sum_{n=1}^{\infty} a_{mn} \sin\frac{m\pi x}{a} \sin\frac{n\pi y}{b},$$

where p_{mn} and a_{mn} represent coefficients yet to be determined.

Notice that $\omega_{(x,y)}$ does satisfy the boundary conditions of the problem.

In order to determine p_{mn},

$$p_{(x,y)} = \sum_{m=1}^{\infty}\sum_{n=1}^{\infty} p_{mn} \sin\frac{m\pi x}{a} \sin\frac{n\pi y}{b}$$

$$\Rightarrow \quad p_{(x,y)} \sin\frac{m'\pi x}{a} \sin\frac{n'\pi y}{b} = \sum_{m=1}^{\infty}\sum_{n=1}^{\infty} p_{mn} \sin\frac{m\pi x}{a} \sin\frac{m'\pi x}{a} \sin\frac{n\pi y}{b} \sin\frac{n'\pi y}{b}$$

$$\Rightarrow \quad \int_{y=0}^{b}\int_{x=0}^{a} p_{(x,y)} \sin\frac{m'\pi x}{a} \sin\frac{n'\pi y}{b} dxdy = \sum_{m=1}^{\infty}\sum_{n=1}^{\infty} p_{mn} \int_{y=0}^{b}\int_{x=0}^{a} \sin\frac{m\pi x}{a} \sin\frac{m'\pi x}{a} \sin\frac{n\pi y}{b} \sin\frac{n'\pi y}{b} dxdy$$

* Orthogonality relation.

$$\int_0^l \sin\frac{m\pi x}{l} \sin\frac{n\pi x}{l} dx = \begin{cases} 0, & m \neq n \\ \frac{l}{2}, & m = n \end{cases}.$$

The proof is as follows:

$$m = n \quad \Rightarrow$$

$$\int_0^l \sin\frac{m\pi x}{l} \sin\frac{n\pi x}{l} dx = \int_0^l \sin^2\frac{m\pi x}{l} dx$$

$$= \frac{1}{2}\int_0^l \left(1 - \cos\frac{2m\pi x}{l}\right) dx$$

$$= \frac{1}{2}\left[x - \frac{l}{2m\pi}\sin\frac{2m\pi x}{l}\right]_0^l$$

$$= \frac{1}{2}(l) = \frac{l}{2.}$$

When $m \neq n$,

$$\int_0^l \sin\frac{m\pi x}{l} \sin\frac{n\pi x}{l} dx$$

$$\cos(a+b) = \cos a\cos b - \sin a\sin b$$

$$cos(a-b) = cosacosb + sinasinb$$

$$2sinasinb = cos(a-b) - cos(a+b)$$

$$\Rightarrow \quad sinasinb = -\frac{1}{2}[\cos(a+b) - \cos(a-b)]$$

$$\Rightarrow \quad \int_0^l \sin\frac{m\pi x}{l}\sin\frac{n\pi x}{l}dx$$

$$-\frac{1}{2}\int_{x=0}^{l}\left[\cos\frac{(m+n)\pi x}{l} \quad cos\frac{(m-n)\pi x}{l}\right]dx$$

$$= -\frac{1}{2}\left[\frac{l}{(m+n)\pi}\sin\frac{(m+n)\pi x}{l} - \frac{l}{(m-n)\pi}\sin\frac{(m-n)\pi x}{l}\right]_{x=0}^{l}$$

$$= 0$$

Therefore,

$$p_{mn}\left(\frac{a}{2}\right)\left(\frac{b}{2}\right) = \int_{y=0}^{b}\int_{x=0}^{a} p_{(x,y)}\sin\frac{m\pi x}{a}\sin\frac{n\pi y}{b}dxdy$$

$$\Rightarrow \quad p_{mn} = \frac{4}{ab}\int_{y=0}^{b}\int_{x=0}^{a} p_{(x,y)}\sin\frac{m\pi x}{a}\sin\frac{n\pi y}{b}dxdy.$$

In order to determine a_{mn},

$$\omega_{(x,y)} = \sum_{m=1}^{\infty}\sum_{n=1}^{\infty} a_{mn}\sin\frac{m\pi x}{a}\sin\frac{n\pi y}{b}$$

$$\Rightarrow \quad \frac{\partial\omega}{\partial x} = \sum_{m=1}^{\infty}\sum_{n=1}^{\infty}(a_{mn})\left(\frac{m\pi}{a}\right)\cos\frac{m\pi x}{a}\sin\frac{n\pi y}{b}$$

$$\Rightarrow \quad \frac{\partial^2\omega}{\partial x^2} = \sum_{m=1}^{\infty}\sum_{n=1}^{\infty} -(a_{mn})\left(\frac{m\pi}{a}\right)^2 \sin\frac{m\pi x}{a}\sin\frac{n\pi y}{b}$$

$$\Rightarrow \quad \frac{\partial^3\omega}{\partial x^3} = \sum_{m=1}^{\infty}\sum_{n=1}^{\infty} -(a_{mn})\left(\frac{m\pi}{a}\right)^3 \cos\frac{m\pi x}{a}\sin\frac{n\pi y}{b}.$$

Also,

$$\frac{\partial^4 \omega}{\partial x^4} = \sum_{m=1}^{\infty}\sum_{n=1}^{\infty}(a_{mn})\left[\frac{m\pi}{a}\right]^4 \sin\frac{m\pi x}{a}\sin\frac{n\pi y}{b}.$$

Similarly,

$$\frac{\partial^4 \omega}{\partial y^4} = \sum_{m=1}^{\infty}\sum_{n=1}^{\infty}(a_{mn})\left(\frac{n\pi}{b}\right)^4 \sin\frac{m\pi x}{a}\sin\frac{n\pi y}{b}.$$

Similarly,

$$\frac{\partial^4 \omega}{\partial x^2\,\partial y^2} = \sum_{m=1}^{\infty}\sum_{n=1}^{\infty}(a_{mn})\left(\frac{m\pi}{a}\right)^2\left(\frac{n\pi}{b}\right)^2 \sin\frac{m\pi x}{a}\sin\frac{n\pi y}{b}$$

$$\Rightarrow \sum_{m=1}^{\infty}\sum_{n=1}^{\infty}\left\{a_{mn}\left[\left(\frac{m\pi}{a}\right)^4 + 2\left(\frac{m\pi}{a}\right)^2\left(\frac{n\pi}{b}\right)^2 + \left(\frac{n\pi}{b}\right)^4\right] - \frac{p_{mn}}{D}\right\}\sin\frac{m\pi x}{a}\sin\frac{n\pi y}{b} = 0$$

$$\Rightarrow\ a_{mn}\left[\left(\frac{m\pi}{a}\right)^4 + 2\left(\frac{m\pi}{a}\right)^2\left(\frac{n\pi}{b}\right)^2 + \left(\frac{n\pi}{b}\right)^4\right] = \frac{p_{mn}}{D}$$

$$\Rightarrow\ a_{mn} = \frac{p_{mn}}{D\pi^4\left[\left(\frac{m^2}{a^2}\right)+\left(\frac{n^2}{b^2}\right)\right]^2}$$

$$\Rightarrow\ \omega_{(x,y)} = \sum_{m=1}^{\infty}\sum_{n=1}^{\infty}\frac{p_{mn}\sin\frac{m\pi x}{a}\sin\frac{n\pi y}{b}}{D\pi^4\left[\left(\frac{m^2}{a^2}\right)+\left(\frac{n^2}{b^2}\right)\right]^2}$$

$$\Rightarrow\ \omega_{(x,y)} = \frac{1}{\pi^4 D}\sum_{m=1}^{\infty}\sum_{n=1}^{\infty}\frac{p_{mn}\sin\frac{m\pi x}{a}\sin\frac{n\pi y}{b}}{\left[\left(\frac{m^2}{a^2}\right)+\left(\frac{n^2}{b^2}\right)\right]^2}.$$

For the special case of a uniformly distributed load:

$$p_{(x,y)} = p_0$$

$$\Rightarrow \quad p_{mn} = \frac{4}{ab}\int_{y=0}^{b}\int_{x=0}^{a} p_0 \sin\frac{m\pi x}{a}\sin\frac{n\pi y}{b}\,dxdy$$

$$= \frac{4p_0}{ab}\int_{y=0}^{b}\int_{x=0}^{a} \sin\frac{m\pi x}{a}\sin\frac{n\pi y}{b}\,dxdy$$

$$= \left(\frac{4p_0}{ab}\right)\left(\frac{2a}{m\pi}\right)\left(\frac{2b}{n\pi}\right) = \frac{16p_0 ab}{abmn\pi^2}$$

$$\Rightarrow \quad p_{mn} = \frac{16p_0}{mn\pi^2}; \quad m,n = 1, 3, 5, 7$$

Since

$$\int_{x=0}^{a} \sin\frac{m\pi x}{a}dx = \left[-\frac{a}{m\pi}\cos\frac{m\pi x}{a}\right]_{x=0}^{a}$$

$$= -\frac{a}{m\pi}(\cos m\pi - \cos 0)$$

$$= \frac{a}{m\pi}(1 - \cos m\pi)$$

$$= \begin{cases} 0 & \text{if m is even} \\ \dfrac{2a}{m\pi} & \text{if m is odd} \end{cases},$$

we conclude that:

$$\omega(x,y) = \frac{16p_0}{\pi^6 D}\sum_{m=1}^{\infty}\sum_{n=1}^{\infty}\frac{\sin\frac{m\pi x}{a}\sin\frac{n\pi y}{b}}{mn\left[\left(\frac{m^2}{a^2}\right)+\left(\frac{n^2}{b^2}\right)\right]^2} \quad m,n = 1, 3, 5, 7, \ldots$$

Maximum deflection takes place at the center of the plate (i.e., at $x = \frac{a}{2}$, $y = \frac{b}{2}$):

$$\omega_{max} = \frac{16p_0}{\pi^6 D}\sum_{m=1}^{\infty}\sum_{n=1}^{\infty}\frac{\sin\frac{m\pi}{2}\sin\frac{n\pi}{2}}{mn\left[\left(\frac{m^2}{a^2}\right)+\left(\frac{n^2}{b^2}\right)\right]^2} \quad m,n = 1, 3, 5, 7, \ldots$$

$$\Rightarrow \omega_{max} = \frac{16p_0}{\pi^6 D}\left\{\frac{(1)(1)}{(1)(1)\left[\left(\frac{1}{a}\right)^2+\left(\frac{1}{b}\right)^2\right]^2} - \frac{1}{(1)(3)\left[\left(\frac{1}{a}\right)^2+\left(\frac{3}{b}\right)^2\right]^2} - \frac{1}{(3)(1)\left[\left(\frac{3}{a}\right)^2+\left(\frac{1}{b}\right)^2\right]^2} + \frac{1}{(3)(3)\left[\left(\frac{3}{a}\right)^2+\left(\frac{3}{b}\right)^2\right]^2}\ldots\right\}.$$

For a square plate (a special case when a = b):

$$\omega_{max} = \frac{16p_0}{\pi^6 D}\left[\frac{1}{\left(\frac{2}{a^2}\right)^2}\right] = \frac{16p_0 a^4}{4\pi^6 D}$$

$$\text{or } \omega_{max} = \frac{4p_0 a^4}{\pi^6 D} \text{ (one term is retained).}$$

9.9 Marcus Solution for the Deflection of a Thin Plate

We showed that:

$$M_x = -D\left(\frac{\partial^2 w}{\partial x^2} + \nu\frac{\partial^2 w}{\partial y^2}\right)$$

$$M_y = -D\left(\frac{\partial^2 w}{\partial y^2} + \nu\frac{\partial^2 w}{\partial x^2}\right).$$

Adding the above equations member to member:

$$M_x + M_y = -D(1+\nu)\left(\frac{\partial^2 w}{\partial x^2} + \frac{\partial^2 w}{\partial y^2}\right).$$

By letting M denote the moment function or so-called moment sum

$$M = \frac{M_x + M_y}{1+\nu},$$

we conclude that

$$\nabla^2 \omega = -\frac{M}{D}.$$

Thus, the fourth-order partial differential equation describing the deflection of the mid-surface of the thin plate,

$$\nabla^4 \omega = \frac{p}{D}$$

$$\text{or} \quad \nabla^2(\nabla^2 \omega) = \frac{p}{D},$$

becomes:

$$\nabla^2\left(-\frac{M}{D}\right) = \frac{p}{D}$$

$$\Rightarrow \quad \frac{\partial^2 M}{\partial x^2} + \frac{\partial^2 M}{\partial y^2} = -p.$$

We conclude that:

$$\frac{\partial^2 M}{\partial x^2} + \frac{\partial^2 M}{\partial y^2} = -p$$

$$\frac{\partial^2 w}{\partial x^2} + \frac{\partial^2 w}{\partial y^2} = -\frac{M}{D}.$$

Thus, the fourth-order thin plate PDE has been reduced to two second-order PDEs that are sometimes preferred, depending on the method of solution employed.

Problem

9.1. A clamped (built-in) circular plate of radius a and thickness t is to close a circuit by deflecting 1 mm at the center at a pressure of $p_0 = 10\ MPa$. What is the required value of t? Take $a = 40$ mm, $E = 70$ GPa, and $\nu = 0.3$.

9.2. A simply supported square plate with thickness $t = 10$ mm carries a uniform loading. The maximum deflection in the plate was found to be $\omega_{max} = 0.5$ mm. Calculate the maximum deflection if the thickness t was reduced to $t = 5$ mm, assuming that everything else was kept the same.

9.3. A 500 mm simply supported square aluminum panel of 20 mm thickness is under uniform pressure p_0. For $E = 70$ GPa, $\nu = 0.3$, and $\sigma_{yield} = 240\ MPa$, and taking into account only the first term of the series solution, calculate the limiting value of p_0 that can be applied to the plate without causing yielding and maximum deflection ω_{max} that would be produced when p_0 reaches its limiting value.

9.4. Compute the maximum deflection for a built-in circular thin plate of radius $a = 40$ mm subject to a uniformly distributed loading $p_0 = 10\ MPa$. (Young's modulus of elasticity $E = 200$ GPa, Poisson's ratio $\nu = 1/3$, and thickness of the plate $t = 2$ mm.)

9.5. A simply supported square plate ($a = b$) is subjected to a uniformly distributed loading $p_{(x,y)} = p_0$. Determine the maximum deflection in the plate by retaining only the first term in Navier in finite series solution. ($a = 2$ m, $t = 20$ mm, $E = 210$ GPa, $\nu = 0.3$, $p_0 = 10\ kPa$.)

9.6. A simply supported square plate ($a = b$) carries a uniform loading p_0.

a) Determine the maximum deflection.

b) Retaining the first two terms of the series solution, evaluate the value of p_0 for which the maximum deflection is not to exceed 8 mm. The following data apply: $a = 3$ m, $t = 25$ mm, $E = 210$ GPa, and $\nu = 0.3$.

Further Reading

Timoshenko, Stephen P., and Woinowsky-Krieger, S. *Theory of Plates and Shells.* 2nd ed. New York City: McGraw-Hill, 1959.

Ugural, Ansel C., and Saul K. Fenster. *Advanced Mechanics of Materials and Applied Elasticity.* 5th ed. Upper Saddle River: Prentice Hall, 2012.

CHAPTER 10

Introduction to Finite Element Analysis

10.1 Brief Historical Background

The finite element method (FEM) is a numerical technique. It originated in an effort to solve complex structural mechanics and analysis problems. However, today, finite element analysis (FEA) is used in many disciplines in engineering and physics, including structural mechanics, electromagnetism, heat transfer, and fluid dynamics. It is interesting that perhaps the first paper published in FEM was written by a mathematician. In 1943, R. Courant[1] published a paper on the torsion of a cylinder in which he discussed the concept of "discretization of a continuous domain" (Courant, 1943). His paper published in the 1940s (prior to the digital computation revolution) went unnoticed by engineers and physicists. Ray Clough[2] from UC Berkeley coined the term "finite element" in the 1960s. O. Zienkiewicz from the University of Swansea and J. Argyris from University of Stuttgart were also among the pioneers in developing the method in the 1970s. NASA sponsored the original version of NASTRAN in 1965, and UC Berkeley made structural analysis programs (SAP) widely available. It is worth noticing that, as in numerical analysis in general, only the rapid decline in the cost of computers together with the tremendous increase in computing power made FEA

---

1 Richard Courant was a famous German American mathematician. He was born on January 8, 1888 in the German Empire and died on January 27, 1972 in New York.

2 Ray William Clough was born in Seattle in 1920. He was a brilliant professor of engineering at UC Berkeley, which is considered by most to be the birthplace of FEM.

attractive and interesting to engineers and physicists. This chapter is an elementary introduction to the topic covering only FEA as applied to structural analysis (stiffness matrix method).

10.2 Derivation of the Stiffness Matrix for a Bar Element

In chapter 1, we derived Hooke's law for a prismatic bar subject to uniaxial state of stress:

$$\delta = \frac{\text{Pl}}{\text{AE}}.$$

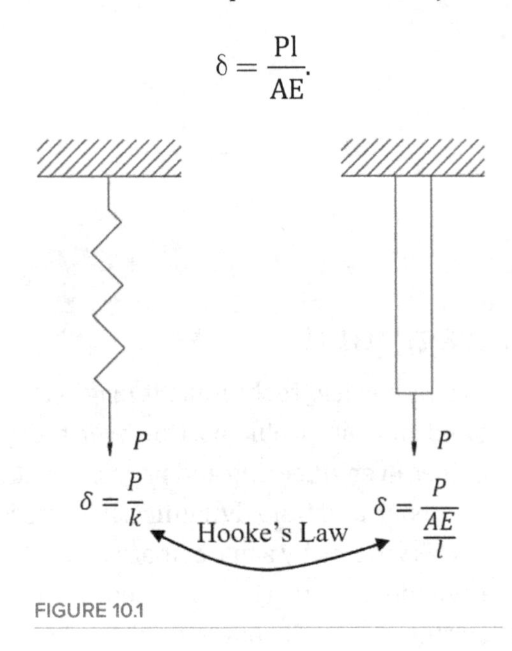

FIGURE 10.1

A prismatic bar when loaded axially with a load *P*, as long as the material is still behaving in the linearly elastic range, will behave like a linear spring with spring constant $k = \frac{\text{AE}}{\text{l}}$.

Notice that k depends on the geometrical properties of the prismatic bar (A and l) and the mechanical property of the material (E). k has the dimension of $\frac{\text{Force}}{\text{Length}}$.

$$\frac{AE}{l} \quad = \quad k$$

FIGURE 10.2

We will derive the stiffness matrix for a bar element (or truss element or axial force element). We adopt the absolute sign convention in deriving the stiffness matrix.

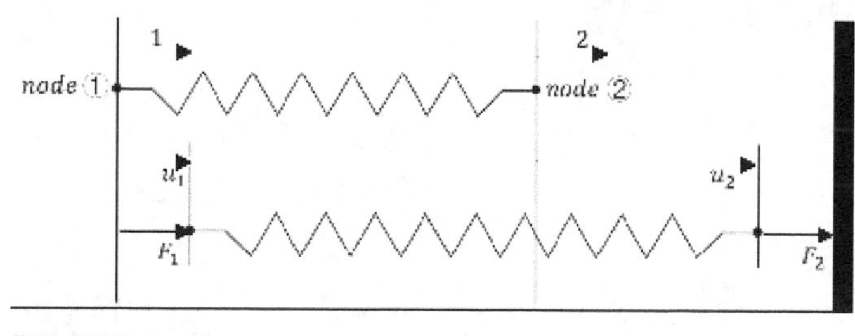

FIGURE 10.3

We are looking for a linear relationship between end forces $\begin{Bmatrix} F_1 \\ F_2 \end{Bmatrix}$ and end displacements $\begin{Bmatrix} u_1 \\ u_2 \end{Bmatrix}$ in the following form:

$$\begin{Bmatrix} F_1 \\ F_2 \end{Bmatrix} = \begin{bmatrix} k_{11} & k_{12} \\ k_{21} & k_{22} \end{bmatrix} \begin{Bmatrix} u_1 \\ u_2 \end{Bmatrix}.$$

- **Case (i):** $u_1 = 1; u_2 = 0$

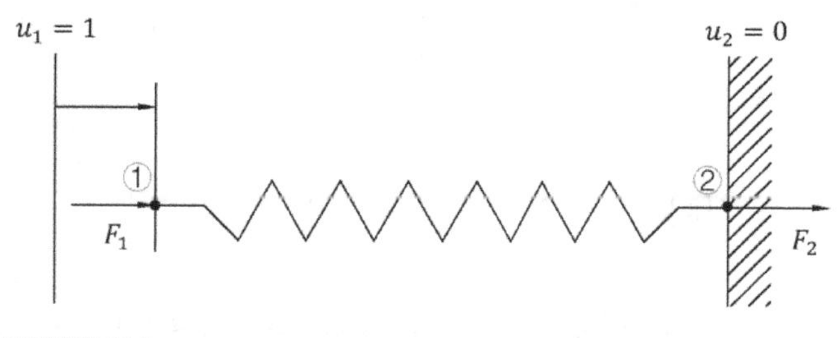

FIGURE 10.4

$$\sum F_x = 0 \Rightarrow F_1 + F_2 = 0$$

$$F_1 = ku_1 = (k)(1) = k$$

$$\Rightarrow \qquad F_2 = -F_1 = -k$$

$$\Rightarrow \qquad k_{11} = k; k_{21} = -k$$

- **Case (ii):** $u_1 = 0; u_2 = 1$

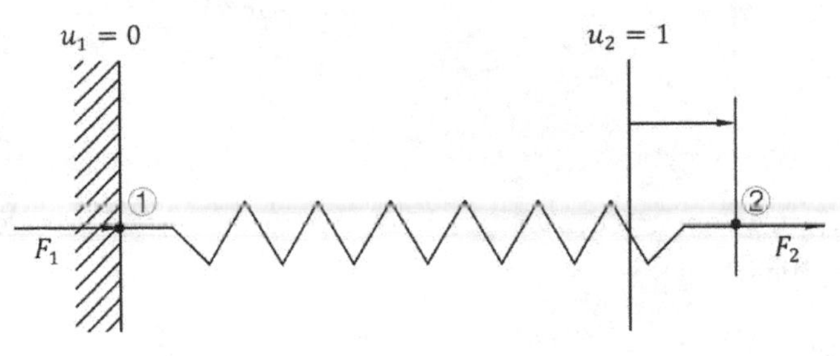

FIGURE 10.5

$$\sum F_x = 0 \Rightarrow F_1 + F_2 = 0$$

$$F_2 = ku_2 = (k)(1) = k$$

$$\Rightarrow \qquad F_1 = -F_2 = -k$$

$$\Rightarrow \qquad k_{12} = -k; \; k_{22} = k$$

$$\Rightarrow \qquad \begin{Bmatrix} F_1 \\ F_2 \end{Bmatrix} = k\begin{bmatrix} 1 & -1 \\ -1 & 1 \end{bmatrix}\begin{Bmatrix} u_1 \\ u_2 \end{Bmatrix} = \frac{AE}{l}\begin{bmatrix} 1 & -1 \\ -1 & 1 \end{bmatrix}\begin{Bmatrix} u_1 \\ u_2 \end{Bmatrix}$$

The matrix is:

$$[k] = k\begin{bmatrix} 1 & -1 \\ -1 & 1 \end{bmatrix} = \frac{AE}{l}\begin{bmatrix} 1 & -1 \\ -1 & 1 \end{bmatrix}.$$

It is the bar element (or axial force element or truss element) stiffness matrix. It is a (2×2) real symmetric singular matrix. Indeed, let us determine the eigenvalues and corresponding eigenvectors of the above matrix. The eigenvalues of the above stiffness matrix can be determined by setting:

$$\begin{vmatrix} k-\lambda & -k \\ -k & k-\lambda \end{vmatrix} = 0$$

$$\Rightarrow \qquad (k-\lambda)^2 - k^2 = 0$$

$$\Rightarrow \qquad (k-\lambda+k)(k-\lambda-k) = 0$$

$$\Rightarrow \qquad (2k-\lambda)(-\lambda) = 0$$

Either $\qquad \lambda = 0 \text{ or } \lambda = 2k.$

In order to determine an eigenvector corresponding to the eigenvalue $\lambda = 0$, we set:

$$\begin{bmatrix} k & -k \\ -k & k \end{bmatrix}\begin{pmatrix} x \\ y \end{pmatrix} = \begin{pmatrix} 0 \\ 0 \end{pmatrix}$$

$$\Rightarrow \qquad kx - ky = 0$$

$$-kx + ky = 0.$$

Therefore, $\begin{pmatrix} 1 \\ 1 \end{pmatrix}$ is an eigenvector corresponding to $\lambda = 0$. $\begin{pmatrix} \frac{1}{\sqrt{2}} \\ \frac{1}{\sqrt{2}} \end{pmatrix}$ is a normalized eigenvector corresponding to the eigenvalue $\lambda = 0$.

In order to determine an eigenvector corresponding to the eigenvalue $\lambda = 2k$, we set:

$$\begin{pmatrix} -k & -k \\ -k & -k \end{pmatrix}\begin{pmatrix} x \\ y \end{pmatrix} = \begin{pmatrix} 0 \\ 0 \end{pmatrix}$$

$$\Rightarrow \qquad -kx - ky = 0$$

$$-kx - ky = 0.$$

Therefore $\begin{pmatrix} 1 \\ -1 \end{pmatrix}$ is an eigenvector corresponding to the eigenvalue $\lambda = 2k$. $\begin{pmatrix} \frac{1}{\sqrt{2}} \\ -\frac{1}{\sqrt{2}} \end{pmatrix}$ is a normalized eigenvector corresponding to the eigenvalue $\lambda = 2k$.

The normalized eigenvector $\begin{pmatrix} \frac{1}{\sqrt{2}} \\ \frac{1}{\sqrt{2}} \end{pmatrix}$ corresponds to a rigid body mode. The strain energy associated with it is zero (no strain). The normalized eigenvector $\begin{pmatrix} \frac{1}{\sqrt{2}} \\ -\frac{1}{\sqrt{2}} \end{pmatrix}$ corresponds to a deformation mode. The strain energy associated with it is non-zero (there is strain).

Assembly of Stiffness Matrices (Direct Stiffness Method)

Consider the following structure in **figure 10.6**.

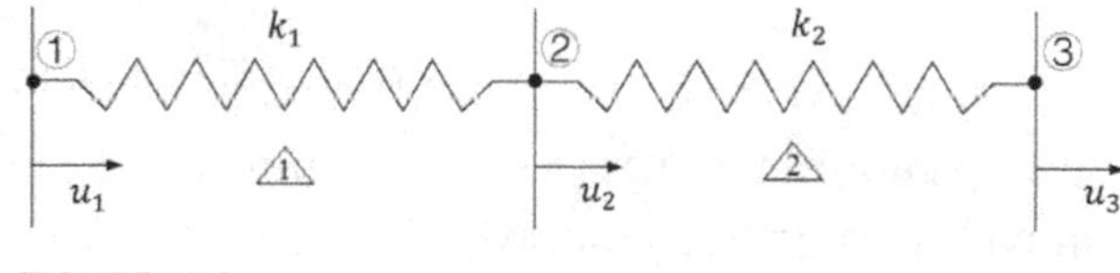

FIGURE 10.6

The structure consists of two elements and has three degrees of freedom. Let us establish its overall stiffness matrix.

The stiffness matrix for an element is $\triangle 1$:

$$\begin{bmatrix} k_1 & -k_1 \\ -k_1 & k_1 \end{bmatrix} \qquad \begin{Bmatrix} u_1 \\ u_2 \end{Bmatrix}.$$

The stiffness matrix for an element is $\triangle 2$:

$$\begin{bmatrix} k_2 & -k_2 \\ -k_2 & k_2 \end{bmatrix} \qquad \begin{Bmatrix} u_2 \\ u_3 \end{Bmatrix}.$$

The overall stiffness matrix is:

$$\begin{bmatrix} k_1 & -k_1 & 0 \\ -k_1 & k_1 + k_2 & -k_2 \\ 0 & -k_2 & k_2 \end{bmatrix} \qquad \begin{Bmatrix} u_1 \\ u_2 \\ u_3 \end{Bmatrix}.$$

Therefore, the overall stiffness matrix for the structure is:

$$[k] = \begin{bmatrix} k_1 & -k_1 & 0 \\ -k_1 & k_1 + k_2 & -k_2 \\ 0 & -k_2 & k_2 \end{bmatrix}.$$

The above overall stiffness matrix is a (3×3) matrix, which is predicted, since the structure has three degrees of freedom. Notice also the following:

i. The above stiffness matrix is real and symmetric (a manifestation of the Maxwell-Betti reciprocity principle).
ii. The (main) diagonal elements are all positive.
iii. If we add the elements of each column (or each row) together, they add up to zero (equilibrium).
iv. Determinant of $[k] = k_1\left[k_2(k_1 + k_2) - k_2^2\right] + k_1(-k_1k_2) = 0$.

Therefore $[k]$ is singular and cannot be inverted at this stage because it contains a rigid body mode. The boundary conditions are not yet determined in the given structure. For instance, we can remove the rigid body mode in the given structure by having a rigid support at node ① (fixing it).

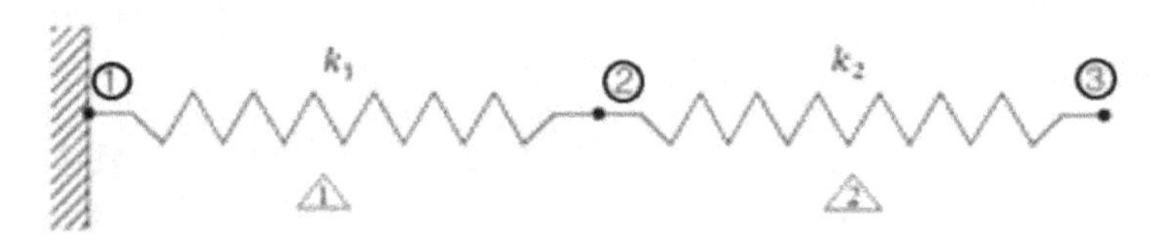

FIGURE 10.7

If we have a rigid support at node ①, the number of degrees of freedom will be reduced to 2, and the overall stiffness matrix becomes:

$$[k]=\begin{bmatrix} k_1 & -k_1 & 0 \\ -k_1 & k_1+k_2 & -k_2 \\ 0 & -k_2 & k_2 \end{bmatrix}=\begin{bmatrix} k_1+k_2 & -k_2 \\ -k_2 & k_2 \end{bmatrix}.$$

The overall stiffness matrix of the new structure becomes:

$$[k]=\begin{bmatrix} k_1+k_2 & -k_2 \\ -k_2 & k_2 \end{bmatrix}.$$

It is now a (2 × 2) real symmetric positive definite and non-singular. Its determinant is non-zero and can be inverted.

EXAMPLE 10.1

For the structure shown in the figure below, determine the (axial) displacement of point C.

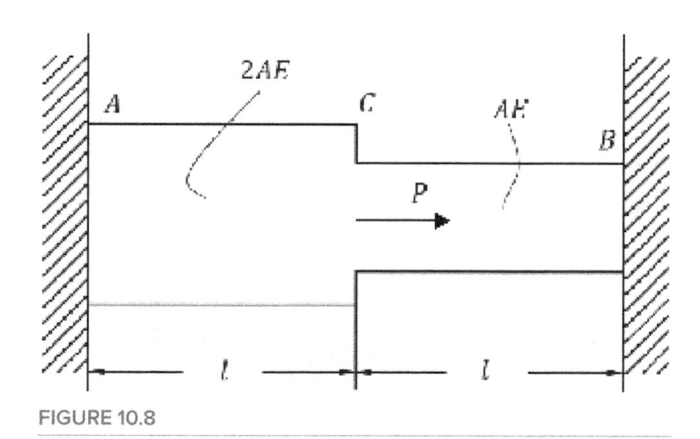

FIGURE 10.8

SOLUTION

Method 1 (Stiffness Matrix Approach)

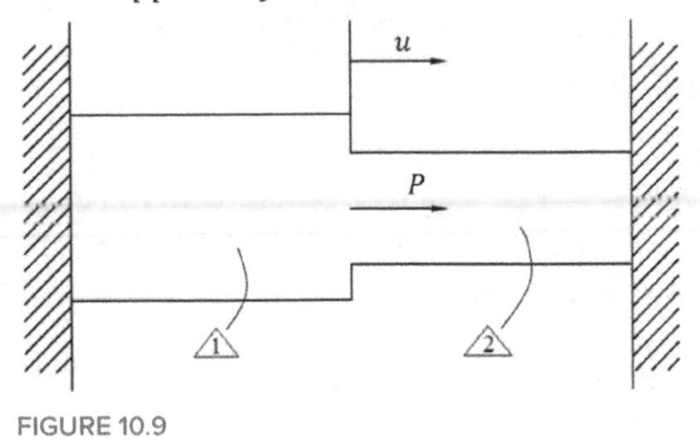

FIGURE 10.9

The structure can be treated as consistent of two elements. It has only one degree of freedom. Therefore, the overall stiffness matrix is expected to be a (3 × 3) matrix.

Stiffness matrix for an element is △1:

$$\frac{2AE}{l}\begin{bmatrix} 1 & -1 \\ -1 & 1 \end{bmatrix} \rightarrow \frac{AE}{l}[2] \qquad \{u\}.$$

Stiffness matrix for an element is △2:

$$\frac{AE}{l}\begin{bmatrix} 1 & -1 \\ -1 & 1 \end{bmatrix} \rightarrow \frac{AE}{l}[1] \qquad \{u\}.$$

Therefore, the overall stiffness matrix is:

$$\frac{AE}{l}[3] \qquad \{u\}.$$

The equilibrium equation is:

$$\frac{3AE}{l}\{u\} = \{P\} \Rightarrow u = \frac{Pl}{3AE}.$$

We conclude that the (axial) deflection of point C is $\frac{Pl}{3AE}$ → (to the right).

Method 2 (Strength of Materials Approach)

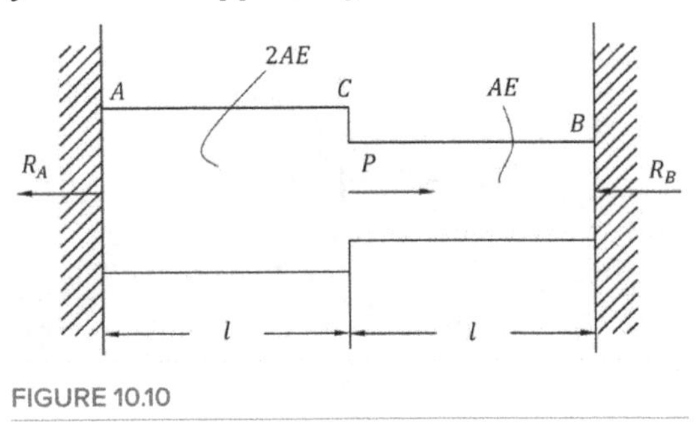

FIGURE 10.10

The structure is statically indeterminate to the first degree (i.e., the degree of indeterminacy is one).

From statics, we know:

$$\sum F_x = 0 \Rightarrow R_A + R_B = P$$

We need another equation based on the geometry of deformation.

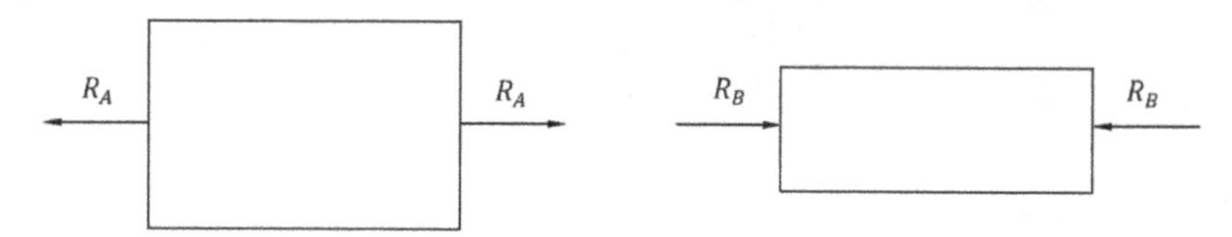

FIGURE 10.11 Free body diagrams of portions AC and CB

The compatibility equation is:

$$\frac{R_A l}{2AE} = \frac{R_B l}{AE}$$

$$\Rightarrow \quad \frac{R_A}{2} = R_B.$$

Using the above relationship in the equilibrium equation:

$$R_A + \frac{R_A}{2} = P \Rightarrow R_A = \frac{2P}{3}.$$

Therefore, $\delta_C = \frac{(\frac{2P}{3})(l)}{2AE} = \frac{Pl}{3AE} \rightarrow$ (to the right),

which is exactly the same result obtained in method 1.

EXAMPLE 10.2

For the structure shown in the figure below, determine the (axial) displacement of points C and D.

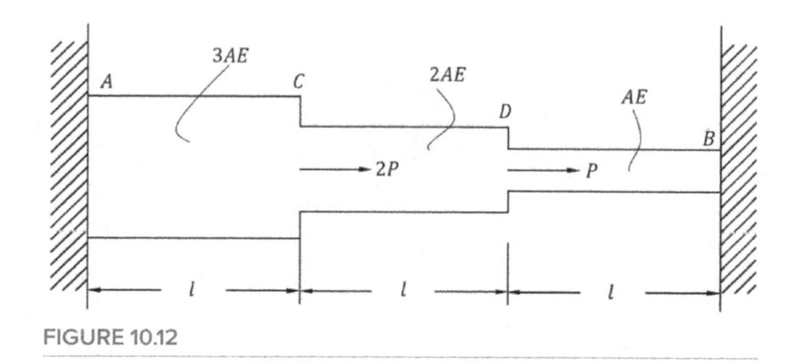

FIGURE 10.12

SOLUTION

Method 1 (Stiffness Matrix approach)

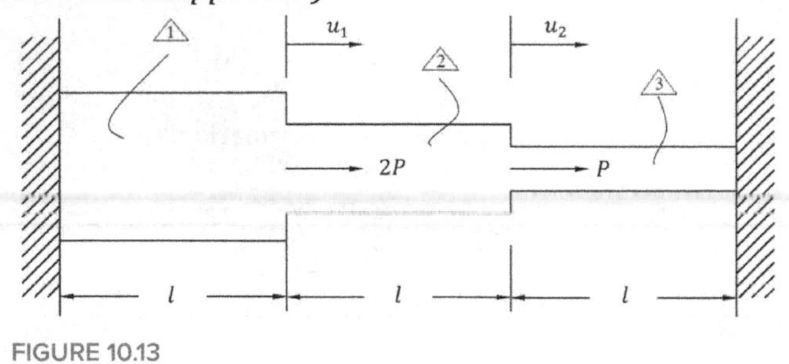

FIGURE 10.13

The structure can be treated as consisting of three elements. It has two degrees of freedom. Therefore, we should expect the overall stiffness matrix to be a (2×2) matrix.

The stiffness matrix for an element is ⚠1:

$$\frac{3AE}{l}\begin{bmatrix} 1 & -1 \\ -1 & 1 \end{bmatrix} \rightarrow \frac{AE}{l}[3] \qquad \{u_1\}.$$

The stiffness matrix for an element is ⚠2:

$$\frac{2AE}{l}\begin{bmatrix} 1 & -1 \\ -1 & 1 \end{bmatrix} \rightarrow \frac{AE}{l}\begin{bmatrix} 2 & -2 \\ -2 & 2 \end{bmatrix} \qquad \begin{Bmatrix} u_1 \\ u_2 \end{Bmatrix}.$$

The stiffness matrix for an element is ⚠3:

$$\frac{AE}{l}\begin{bmatrix} 1 & -1 \\ -1 & 1 \end{bmatrix} \rightarrow \frac{AE}{l}[1] \qquad \{u_2\}.$$

The overall stiffness matrix is:

$$\frac{AE}{l}\begin{bmatrix} 3+2 & -2 \\ -2 & 2+1 \end{bmatrix} \qquad \begin{Bmatrix} u_1 \\ u_2 \end{Bmatrix}.$$

Therefore, the equilibrium equations become:

$$\frac{AE}{l}\begin{bmatrix} 5 & -2 \\ -2 & 3 \end{bmatrix}\begin{Bmatrix} u_1 \\ u_2 \end{Bmatrix} = \begin{Bmatrix} 2P \\ P \end{Bmatrix}$$

$$\Rightarrow \qquad \begin{Bmatrix} u_1 \\ u_2 \end{Bmatrix} = \frac{l}{AE}\begin{bmatrix} 5 & -2 \\ -2 & 3 \end{bmatrix}^{-1}\begin{Bmatrix} 2P \\ P \end{Bmatrix} = \left(\frac{l}{AE}\right)\left(\frac{1}{11}\right)\begin{bmatrix} 3 & 2 \\ 2 & 5 \end{bmatrix}\begin{Bmatrix} 2P \\ P \end{Bmatrix}$$

$$= \begin{Bmatrix} \dfrac{8Pl}{11AE} \\ \dfrac{9Pl}{11AE} \end{Bmatrix}.$$

We conclude that:

The axial displacement of C is: $\frac{8Pl}{11AE}$ → (to the right).

The axial displacement of D is: $\frac{9Pl}{11AE}$ → (to the right).

Method 2 (Strength of Materials Approach)

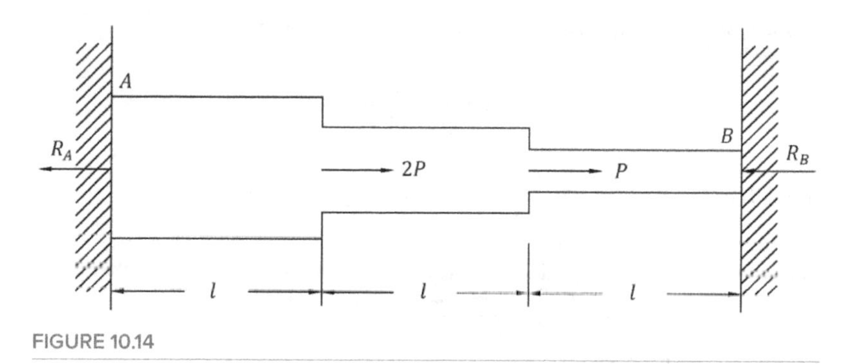

FIGURE 10.14

The problem is statically indeterminate to the first degree (i.e., the degree of indeterminacy is one).

From statics, we know:

$$\sum F_x = 0 \Rightarrow R_A + R_B = 3P$$

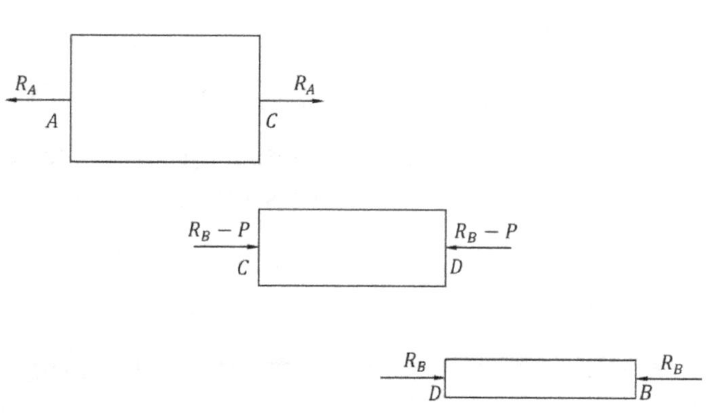

FIGURE 10.15 Free body diagrams of portions AC, CD, and DB

The compatibility equation is:

$$\frac{R_A l}{3AE} - \frac{(R_B - P)l}{2AE} - \frac{R_B l}{AE} = 0$$

$$\Rightarrow \qquad 2R_A - 3(R_B - P) - 6R_B = 0$$

$$\Rightarrow \qquad 2R_A - 9R_B = -3P.$$

Combining the above compatibility equation with the equilibrium equation, we get a system of two equations and two unknowns:

$$R_A + R_B = 3P$$

$$2R_A - 9R_B = -3P.$$

Solving the above system of equations simultaneously, we obtain:

$$R_A = \frac{24P}{11} \text{ and } R_B = \frac{9P}{11}.$$

Therefore, axial displacement of point C is

$$\frac{\left(\frac{24P}{11}\right)(l)}{3AE} = \frac{8Pl}{11AE} \rightarrow \text{(to the right)},$$

axial displacement of Point D is

$$\frac{\left(\frac{9P}{11}\right)(l)}{AE} = \frac{9Pl}{11AE} \rightarrow \text{(to the right)},$$

and the above results are exactly the same obtained in method 1.

10.3 Derivation of the Stiffness Matrix for a Truss Element

We derived in the previous section the stiffness matrix for a bar element that has two degrees of freedom. For this reason, its stiffness matrix was a (2×2) real symmetric matrix.

F_A, u_A → A ——— B → F_B, u_B

FIGURE 10.16

$$\begin{Bmatrix} F_A \\ F_B \end{Bmatrix} = \frac{AE}{l}\begin{bmatrix} 1 & -1 \\ -1 & 1 \end{bmatrix}\begin{Bmatrix} u_A \\ u_B \end{Bmatrix}$$

A plane truss is a collection of truss elements, bar elements, or axial force elements. A truss element does not have to be horizontal, such as element AB shown in the figure above. Its orientation in the plane can be determined by angle θ that AB makes with the horizontal axis, as shown in the **figure 10.17**.

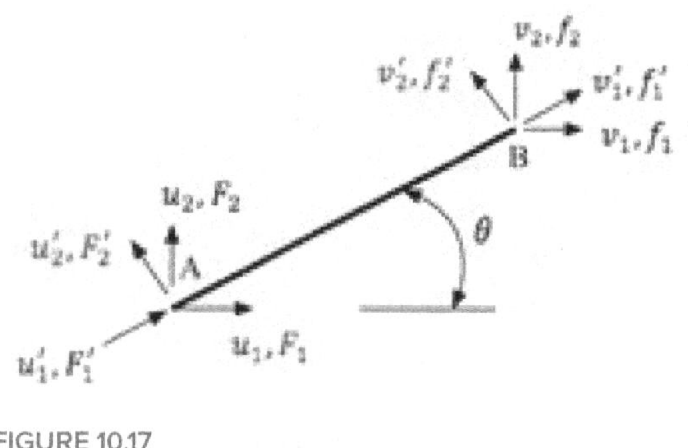

FIGURE 10.17

It is clear that plane truss element AB now has four degrees of freedom. Therefore, its stiffness matrix will be a (4×4) real symmetric matrix. In order to derive such a (4×4) matrix, we enlarge the (2×2) matrix derived in the previous section using the (2×2) orthonormal transformation matrix that takes us from the old unprimed coordinate system to the new primed coordinate system.

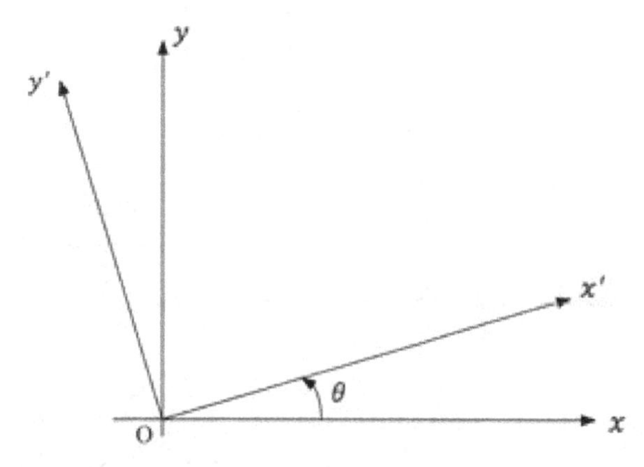

FIGURE 10.18

$$\begin{pmatrix} x' \\ y' \end{pmatrix} = \begin{pmatrix} \cos\theta & \sin\theta \\ -\sin\theta & \cos\theta \end{pmatrix} \begin{pmatrix} x \\ y \end{pmatrix}$$

$$\begin{Bmatrix} F_1' \\ F_2' \\ f_1' \\ f_2' \end{Bmatrix} = \begin{bmatrix} \cos\theta & \sin\theta & 0 & 0 \\ -\sin\theta & \cos\theta & 0 & 0 \\ 0 & 0 & \cos\theta & \sin\theta \\ 0 & 0 & -\sin\theta & \cos\theta \end{bmatrix} \begin{Bmatrix} F_1 \\ F_2 \\ f_1 \\ f_2 \end{Bmatrix}$$

$$\begin{Bmatrix} F_1' \\ F_2' \\ f_1' \\ f_2' \end{Bmatrix} = [T] \begin{Bmatrix} F_1 \\ F_2 \\ f_1 \\ f_2 \end{Bmatrix}$$

$$\begin{Bmatrix} u_1' \\ u_2' \\ v_1' \\ v_2' \end{Bmatrix} = [T] \begin{Bmatrix} u_1 \\ u_2 \\ v_1 \\ v_2 \end{Bmatrix}$$

$$[k'] = k \begin{bmatrix} 1 & 0 & -1 & 0 \\ 0 & 0 & 0 & 0 \\ -1 & 0 & 1 & 0 \\ 0 & 0 & 0 & 0 \end{bmatrix}$$

$$[k] = [T]^T [k'][T]$$

$$= k \begin{bmatrix} \cos\theta & -\sin\theta & 0 & 0 \\ \sin\theta & \cos\theta & 0 & 0 \\ 0 & 0 & \cos\theta & -\sin\theta \\ 0 & 0 & \sin\theta & \cos\theta \end{bmatrix} \begin{bmatrix} 1 & 0 & -1 & 0 \\ 0 & 0 & 0 & 0 \\ -1 & 0 & 1 & 0 \\ 0 & 0 & 0 & 0 \end{bmatrix} \begin{bmatrix} \cos\theta & \sin\theta & 0 & 0 \\ -\sin\theta & \cos\theta & 0 & 0 \\ 0 & 0 & \cos\theta & \sin\theta \\ 0 & 0 & -\sin\theta & \cos\theta \end{bmatrix}$$

$$= k \begin{bmatrix} \cos^2\theta & \cos\theta\sin\theta & -\cos^2\theta & -\cos\theta\sin\theta \\ & \sin^2\theta & -\cos\theta\sin\theta & -\sin^2\theta \\ & & \cos^2\theta & \cos\theta\sin\theta \\ & \text{Symmetric} & & \sin^2\theta \end{bmatrix}$$

$$\Rightarrow \begin{Bmatrix} F_1 \\ F_2 \\ f_1 \\ f_2 \end{Bmatrix} = k \begin{bmatrix} \lambda^2 & \lambda\mu & -\lambda^2 & -\lambda\mu \\ \lambda\mu & \mu^2 & -\lambda\mu & -\mu^2 \\ -\lambda^2 & -\lambda\mu & \lambda^2 & \lambda\mu \\ -\lambda\mu & -\mu^2 & \lambda\mu & \mu^2 \end{bmatrix} \begin{Bmatrix} u_1 \\ u_2 \\ v_1 \\ v_2 \end{Bmatrix},$$

where $\lambda = \cos\theta$ and $\mu = \sin\theta$.

We conclude that the (4 × 4) truss element stiffness matrix is:

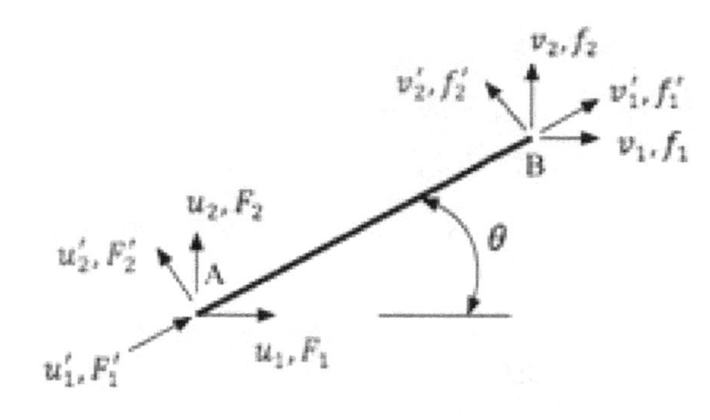

FIGURE 10.19

$$\begin{bmatrix} F_1 \\ F_2 \\ f_1 \\ f_2 \end{bmatrix} = k \begin{bmatrix} \lambda^2 & \lambda\mu & -\lambda^2 & -\lambda\mu \\ \lambda\mu & \mu^2 & -\lambda\mu & -\mu^2 \\ -\lambda^2 & -\lambda\mu & \lambda^2 & \lambda\mu \\ -\lambda\mu & -\mu^2 & \lambda\mu & \mu^2 \end{bmatrix} \begin{bmatrix} u_1 \\ u_2 \\ v_1 \\ v_2 \end{bmatrix},$$

where $k = \frac{AE}{l}$; $\lambda = \cos\theta$; $\mu = \sin\theta$.

EXAMPLE 10.3

For the statically determinate simply supported plane truss shown in the figure below, compute the horizontal displacement and the vertical displacement of joint C. For simplicity, assume that all three members of the truss are identical (i.e., same length l, same cross-sectional area A, and same Young's modulus of elasticity E).

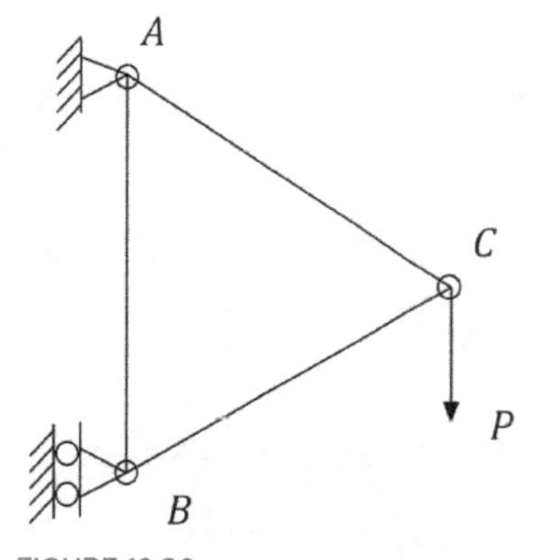

FIGURE 10.20

SOLUTION

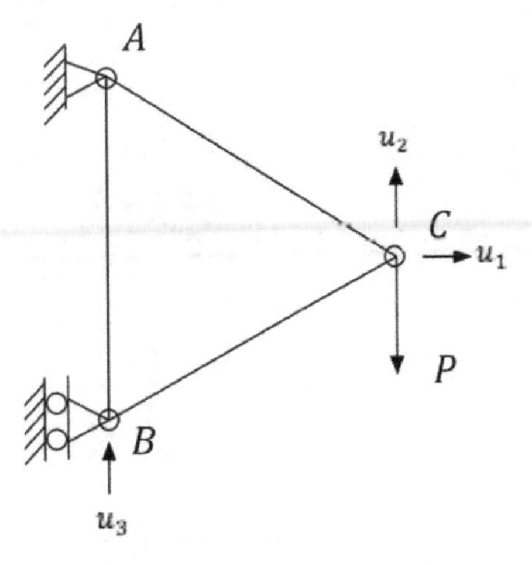

FIGURE 10.21

The truss has three degrees of freedom. Therefore, the global stiffness matrix should be a (3 × 3) real symmetric matrix.

The stiffness matrix for element A is:

$$\frac{AE}{l}\begin{bmatrix} \lambda^2 & \lambda\mu & -\lambda^2 & -\lambda\mu \\ \lambda\mu & \mu^2 & -\lambda\mu & -\mu^2 \\ -\lambda^2 & -\lambda\mu & \lambda^2 & \lambda\mu \\ -\lambda\mu & -\mu^2 & \lambda\mu & \mu^2 \end{bmatrix} \rightarrow \frac{AE}{l}[\mu^2]$$

$$\theta = 90^\circ \Rightarrow \lambda = 0; \mu = 1.$$

⇒ The stiffness matrix for element AB is:

$$\frac{AE}{l}[1] \qquad \{u_3\}.$$

The stiffness matrix for element BC is:

$$\frac{AE}{l}\begin{bmatrix} \lambda^2 & \lambda\mu & -\lambda^2 & -\lambda\mu \\ \lambda\mu & \mu^2 & -\lambda\mu & -\mu^2 \\ -\lambda^2 & -\lambda\mu & \lambda^2 & \lambda\mu \\ -\lambda\mu & -\mu^2 & \lambda\mu & \mu^2 \end{bmatrix} \rightarrow \frac{AE}{l}\begin{bmatrix} \mu^2 & -\lambda\mu & -\mu^2 \\ -\lambda\mu & \mu^2 & \lambda\mu \\ -\mu^2 & \lambda\mu & \mu^2 \end{bmatrix}$$

$$\theta = 30^\circ \Rightarrow \lambda = \frac{\sqrt{3}}{2}; \mu = \frac{1}{2}.$$

⇒ The stiffness matrix for element BC is:

$$\frac{AE}{l}\begin{bmatrix} \frac{1}{4} & -\frac{\sqrt{3}}{4} & -\frac{1}{4} \\ -\frac{\sqrt{3}}{4} & \frac{3}{4} & \frac{\sqrt{3}}{4} \\ -\frac{1}{4} & \frac{\sqrt{3}}{4} & \frac{1}{4} \end{bmatrix} \begin{Bmatrix} u_3 \\ u_1 \\ u_2 \end{Bmatrix}.$$

The stiffness matrix for element AC is:

$$\frac{AE}{l}\begin{bmatrix} \lambda^2 & \lambda\mu & -\lambda^2 & -\lambda\mu \\ \lambda\mu & \mu^2 & -\lambda\mu & -\mu^2 \\ -\lambda^2 & -\lambda\mu & \lambda^2 & \lambda\mu \\ -\lambda\mu & -\mu^2 & \lambda\mu & \mu^2 \end{bmatrix} \rightarrow \frac{AE}{l}\begin{bmatrix} \lambda^2 & \lambda\mu \\ \lambda\mu & \mu^2 \end{bmatrix}$$

$$\theta = 150^\circ \Rightarrow \lambda = -\frac{\sqrt{3}}{2}; \mu = \frac{1}{2}.$$

⇒ The stiffness matrix for element AC is:

$$\frac{AE}{l}\begin{bmatrix} \frac{3}{4} & \frac{\sqrt{3}}{4} \\ -\frac{\sqrt{3}}{4} & \frac{1}{4} \end{bmatrix} \begin{Bmatrix} u_1 \\ u_2 \end{Bmatrix}.$$

The overall (or global) stiffness matrix is:

$$\frac{AE}{l}\begin{bmatrix} \frac{5}{4} & -\frac{\sqrt{3}}{4} & -\frac{1}{4} \\ -\frac{\sqrt{3}}{4} & \frac{6}{4} & 0 \\ -\frac{1}{4} & 0 & \frac{2}{4} \end{bmatrix} \begin{Bmatrix} u_3 \\ u_1 \\ u_2 \end{Bmatrix}.$$

The above overall stiffness matrix can be reshuffled and be written as follows:

$$\frac{AE}{l}\begin{bmatrix} \frac{6}{4} & 0 & -\frac{\sqrt{3}}{4} \\ 0 & \frac{2}{4} & -\frac{1}{4} \\ -\frac{\sqrt{3}}{4} & -\frac{1}{4} & \frac{5}{4} \end{bmatrix} \begin{Bmatrix} u_1 \\ u_2 \\ u_3 \end{Bmatrix}.$$

The equilibrium equations are:

$$\frac{AE}{l}\begin{bmatrix} \frac{6}{4} & 0 & -\frac{\sqrt{3}}{4} \\ 0 & \frac{2}{4} & -\frac{1}{4} \\ -\frac{\sqrt{3}}{4} & -\frac{1}{4} & \frac{5}{4} \end{bmatrix} \begin{Bmatrix} u_1 \\ u_2 \\ u_3 \end{Bmatrix} = \begin{Bmatrix} 0 \\ -P \\ 0 \end{Bmatrix}$$

$$\Rightarrow \qquad \begin{Bmatrix} u_1 \\ u_2 \\ u_3 \end{Bmatrix} = \begin{Bmatrix} \frac{-\sqrt{3}Pl}{12AE} \\ -\frac{9Pl}{4AE} \\ -\frac{Pl}{2AE} \end{Bmatrix}.$$

Therefore, the horizontal displacement of joint C is

$$\frac{\sqrt{3}Pl}{12AE} \leftarrow \text{(to the left)},$$

and the vertical displacement of joint C is

$$\frac{9Pl}{4AE} \downarrow \text{downward.}$$

From the above solution, we also obtain a bonus information that the vertical displacement of roller B is $\frac{Pl}{2AE} \downarrow$ downward.

10.4 Derivation of the Stiffness Matrix for a Circular Rod Element Subject to Torsion

In section 10.2, we saw that a bar element loaded axially with a load *P* in the linearly elastic range behaves like a linear spring with spring constant k:

$$\delta = \frac{P}{\frac{AE}{l}} = \frac{P}{k},$$

where $k = \frac{AE}{l}$ is the equivalent linear spring constant (N/m).

We then concluded that the (2×2) real symmetric stiffness matrix for a bar element was (see **figure 10.22**):

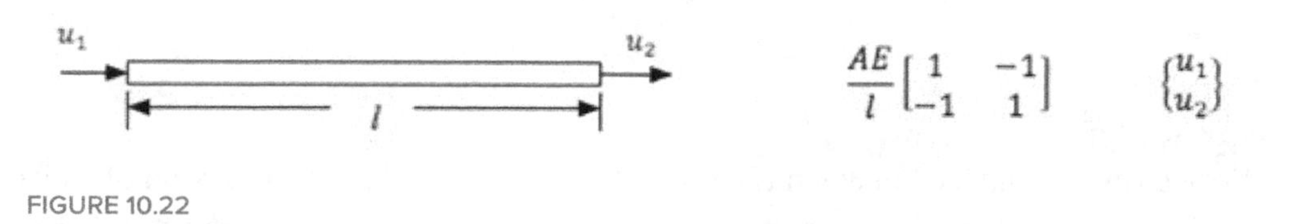

FIGURE 10.22

For a circular rod subject to twisting moment T(N × m) (see **figure 10.23**):

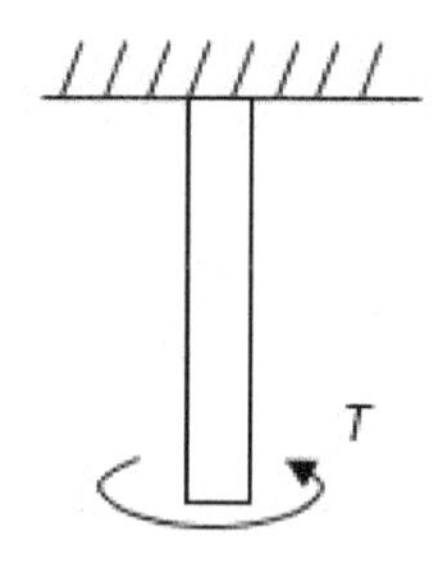

FIGURE 10.23

It can be shown that:

$$\phi = \frac{Tl}{GJ} = \frac{T}{\frac{GJ}{l}},$$

where ϕ is the angle of twist at the free end.

A circular rod subject to torsion in the linearly elastic range behaves like a torsional spring with a torsional spring constant $k_T\left(\frac{N\times m}{rad}\right)$.

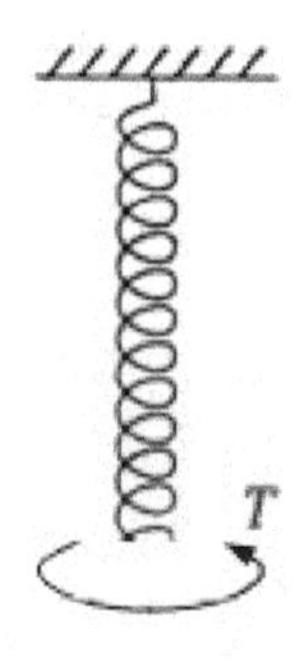

FIGURE 10.24

$$\phi = \frac{T}{k_T},$$

where $k_T = \frac{GJ}{l}$.

Notice the similarity between the formulas in axial loading and torsion of a circular rod. Young modulus of elasticity E is now replaced by modulus of rigidity G. Cross sectional area A is now replaced by area polar moment of inertia J. The axial load P is now replaced by the twisting moment T. It is obvious now that a circular rod subject to twisting has two degrees of freedom, and its (2×2) real symmetric matrix becomes (see **figure 10.25**):

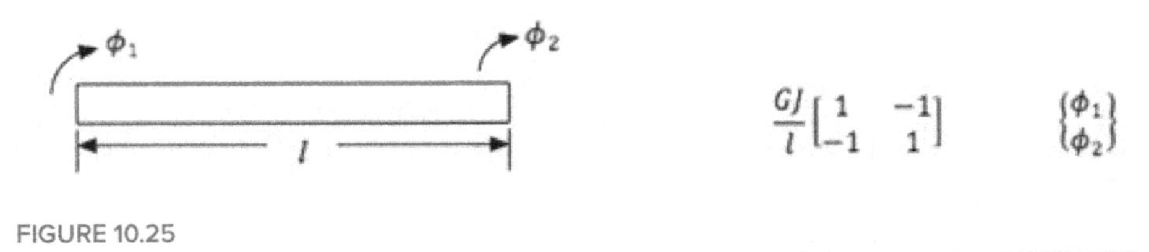

FIGURE 10.25

EXAMPLE 10.4

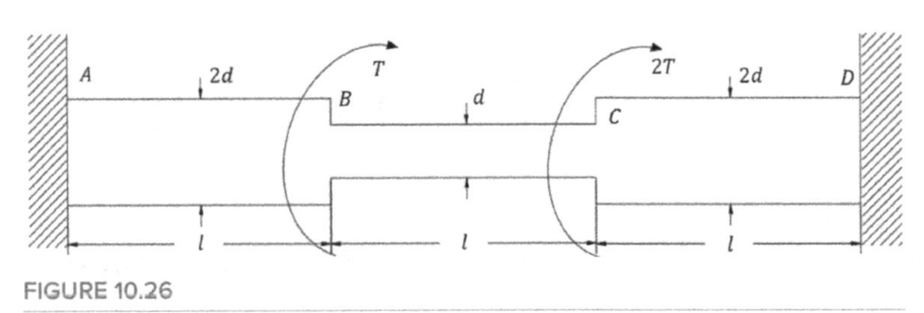

FIGURE 10.26

A solid circular shaft AD is fixed to rigid walls at both ends and subjected to a torque T at B and a torque 2T at C, as shown in **figure 10.26**. Compute the angles of twist at B and C. Assume that the modulus of rigidity G is constant throughout (the same material).

SOLUTION

Method 1 (Stiffness Matrix Approach)

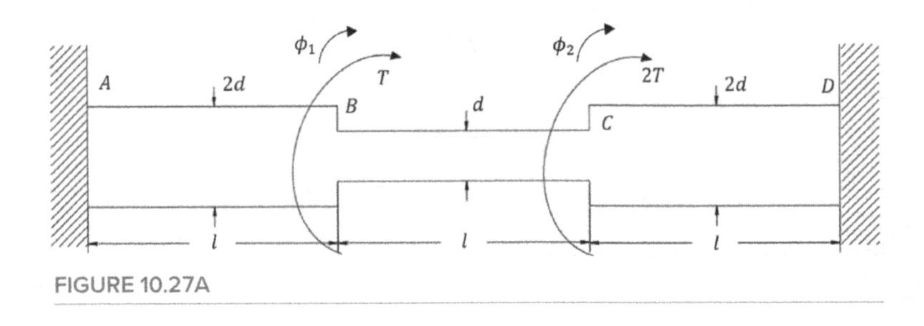

FIGURE 10.27A

The structure can be treated as consisting of three elements. It has two degrees of freedom.
The stiffness matrix for element AB is:

$$\frac{G\left(\frac{\pi}{32}\right)(2d)^4}{l}\begin{bmatrix} 1 & -1 \\ -1 & 1 \end{bmatrix}$$

$$= \frac{G\left(\frac{\pi}{32}\right)(2d)^4}{l}[1] \qquad \{\phi_1\}.$$

The stiffness matrix for element BC is:

$$\frac{G\left(\frac{\pi}{32}\right)(d)^4}{l}\begin{bmatrix} 1 & -1 \\ -1 & 1 \end{bmatrix}$$

$$= \frac{\pi G d^4}{32l}\begin{bmatrix} 1 & -1 \\ -1 & 1 \end{bmatrix} \qquad \begin{Bmatrix} \phi_1 \\ \phi_2 \end{Bmatrix}.$$

The stiffness matrix for element CD is:

$$\frac{G\left(\frac{\pi}{32}\right)(2d)^4}{l}\begin{bmatrix} 1 & -1 \\ -1 & 1 \end{bmatrix}$$

$$= \frac{\pi G d^4}{32l}[16] \qquad \{\phi_2\}.$$

Therefore, the overall (or global) stiffness matrix is:

$$\frac{\pi G d^4}{32l}\begin{bmatrix} 16+1 & -1 \\ -1 & 1+16 \end{bmatrix}$$

$$= \frac{\pi G d^4}{32l}\begin{bmatrix} 17 & -1 \\ -1 & 17 \end{bmatrix} \qquad \begin{Bmatrix} \phi_1 \\ \phi_2 \end{Bmatrix}.$$

The equilibrium equations are:

$$\frac{\pi G d^4}{32l}\begin{bmatrix} 17 & -1 \\ -1 & 17 \end{bmatrix}\begin{Bmatrix} \phi_1 \\ \phi_2 \end{Bmatrix} = \begin{Bmatrix} T \\ 2T \end{Bmatrix}$$

$$\Rightarrow \qquad \begin{Bmatrix} \phi_1 \\ \phi_2 \end{Bmatrix} = \frac{32l}{\pi G d^4}\begin{bmatrix} 17 & -1 \\ -1 & 17 \end{bmatrix}^{-1}\begin{Bmatrix} T \\ 2T \end{Bmatrix}$$

$$\Rightarrow \qquad \begin{Bmatrix} \phi_1 \\ \phi_2 \end{Bmatrix} = \left(\frac{32l}{\pi G d^4}\right)\left(\frac{1}{288}\right)\begin{bmatrix} 17 & 1 \\ 1 & 17 \end{bmatrix}\begin{Bmatrix} T \\ 2T \end{Bmatrix}$$

$$\Rightarrow \qquad \begin{Bmatrix} \phi_1 \\ \phi_2 \end{Bmatrix} = \begin{Bmatrix} \dfrac{19Tl}{9\pi Gd^4} \\ \dfrac{35Tl}{9\pi Gd^4} \end{Bmatrix}.$$

We conclude that:

$$\phi_1 = \frac{19Tl}{9\pi Gd^4}\ ;\ \phi_2 = \frac{35Tl}{9\pi Gd^4}.$$

Notice that ϕ_1 and ϕ_2 are unitless or dimensionless (radians).

Method 2 (Elementary Mechanics of Materials Approach)

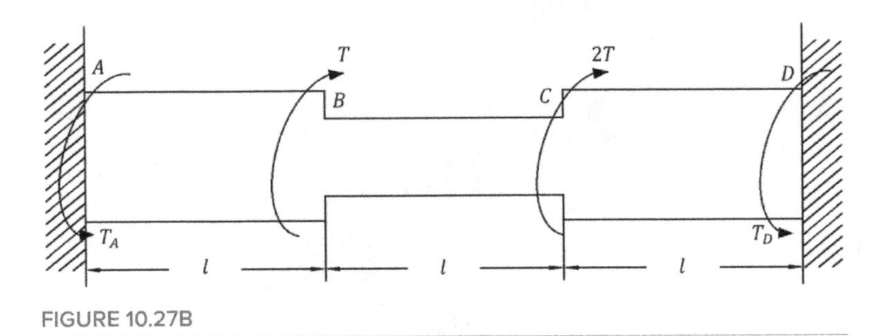

FIGURE 10.27B

$T_A = ?$

$T_D = ?$

From statics, we know:

$$T_A + T_D - T - 2T = 0$$

$$\Rightarrow T_A + T_D = 3T.$$

The problem is statically indeterminate to the first degree (i.e., the degree of indeterminacy is one).

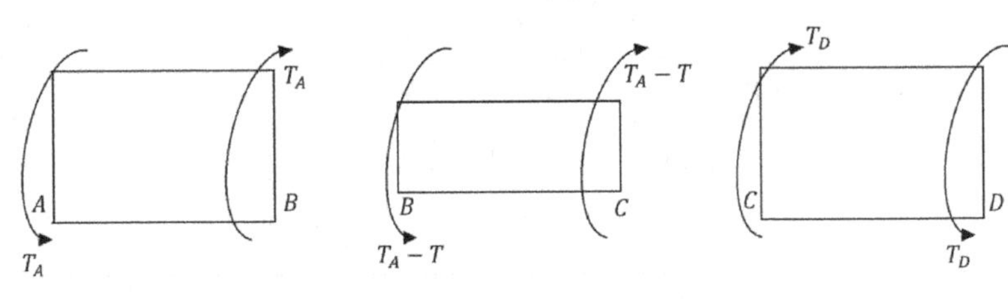

FIGURE 10.27C

The compatibility equation is: $\sum \phi_i = 0$

$$\Rightarrow \quad \frac{T_A l}{G\left(\frac{\pi}{32}\right)(2d)^4} + \frac{(T_A - T)l}{G\left(\frac{\pi}{32}\right)(d)^4} - \frac{T_D l}{G\left(\frac{\pi}{32}\right)(2d)^4} = 0$$

$$\Rightarrow \quad \frac{T_A}{16d^4} + \frac{(T_A - T)}{d^4} - \frac{T_D}{16d^4} = 0$$

$$\Rightarrow \quad \frac{T_A}{16} + \frac{(T_A - T)}{1} - \frac{T_D}{16} = 0$$

$$\Rightarrow \quad T_A + 16(T_A - T) - T_D = 0$$

$$\Rightarrow \quad T_A + 16T_A - 16T - T_D = 0$$

$$\Rightarrow \quad 17T_A - T_D = 16T.$$

Combining the above compatibility equation with the equilibrium equation $T_A + T_D = 3T$, we obtain a system of two equations and two unknowns. Solving simultaneously, we obtain:

$$T_A = \frac{19T}{18} \text{ and } T_D = \frac{35T}{18}$$

$$\phi_1 = \frac{\left(\frac{19T}{18}\right)(l)}{G\left(\frac{\pi}{32}\right)(2d)^4} = \frac{\frac{19}{18}Tl}{(G)\left(\frac{\pi}{32}\right)(16d^4)}$$

$$= \left(\frac{19Tl}{18}\right)\left(\frac{2}{G\pi d^4}\right) = \frac{19Tl}{9\pi Gd^4}$$

$$\Rightarrow \quad \phi_1 = \frac{19Tl}{9\pi Gd^4}$$

$$\phi_2 = \frac{\left(\frac{35}{18}T\right)(l)}{G\left(\frac{\pi}{32}\right)(2d)^4} = \frac{\frac{35}{18}Tl}{\frac{G\pi d^4}{2}}$$

$$= \left(\frac{35Tl}{18}\right)\left(\frac{2}{\pi Gd^4}\right) = \frac{35Tl}{9\pi Gd^4}$$

$$\Rightarrow \quad \phi_2 = \frac{35Tl}{9\pi Gd^4}.$$

These are exactly the same results we obtained using method 1 (FEA approach).

10.5 Derivation of the Stiffness Matrix for a Beam Element

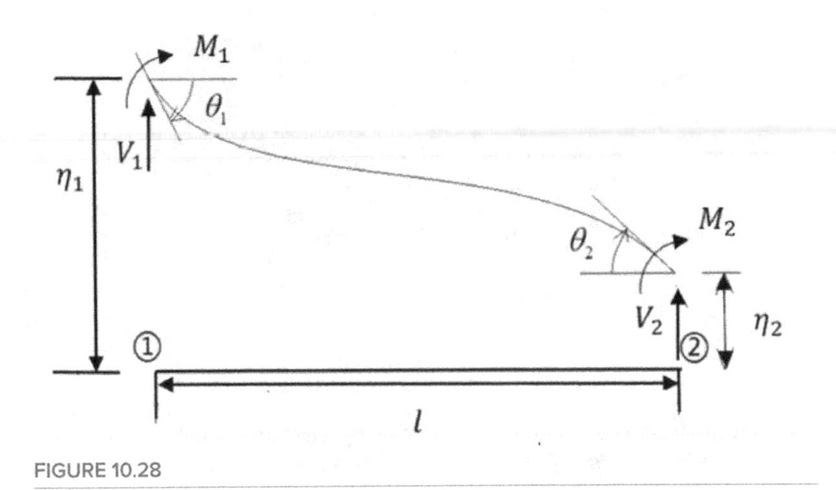

FIGURE 10.28

We are looking for a linear relationship between end forces $\begin{Bmatrix} M_1 \\ V_1 \\ M_2 \\ V_2 \end{Bmatrix}$ and end displacements $\begin{Bmatrix} \theta_1 \\ \eta_1 \\ \theta_2 \\ \eta_2 \end{Bmatrix}$ in the following form:

$$\begin{Bmatrix} M_1 \\ V_1 \\ M_2 \\ V_2 \end{Bmatrix} = \begin{bmatrix} k_{11} & k_{12} & k_{13} & k_{14} \\ k_{21} & k_{22} & k_{23} & k_{24} \\ k_{31} & k_{32} & k_{33} & k_{34} \\ k_{41} & k_{42} & k_{43} & k_{44} \end{bmatrix} \begin{Bmatrix} \theta_1 \\ \eta_1 \\ \theta_2 \\ \eta_2 \end{Bmatrix}.$$

- **Case (i):** $\theta_1 = 1; \eta_1 = \theta_2 = \eta_2 = 0$
- **Case (ii):** $\eta_1 = 1; \theta_1 = \theta_2 = \eta_2 = 0$
- **Case (iii):** $\theta_2 = 1; \theta_1 = \eta_1 = \eta_2 = 0$
- **Case (iv):** $\eta_2 = 1; \theta_1 = \eta_1 = \theta_2 = 0$

Case (i) corresponds to **figure 10.29**.

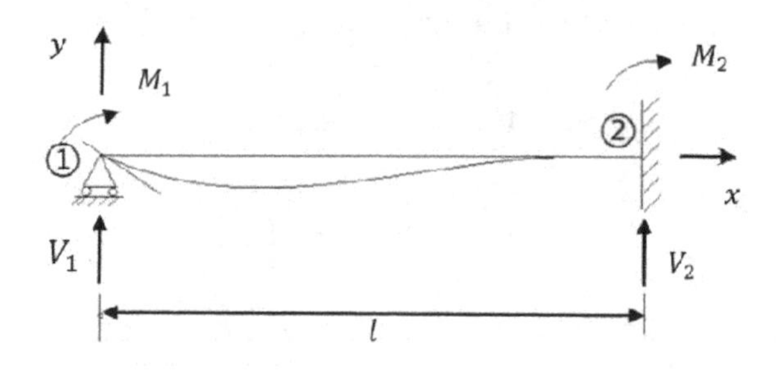

FIGURE 10.29 EI is constant throughout

From statics, we know:

$$\sum F_y = 0 \Rightarrow V_1 + V_2 = 0$$

$$\sum M_{②} = 0 \Rightarrow M_1 + M_2 + V_1 l = 0$$

The differential equation describing the elastic curve of the beam:

$$EIy'' = M_{(x)}$$

$$\Rightarrow \qquad EIy'' = V_1 x + M_1$$

$$\Rightarrow \qquad EIy' = V_1 \frac{x^2}{2} + M_1 x + C.$$

At $x = 0: y' = -1$

$$\Rightarrow \qquad EIy' = V_1 \frac{x^2}{2} + M_1 x - EI$$

$$\Rightarrow \qquad EIy = \frac{V_1}{2}\frac{x^3}{3} + M_1 \frac{x^2}{2} - EIx + D.$$

At $x = 0: y = 0$

$$\Rightarrow \qquad EIy = \frac{V_1}{6}x^3 + \frac{M_1}{2}x^2 - EIx.$$

At $x = l$: $y' = 0$ and $y = 0$.
Therefore,

$$\frac{V_1 l^2}{2} + M_1 l = EI$$

$$\frac{V_1 l^3}{6} + M_1 \frac{l^2}{2} = EIl.$$

The above system of equations can be simplified:

$$V_1 \frac{l^2}{2} + M_1 l = EI$$

$$V_1 \frac{l^2}{6} + M_1 \frac{l}{2} = EI.$$

Solving the above system of equations simultaneously, we get:

$$M_1 = \frac{4EI}{l} \text{ and } V_1 = -\frac{6EI}{l^2}$$

$$V_1 + V_2 = 0 \Rightarrow V_2 = \frac{6EI}{l^2}$$

$$M_1 + M_2 + V_1 l = 0 \Rightarrow M_2 = -\frac{4EI}{l} - \left(-\frac{6EI}{l^2}\right)(l) = \frac{2EI}{l}.$$

Therefore,

$$k_{11} = M_1 = \frac{4EI}{l}$$

$$k_{21} = V_1 = -\frac{6EI}{l^2}$$

$$k_{31} = M_2 = \frac{2EI}{l}$$

$$k_{41} = V_2 = \frac{6EI}{l^2}.$$

Case (ii), case (iii), and case (iv) will determine the second column, the third column, and the fourth column in the stiffness matrix, respectively.

$$\begin{Bmatrix} M_1 \\ V_1 \\ M_2 \\ V_2 \end{Bmatrix} = \frac{2EI}{l^3} \begin{bmatrix} 2l^2 & -3l & l^2 & 3l \\ -3l & 6 & -3l & -6 \\ l^2 & -3l & 2l^2 & 3l \\ 3l & -6 & 3l & 6 \end{bmatrix} \begin{Bmatrix} \theta_1 \\ \eta_1 \\ \theta_2 \\ \eta_2 \end{Bmatrix}$$

The stiffness matrix for a beam element is the (4×4) matrix:

$$[k] = \frac{2EI}{l^3}\begin{bmatrix} 2l^2 & -3l & l^2 & 3l \\ -3l & 6 & -3l & -6 \\ l^2 & -3l & 2l^2 & 3l \\ 3l & -6 & 3l & 6 \end{bmatrix}.$$

Notice that the above stiffness matrix is (4×4) real, symmetric, and singular.

It is worth mentioning here that the stiffness matrix can be reshuffled when rearranging the end forces and end displacements.

For instance, we can write:

$$\begin{Bmatrix} M_1 \\ M_2 \\ V_1 \\ V_2 \end{Bmatrix} = \frac{2EI}{l^3}\begin{bmatrix} 2l^2 & l^2 & -3l & 3l \\ l^2 & 2l^2 & -3l & 3l \\ -3l & -3l & 6 & -6 \\ 3l & 3l & -6 & 6 \end{bmatrix}\begin{Bmatrix} \theta_1 \\ \theta_2 \\ \eta_1 \\ \eta_2 \end{Bmatrix}.$$

Alternatively, we can write:

$$\begin{Bmatrix} V_1 \\ M_1 \\ V_2 \\ M_2 \end{Bmatrix} = \frac{2EI}{l^3}\begin{bmatrix} 6 & -3l & -6 & -3l \\ -3l & 2l^2 & 3l & l^2 \\ -6 & 3l & 6 & 3l \\ -3l & l^2 & 3l & 2l^2 \end{bmatrix}\begin{Bmatrix} \eta_1 \\ \theta_1 \\ \eta_2 \\ \theta_2 \end{Bmatrix}.$$

EXAMPLE 10.5

For the statically determinate cantilevered beam shown in the figure below, compute the vertical displacement and the rotation at the free end. Assume EI to be constant throughout.

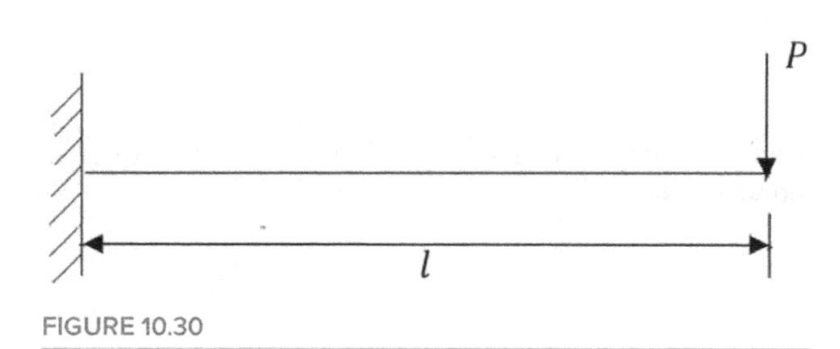

FIGURE 10.30

SOLUTION

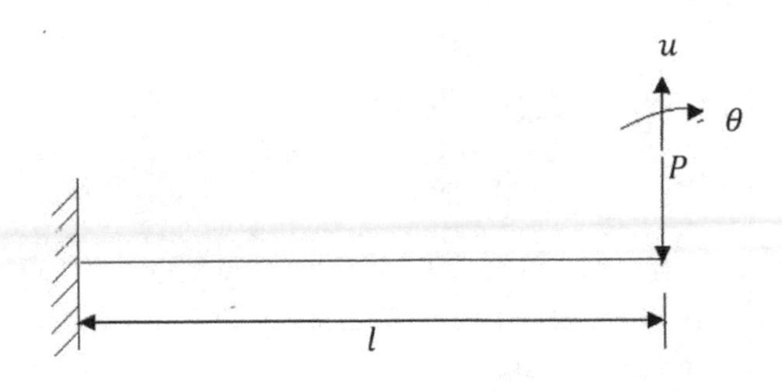

FIGURE 10.31

The cantilevered beam can be treated as consistent of only one beam element. The structure has two degrees of freedom. Therefore, we should expect its stiffness matrix to be a (4 × 4) matrix.

The stiffness matrix of the structure is:

$$\frac{2EI}{l^3}\begin{bmatrix} 2l^2 & -3l & l^2 & 3l \\ -3l & 6 & -3l & -6 \\ l^2 & -3l & 2l^2 & 3l \\ 3l & -6 & 3l & 6 \end{bmatrix} \rightarrow \frac{2EI}{l^3}\begin{bmatrix} 2l^2 & 3l \\ 3l & 6 \end{bmatrix} \qquad \begin{Bmatrix} \theta \\ u \end{Bmatrix}.$$

Notice, as predicted, the stiffness matrix for the structure is a (2 × 2) real symmetric positive definite and nonsingular matrix. The equilibrium equations are:

$$\frac{2EI}{l^3}\begin{bmatrix} 2l^2 & 3l \\ 3l & 6 \end{bmatrix}\begin{Bmatrix} \theta \\ u \end{Bmatrix} = \begin{Bmatrix} 0 \\ -P \end{Bmatrix}$$

$$\Rightarrow \qquad \begin{Bmatrix} \theta \\ u \end{Bmatrix} = \frac{l^3}{2EI}\begin{bmatrix} 2l^2 & 3l \\ 3l & 6 \end{bmatrix}^{-1}\begin{Bmatrix} 0 \\ -P \end{Bmatrix}$$

$$= \left(\frac{l^3}{2EI}\right)\left(\frac{1}{3l^2}\right)\begin{bmatrix} 6 & -3l \\ -3l & 2l^2 \end{bmatrix}\begin{Bmatrix} 0 \\ -P \end{Bmatrix}$$

$$= \begin{Bmatrix} \dfrac{Pl^2}{2EI} \\ \dfrac{-Pl^3}{3EI} \end{Bmatrix}.$$

We conclude that the rotation at the free end is $\frac{Pl^2}{2EI}$ ↻ (clockwise) and the vertical displacement at the free end is $\frac{Pl^3}{3EI}$ ↓ (downward).

10.6 Fixed-End Moments and Fixed-End Shears

In example 10.5, the concentrated load P acted at the node. In the event that loading takes place between the nodes (concentrated force between the nodes, distributed load, etc.), the finite element method does not recognize such loading. Instead, it must be replaced by lumping it at the nodes. This can be done by computing the corresponding fixed-end moments and fixed-end shears for it. Below is a brief table depicting such fixed-end moments and fixed-end shears for some simple forms of loading.

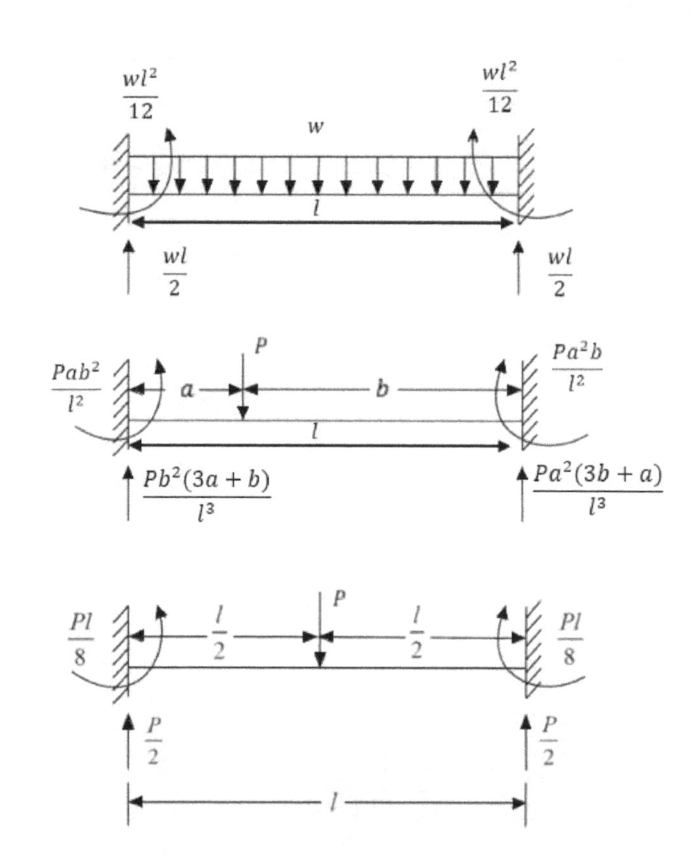

FIGURE 10.32 Fixed-end moments and fixed-end shears for some simple forms of loading

EXAMPLE 10.6

For the statically determinate cantilevered beam shown in **figure 10.33**, compute the vertical deflection and the rotation at the free end. Assume EI to be constant throughout.

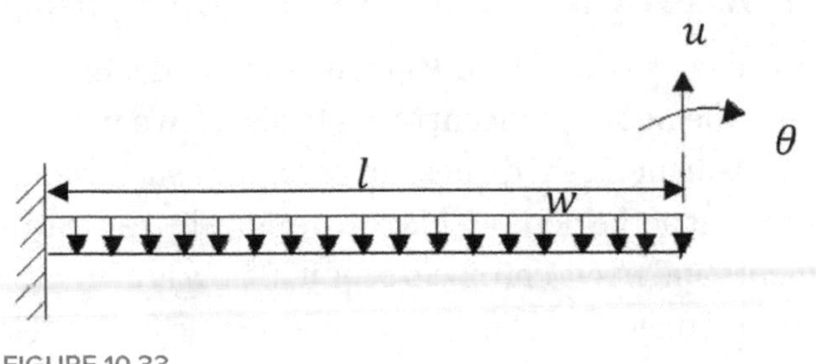

FIGURE 10.33

SOLUTION

The structure can be treated as consisting of one single element. It has two degrees of freedom. Its stiffness matrix is:

$$\frac{2EI}{l^3}\begin{bmatrix} 2l^2 & -3l & l^2 & 3l \\ -3l & 6 & -3l & -6 \\ l^2 & -3l & 2l^2 & 3l \\ 3l & -6 & 3l & 6 \end{bmatrix} \rightarrow \frac{2EI}{l^3}\begin{bmatrix} 2l^2 & 3l \\ 3l & 6 \end{bmatrix} \quad \begin{Bmatrix} \theta \\ u \end{Bmatrix}.$$

The equilibrium equations are:

$$\frac{2EI}{l^3}\begin{bmatrix} 2l^2 & 3l \\ 3l & 6 \end{bmatrix}\begin{Bmatrix} \theta \\ u \end{Bmatrix} = \begin{Bmatrix} -\dfrac{wl^2}{12} \\ -\dfrac{wl}{2} \end{Bmatrix}$$

$$\Rightarrow \qquad \begin{Bmatrix} \theta \\ u \end{Bmatrix} = \frac{l^3}{2EI}\begin{bmatrix} 2l^2 & 3l \\ 3l & 6 \end{bmatrix}^{-1}\begin{Bmatrix} -\dfrac{wl^2}{12} \\ -\dfrac{wl}{2} \end{Bmatrix}$$

$$\Rightarrow \qquad \begin{Bmatrix} \theta \\ u \end{Bmatrix} = \left(\frac{l^3}{2EI}\right)\left(\frac{1}{3l^2}\right)\begin{bmatrix} 6 & -3l \\ -3l & 2l^2 \end{bmatrix}\begin{Bmatrix} -\dfrac{wl^2}{12} \\ -\dfrac{wl}{2} \end{Bmatrix}$$

$$\Rightarrow \qquad \begin{Bmatrix} \theta \\ u \end{Bmatrix} = \begin{Bmatrix} \dfrac{wl^3}{6EI} \\ \dfrac{-wl^4}{8EI} \end{Bmatrix}.$$

We conclude that rotation at the free end is $\frac{wl^3}{6EI}$ ↻ (clockwise), and vertical deflection at the free end is $\frac{wl^4}{8EI}$ ↓ (downward).

EXAMPLE 10.7

For the statically determinate cantilevered beam shown in the figure below, compute the vertical deflection and the rotation at the free end. Assume EI to be constant throughout.

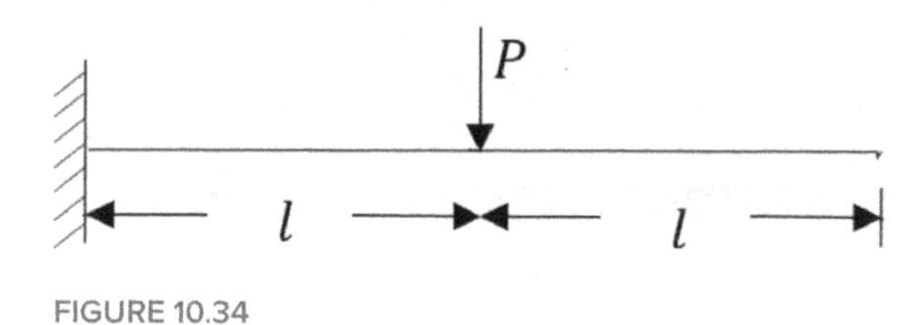

FIGURE 10.34

SOLUTION

The structure can be treated as consistent of one single element. It has two degrees of freedom.

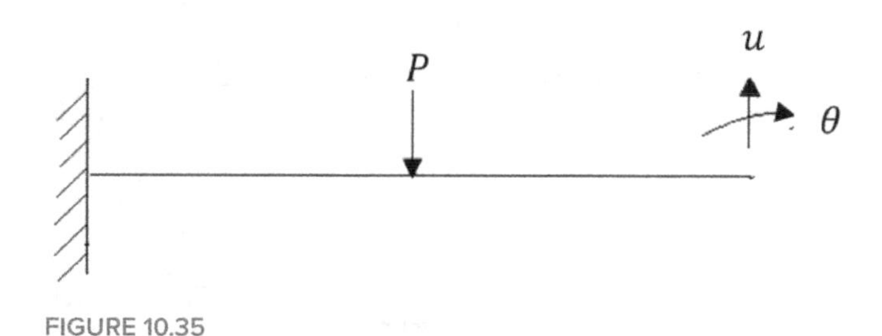

FIGURE 10.35

Its stiffness matrix is:

$$\frac{2EI}{l^3}\begin{bmatrix} 2l^2 & 3l \\ 3l & 6 \end{bmatrix} \qquad \begin{Bmatrix} \theta \\ u \end{Bmatrix}.$$

The equilibrium equations are:

$$\frac{2EI}{l^3}\begin{bmatrix} 2l^2 & 3l \\ 3l & 6 \end{bmatrix}\begin{Bmatrix} \theta \\ u \end{Bmatrix} = \begin{Bmatrix} -\frac{Pl}{8} \\ -\frac{P}{2} \end{Bmatrix}$$

$$\Rightarrow \qquad \theta = \frac{Pl^2}{8EI} \text{ and } u = -\frac{5Pl^3}{48EI}.$$

We conclude that rotation at the free end is $\frac{Pl^2}{8EI}$ ↻ (clockwise), and the vertical deflection at the free end is $\frac{5Pl^3}{48EI}$ ↓ (downward).

It is worth noticing that in example 10.5, example 10.6, and example 10.7, the stiffness matrix is the same, since we are dealing with the same structure but different loadings. For this reason, in the equilibrium equations pertaining to all three examples, the left-hand side of the equations did not change—only the right-hand side (different loading) changed.

10.7 Using the Stiffness Matrix Method in Solving Frame Problems

A frame is a collection of beam elements. In the next two examples, we will illustrate how the stiffness matrix method can be used to solve statically indeterminate frames.

EXAMPLE 10.8

The frame shown in the figure below is statically indeterminate to the first degree. Our objective is to evaluate the horizontal displacement at B, the rotation at B, and the rotation at C. Ignore axial deformation. Assume EI to be constant throughout.

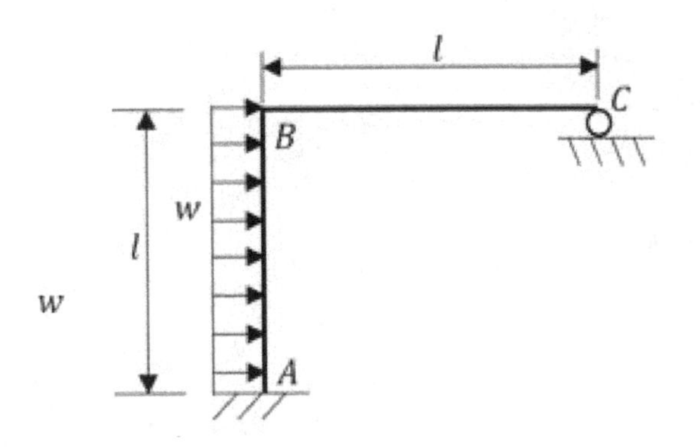

FIGURE 10.36

i. Evaluate the horizontal displacement at B, the rotation at B, and the rotation at C, using the stiffness matrix displacement method.
ii. Redo part (i) using the method of consistent deformations.
iii. Draw the deformed shape of the frame.

SOLUTION

i. The frame can be treated as consisting of two beam elements. Ignoring axial deformation, it has only three degrees of freedom.

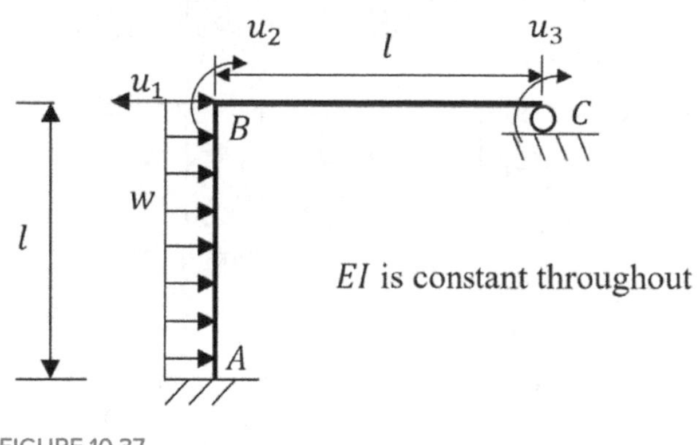

FIGURE 10.37

The stiffness matrix for element AB is:

$$\frac{2EI}{l^3}\begin{bmatrix} 2l^2 & -3l & l^2 & -3l \\ -3l & 6 & -3l & -6 \\ l^2 & -3l & 2l^2 & 3l \\ 3l & -6 & 3l & 6 \end{bmatrix} \rightarrow \frac{2EI}{l^3}\begin{bmatrix} 2l^2 & 3l \\ 3l & 6 \end{bmatrix} \quad \begin{Bmatrix} u_2 \\ u_1 \end{Bmatrix}$$

$$\Rightarrow \quad \frac{2EI}{l^3}\begin{bmatrix} 6 & 3l \\ 3l & 2l^2 \end{bmatrix} \quad \begin{Bmatrix} u_1 \\ u_2 \end{Bmatrix}.$$

The stiffness matrix for element BC is:

$$\frac{2EI}{l^3}\begin{bmatrix} 2l^2 & -3l & l^2 & 3l \\ -3l & 6 & -3l & -6 \\ l^2 & -3l & 2l^2 & 3l \\ 3l & -6 & 3l & 6 \end{bmatrix} \rightarrow \frac{2EI}{l^3}\begin{bmatrix} 2l^2 & l^2 \\ l^2 & 2l^2 \end{bmatrix} \quad \begin{Bmatrix} u_2 \\ u_3 \end{Bmatrix}.$$

The overall stiffness matrix for the entire frame is:

$$\frac{2EI}{l^3}\begin{bmatrix} 6 & 3l & 0 \\ 3l & 4l^2 & l^2 \\ 0 & l^2 & 2l^2 \end{bmatrix} \quad \begin{Bmatrix} u_1 \\ u_2 \\ u_3 \end{Bmatrix}.$$

The equilibrium equations are:

$$\frac{2EI}{l^3}\begin{bmatrix} 6 & 3l & 0 \\ 3l & 4l^2 & l^2 \\ 0 & l^2 & 2l^2 \end{bmatrix}\begin{Bmatrix} u_1 \\ u_2 \\ u_3 \end{Bmatrix} = \begin{Bmatrix} -\dfrac{wl}{2} \\ -\dfrac{wl^2}{12} \\ 0 \end{Bmatrix}$$

$$\Rightarrow \quad \begin{Bmatrix} u_1 \\ u_2 \\ u_3 \end{Bmatrix} = \frac{l^3}{2EI}\begin{bmatrix} 6 & 3l & 0 \\ 3l & 4l^2 & l^2 \\ 0 & l^2 & 2l^2 \end{bmatrix}^{-1} \begin{Bmatrix} -\dfrac{wl}{2} \\ -\dfrac{wl^2}{12} \\ 0 \end{Bmatrix}$$

$$\Rightarrow \quad \begin{Bmatrix} u_1 \\ u_2 \\ u_3 \end{Bmatrix} = \left(\frac{l^3}{2EI}\right)\left(\frac{1}{24l^4}\right)\begin{bmatrix} 7l^4 & -6l^3 & 3l^3 \\ -6l^3 & 12l^2 & -6l^2 \\ 3l^3 & -6l^2 & 15l^2 \end{bmatrix} \begin{Bmatrix} -\dfrac{wl}{2} \\ -\dfrac{wl^2}{12} \\ 0 \end{Bmatrix}$$

$$u_1 = -\frac{wl^4}{16EI};\ u_2 = \frac{wl^3}{24EI};\ u_3 = -\frac{wl^3}{48EI}.$$

Therefore, we conclude that the horizontal displacement at *B* is $\frac{wl^4}{16EI}$ → (to the right), the rotation at *B* is $\frac{wl^3}{24EI}$ ↻ (clockwise), and the rotation at *C* is: $\frac{wl^3}{48EI}$ ↺ (counterclockwise).

ii.

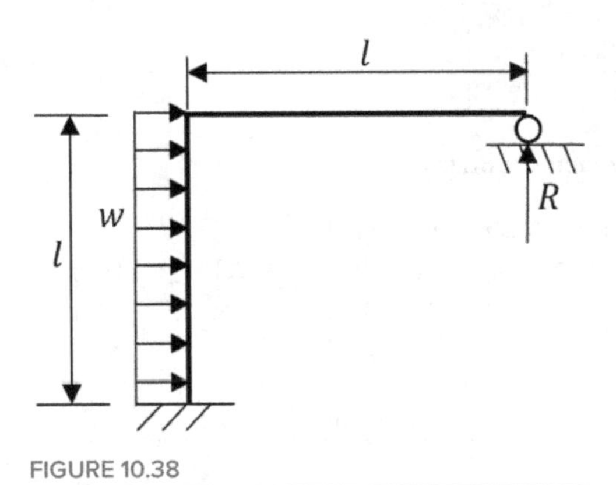

FIGURE 10.38

The frame is statically indeterminate to the first degree. Let the vertical reaction at roller C, R to be the redundant.

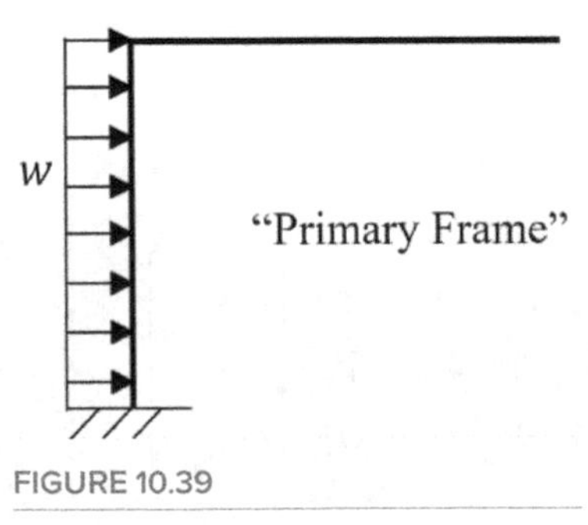

FIGURE 10.39

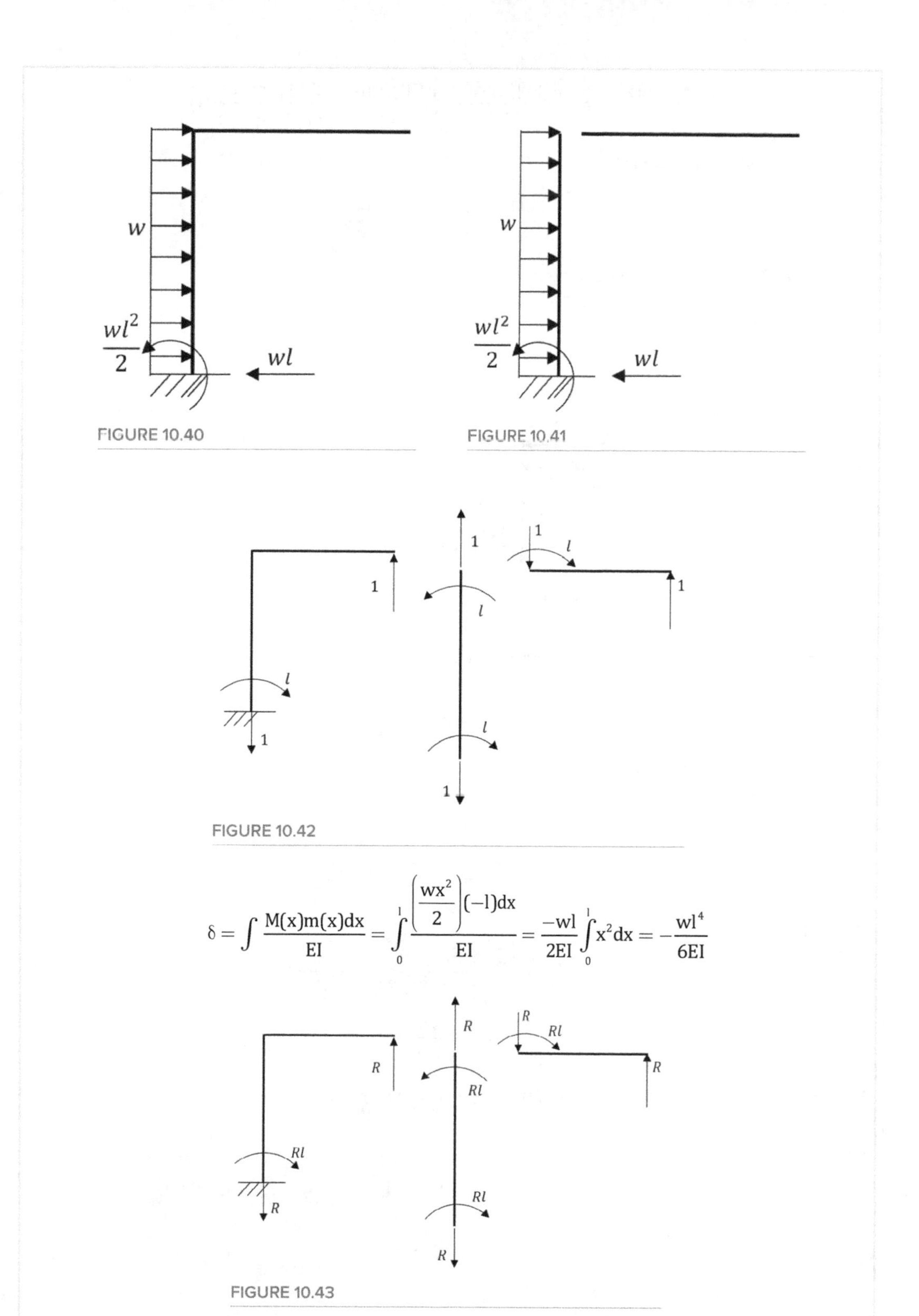

FIGURE 10.40

FIGURE 10.41

FIGURE 10.42

$$\delta = \int \frac{M(x)m(x)dx}{EI} = \int_0^l \frac{\left(\frac{wx^2}{2}\right)(-l)dx}{EI} = \frac{-wl}{2EI}\int_0^l x^2 dx = -\frac{wl^4}{6EI}$$

FIGURE 10.43

$$\delta = \int \frac{M(x)m(x)dx}{EI} = \int_0^l \frac{(Rx)(x)dx}{EI} + \int_0^l \frac{(Rl)(l)dx}{EI} = \frac{R}{EI}\left(\frac{1}{3}l^3\right) + \frac{Rl^2}{EI}(l) = \frac{4Rl^3}{3EI}$$

The compatibility equation is:

$$\frac{4Rl^3}{3EI} = \frac{wl^4}{6EI} \Rightarrow R = \frac{wl}{8}.$$

The remaining reactions can be determined using statics.

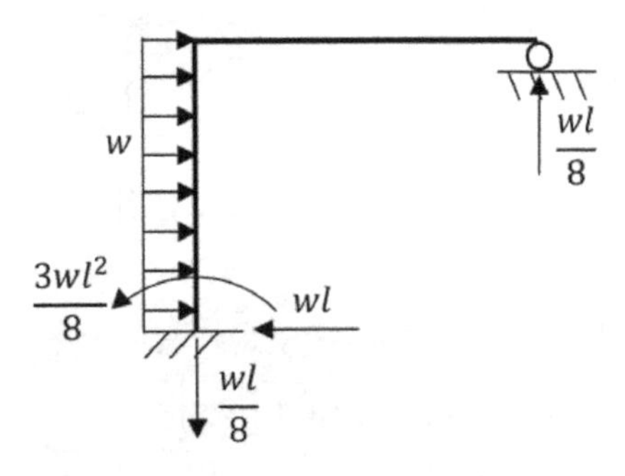

FIGURE 10.44

The differential equation describing the elastic curve in element AB is:

$$EIy'' = M(x) = wlx - \frac{3wl^2}{8} - \frac{wx^2}{2}$$

$$\Rightarrow \quad EIy' = wl\frac{x^2}{2} - \frac{3wl^2}{8}x - \frac{wx^3}{6}$$

$$\Rightarrow \quad EIy = wl\frac{x^3}{6} - \frac{3wl^2x^2}{16} - \frac{wx^4}{24}.$$

At $x = l$:

$$EIy = \frac{wl^4}{6} - \frac{3wl^4}{16} - \frac{wl^4}{24} = -\frac{wl^4}{16}$$

$$\Rightarrow \quad y = -\frac{wl^4}{16EI}.$$

Therefore, horizontal displacement of B is: $\frac{wl^4}{16EI} \rightarrow$ (to the right).

At $x = l$:

$$EIy' = \frac{wl^3}{2} - \frac{3wl^3}{8} - \frac{wl^3}{6} = -\frac{wl^3}{24}$$

$$\Rightarrow \quad y' = -\frac{wl^3}{24EI}.$$

Therefore, rotation at B is $\frac{wl^3}{24EI}$ ↻ (clockwise).

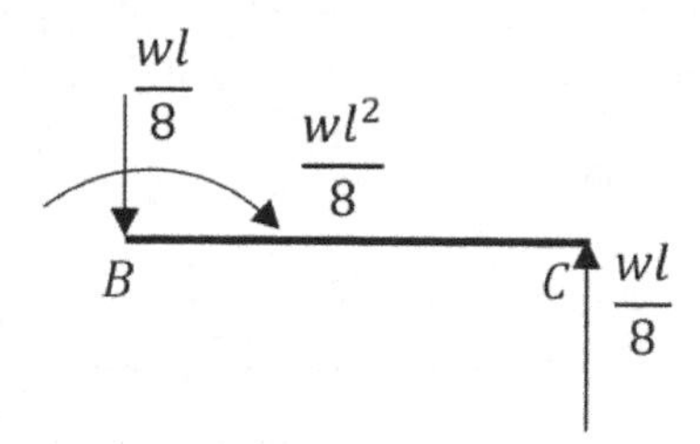

FIGURE 10.45

The differential equation describing the elastic curve of the BC element is:

$$EIy'' = M(x) = \frac{wl^2}{8} - \frac{wl}{8}x$$

$$\Rightarrow \quad EIy' = \frac{wl^2}{8}x - \frac{wl}{16}x^2 - \frac{wl^3}{24}$$

$$EIy = \frac{wl^2}{16}x^2 - \frac{wl}{48}x^3 - \frac{wl^3}{24}x.$$

At $x = l$:

$$EIy' = \frac{wl^3}{8} - \frac{wl^3}{16} - \frac{wl^3}{24} = \frac{wl^3}{48}$$

$$\Rightarrow \quad y' = \frac{wl^3}{48EI}.$$

We conclude that the rotation at C is $\frac{wl^3}{48EI}$ ↺ (counterclockwise).

The above results are identical to the ones obtained in method (i). It is also interesting that at $x = 1$ for the BC element, $EIy = \frac{wl^4}{16} - \frac{wl^4}{48} - \frac{wl^4}{24} = 0$ as predicted.

iii.

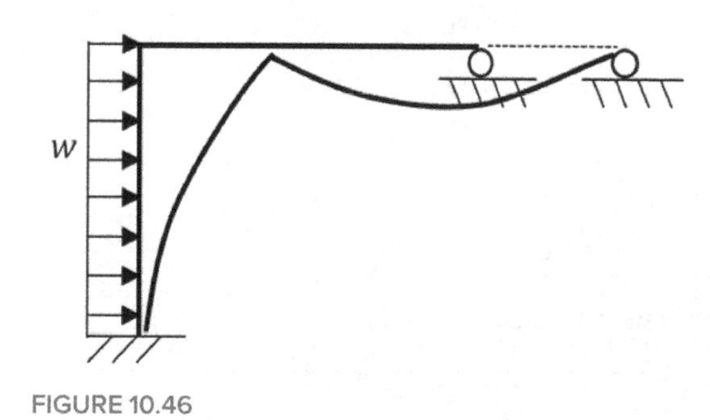

FIGURE 10.46

EXAMPLE 10.9

The frame shown in the figure below is second statically indeterminate to the second degree. Our objective is to evaluate the rotation at B and the rotation at C. Ignore axial deformation. Assume EI to be constant throughout.

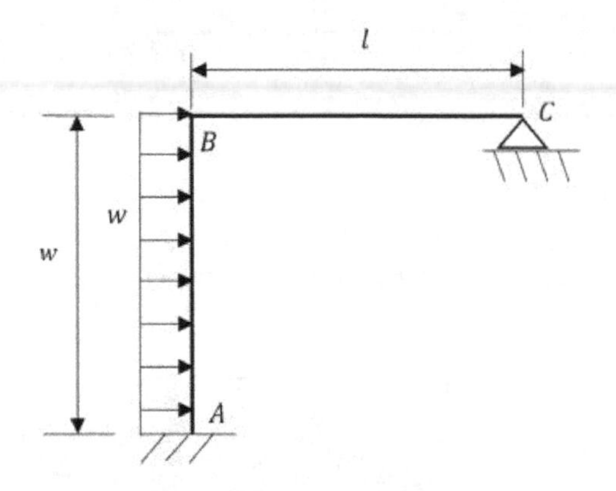

FIGURE 10.47

i. Evaluate the rotation at B and the rotation at C using the stiffness matrix displacement method.
ii. Redo part (i) using the method of consistent deformations.
iii. Draw the deformed shape of the frame.

SOLUTION

i. The frame can be treated as consistent of two beam elements. Ignoring axial deformation, it has only two degrees of freedom.

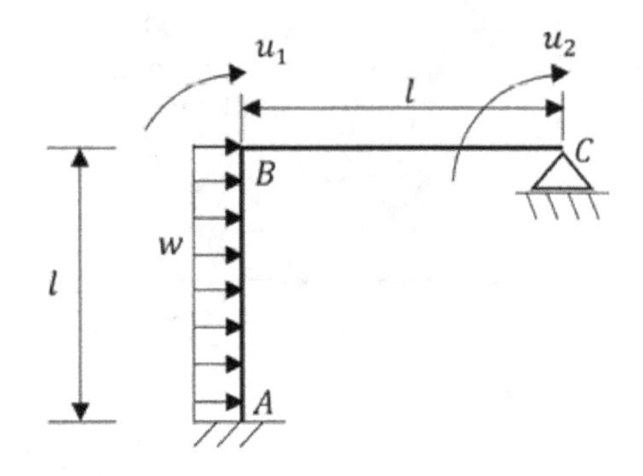

FIGURE 10.48

The stiffness matrix for element AB is:

$$\frac{2EI}{l^3}\begin{bmatrix} 2l^2 & -3l & l^2 & 3l \\ -3l & 6 & -3l & -6 \\ l^2 & -3l & 2l^2 & 3l \\ 3l & -6 & 3l & 6 \end{bmatrix} \rightarrow \frac{2EI}{l^3}\left[2l^2\right] \qquad \left\{u_1\right\}.$$

The stiffness matrix for element BC is:

$$\frac{2EI}{l^3}\begin{bmatrix} 2l^2 & -3l & l^2 & 3l \\ -3l & 6 & -3l & -6 \\ l^2 & -3l & 2l^2 & 3l \\ 3l & -6 & 3l & 6 \end{bmatrix} \rightarrow \frac{2EI}{l^3}\begin{bmatrix} 2l^2 & l^2 \\ l^2 & 2l^2 \end{bmatrix} \qquad \begin{Bmatrix} u_1 \\ u_2 \end{Bmatrix}.$$

The overall stiffness matrix for the frame is:

$$\frac{2EI}{l^3}\begin{bmatrix} 4l^2 & l^2 \\ l^2 & 2l^2 \end{bmatrix} \qquad \begin{Bmatrix} u_1 \\ u_2 \end{Bmatrix}.$$

The equilibrium equations are:

$$\frac{2EI}{l}\begin{bmatrix} 4 & 1 \\ 1 & 2 \end{bmatrix}\begin{Bmatrix} u_1 \\ u_2 \end{Bmatrix} = \begin{Bmatrix} -\dfrac{wl^2}{12} \\ 0 \end{Bmatrix}$$

$$\Rightarrow \qquad \begin{Bmatrix} u_1 \\ u_2 \end{Bmatrix} = \frac{1}{2EI}\begin{bmatrix} 4 & 1 \\ 1 & 2 \end{bmatrix}^{-1}\begin{Bmatrix} -\dfrac{wl^2}{12} \\ 0 \end{Bmatrix}$$

$$\Rightarrow \qquad \begin{Bmatrix} u_1 \\ u_2 \end{Bmatrix} = \begin{Bmatrix} \dfrac{-wl^3}{84EI} \\ \dfrac{wl^3}{168EI} \end{Bmatrix}.$$

We conclude that the rotation at B is $\frac{wl^3}{84EI}$ ↺ (counterclockwise), and the rotation at C is $\frac{wl^3}{168EI}$ ↻ (clockwise).

ii.

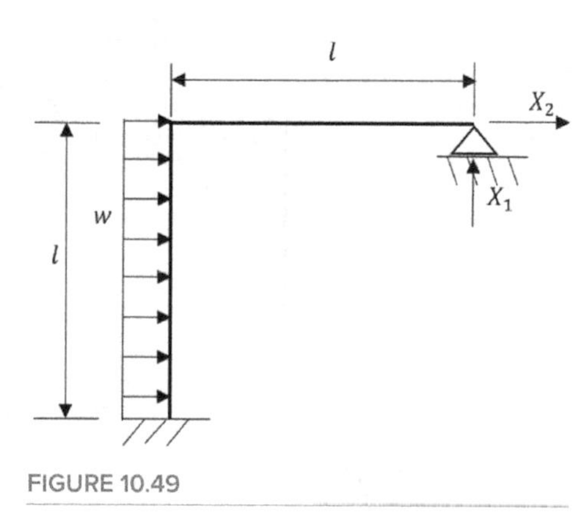

FIGURE 10.49

The frame is statically indeterminate to the second degree. Let X_1, the vertical reaction at the pin and X_2, the horizontal reaction at the pin be the two redundants.

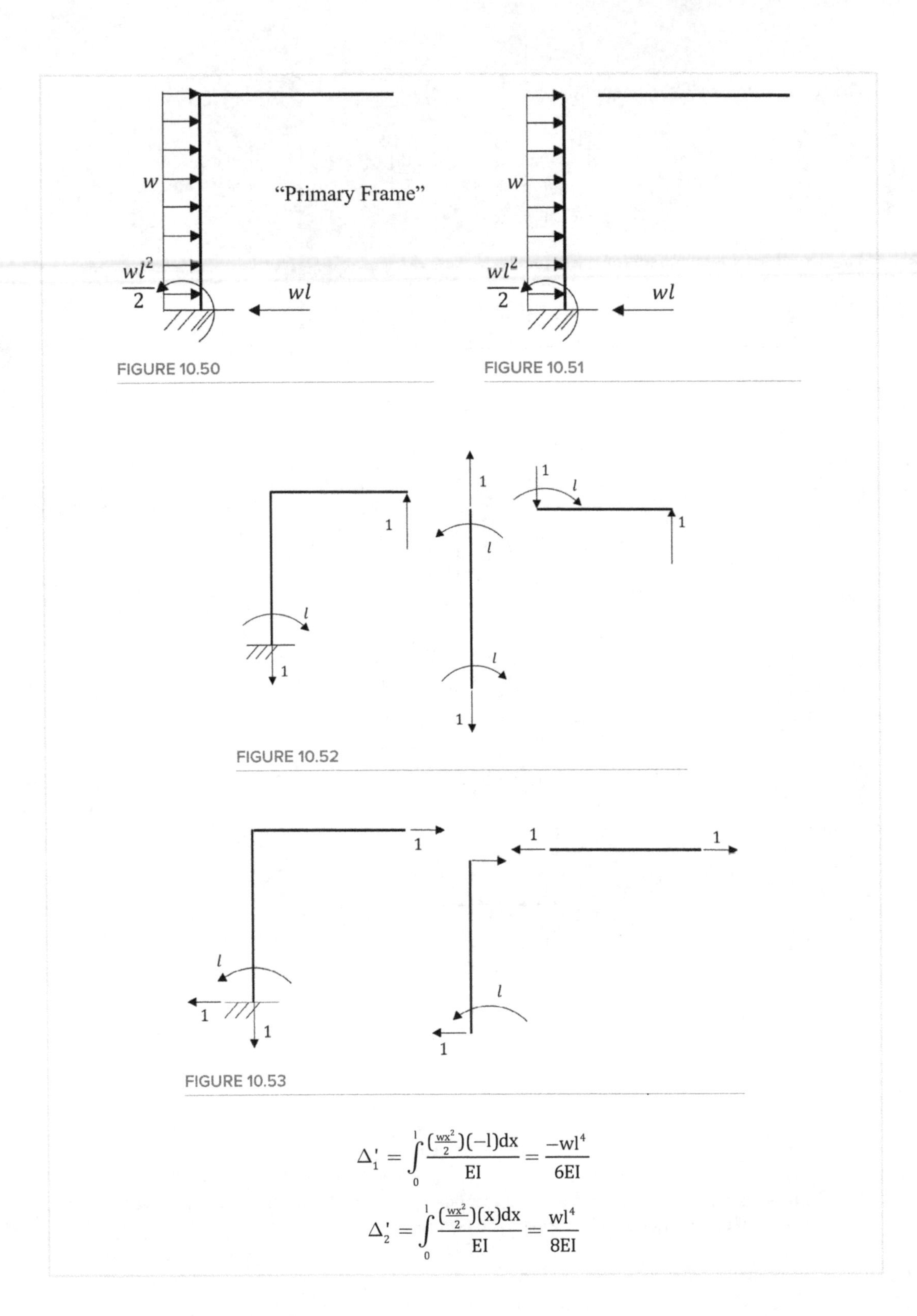

FIGURE 10.50

FIGURE 10.51

FIGURE 10.52

FIGURE 10.53

$$\Delta_1' = \int_0^l \frac{\left(\frac{wx^2}{2}\right)(-l)dx}{EI} = \frac{-wl^4}{6EI}$$

$$\Delta_2' = \int_0^l \frac{\left(\frac{wx^2}{2}\right)(x)dx}{EI} = \frac{wl^4}{8EI}$$

$$\delta_{11} = \int_0^l \frac{x^2 dx}{EI} + \int_0^l \frac{l^2 dx}{EI} = \frac{4l^3}{3EI}$$

$$\delta_{22} = \int_0^l \frac{x^2 dx}{EI} = \frac{l^3}{3EI}$$

$$\delta_{12} = \delta_{21} = \int_0^l \frac{(x)(-l)dx}{EI} = -\frac{l^3}{2EI}$$

$$\left[\delta_{ij}\right] = \begin{bmatrix} \delta_{11} & \delta_{12} \\ \delta_{21} & \delta_{22} \end{bmatrix} = \begin{bmatrix} \frac{4l^3}{3EI} & \frac{-l^3}{2EI} \\ \frac{-l^3}{2EI} & \frac{l^3}{3EI} \end{bmatrix}$$

$[\delta_{ij}]$ is a (2×2) real symmetric matrix called the flexibility matrix.

The compatibility equations are:

$$\left[\delta_{ij}\right]\left\{X_i\right\} + \left\{\Delta_i'\right\} = \left\{0\right\}$$

$$\Rightarrow \quad \begin{bmatrix} \frac{4l^3}{3EI} & \frac{-l^3}{2EI} \\ \frac{-l^3}{2EI} & \frac{l^3}{3EI} \end{bmatrix} \begin{Bmatrix} X_1 \\ X_2 \end{Bmatrix} + \begin{Bmatrix} \frac{-wl^4}{6EI} \\ \frac{wl^4}{8EI} \end{Bmatrix} = \begin{Bmatrix} 0 \\ 0 \end{Bmatrix}$$

$$\Rightarrow \quad \frac{l^3}{6EI} \begin{bmatrix} 8 & -3 \\ -3 & 2 \end{bmatrix} \begin{Bmatrix} X_1 \\ X_2 \end{Bmatrix} = \begin{Bmatrix} \frac{wl^4}{6EI} \\ \frac{-wl^4}{8EI} \end{Bmatrix}$$

$$\Rightarrow \quad \begin{Bmatrix} X_1 \\ X_2 \end{Bmatrix} = \frac{6EI}{l^3} \begin{bmatrix} 8 & -3 \\ -3 & 2 \end{bmatrix}^{-1} \begin{Bmatrix} \frac{wl^4}{6EI} \\ \frac{-wl^4}{8EI} \end{Bmatrix} = \left(\frac{6EI}{l^3}\right)\left(\frac{1}{7}\right) \begin{bmatrix} 2 & 3 \\ 3 & 8 \end{bmatrix} \begin{Bmatrix} \frac{wl^4}{6EI} \\ \frac{-wl^4}{8EI} \end{Bmatrix}$$

$$= \begin{Bmatrix} \frac{-wl}{28} \\ \frac{-3wl}{7} \end{Bmatrix}.$$

Therefore,

$$X_1 = -\frac{wl}{28} \text{ and } X_2 = -\frac{3wl}{7}.$$

The remaining reactions can be obtained from statics.

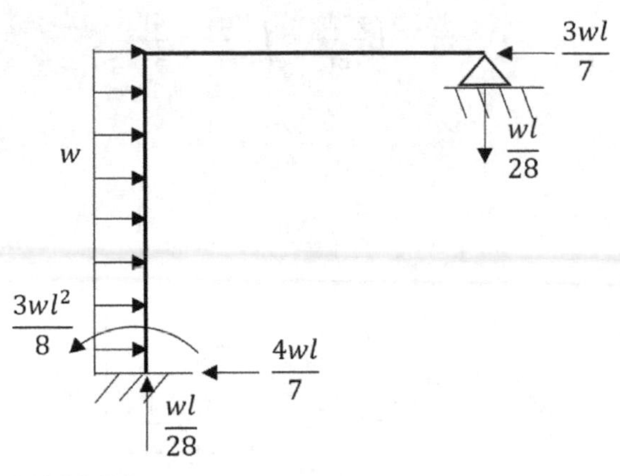

FIGURE 10.54

The differential equation describing the elastic curve of element AB is:

$$EIy'' = M(x)$$

$$\Rightarrow \quad EIy'' = \frac{4wl}{7}x - \frac{3wl^2}{28} - \frac{wx^2}{2}$$

$$\Rightarrow \quad EIy' = \frac{2wlx^2}{7} - \frac{3wl^2x}{28} - \frac{wx^3}{6}$$

$$\Rightarrow \quad EIy = \frac{2wlx^3}{21} - \frac{3wl^2x^2}{56} - \frac{wx^4}{24}.$$

At x = l:

$$\Rightarrow \quad EIy' = \frac{2}{7}wl^3 - \frac{3wl^3}{28} - \frac{wl^3}{6} = \frac{wl^3}{84}$$

$$\Rightarrow \quad y' = \frac{wl^3}{84EI}.$$

We conclude that the rotation at B is $\frac{wl^3}{84EI}$ ↺ (counterclockwise).

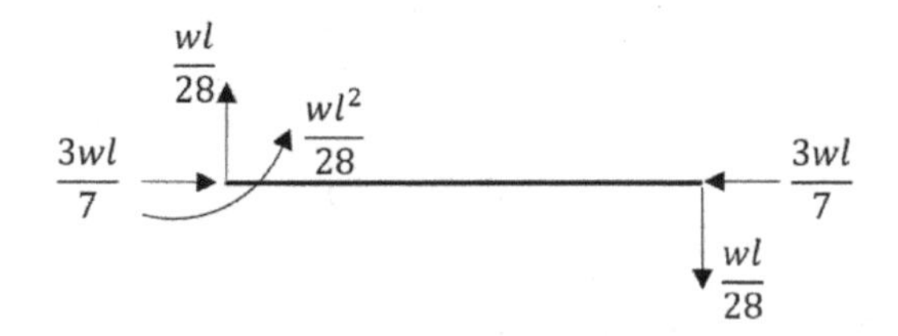

FIGURE 10.55 Member BC

The differential equation describing the elastic curve of element BC is:

$$EIy'' = M(x)$$

$$\Rightarrow \qquad EIy'' = \frac{wl}{28}x - \frac{wl^2}{28}$$

$$\Rightarrow \qquad EIy' = \frac{wlx^2}{56} - \frac{wl^2x}{28} + \frac{wl^3}{84}.$$

At $x = l$:

$$\Rightarrow \qquad EIy' = \frac{wl^3}{56} - \frac{wl^3}{28} + \frac{wl^3}{84} = -\frac{wl^3}{168}$$

$$\Rightarrow \qquad y' = -\frac{wl^3}{168EI}.$$

We conclude that the rotation at C is $\frac{wl^3}{168EI}$ ↻ (clockwise).

The results obtained in method (ii) are identical to the results obtained in method (i).

Notice that if we compute EIy in member BC, we obtain:

$$EIy = \frac{wlx^3}{168} - \frac{wl^2x^2}{56} + \frac{wl^3x}{84}.$$

At $x = l$:

$$EIy = \frac{wl^4}{168} - \frac{wl^4}{56} + \frac{wl^4}{84} = 0 \text{ (as predicted)}.$$

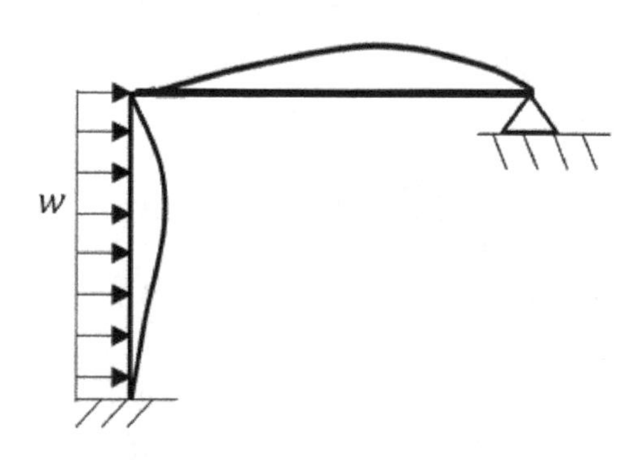

FIGURE 10.56

10.8 Stiffness Matrix for a Beam–Bar Element

The (2×2) stiffness matrix for a bar element and the (4×4) stiffness matrix for a beam element can be combined into a (6×6) stiffness matrix for a beam–bar element:

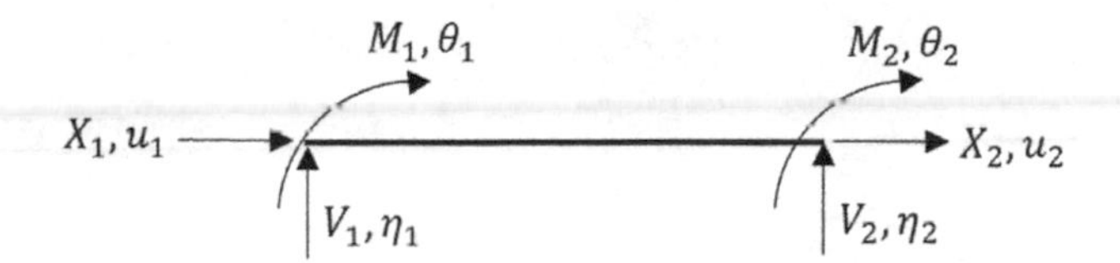

FIGURE 10.57

$$\begin{Bmatrix} M_1 \\ V_1 \\ X_1 \\ M_2 \\ V_2 \\ X_2 \end{Bmatrix} = E \begin{bmatrix} \frac{4I}{l} & -\frac{6I}{l^2} & 0 & \frac{2I}{l} & \frac{6I}{l^2} & 0 \\ -\frac{6I}{l^2} & \frac{12I}{l^3} & 0 & -\frac{6I}{l^2} & -\frac{12I}{l^3} & 0 \\ 0 & 0 & \frac{A}{l} & 0 & 0 & -\frac{A}{l} \\ \frac{2I}{l} & -\frac{6I}{l^2} & 0 & \frac{4I}{l} & \frac{6I}{l^2} & 0 \\ \frac{6I}{l^2} & -\frac{12I}{l^3} & 0 & \frac{6I}{l^2} & \frac{12I}{l^3} & 0 \\ 0 & 0 & -\frac{A}{l} & 0 & 0 & \frac{A}{l} \end{bmatrix} \begin{Bmatrix} \theta_1 \\ \eta_1 \\ u_1 \\ \theta_2 \\ \eta_2 \\ u_2 \end{Bmatrix}$$

or

$$\begin{Bmatrix} M_1 \\ V_1 \\ X_1 \\ M_2 \\ V_2 \\ X_2 \end{Bmatrix} = \frac{E}{l} \begin{bmatrix} 4I & -\frac{6I}{l} & 0 & 2I & \frac{6I}{l} & 0 \\ -\frac{6I}{l} & \frac{12I}{l^2} & 0 & -\frac{6I}{l} & -\frac{12I}{l^2} & 0 \\ 0 & 0 & A & 0 & 0 & -A \\ 2I & -\frac{6I}{l} & 0 & 4I & \frac{6I}{l} & 0 \\ \frac{6I}{l} & -\frac{12I}{l^2} & 0 & \frac{6I}{l} & \frac{12I}{l^2} & 0 \\ 0 & 0 & -A & 0 & 0 & A \end{bmatrix} \begin{Bmatrix} \theta_1 \\ \eta_1 \\ u_1 \\ \theta_2 \\ \eta_2 \\ u_2 \end{Bmatrix}$$

(6×1) $\qquad$ (6×6) $\qquad$ (6×1).

10.9 Development of a Plane Stress Element

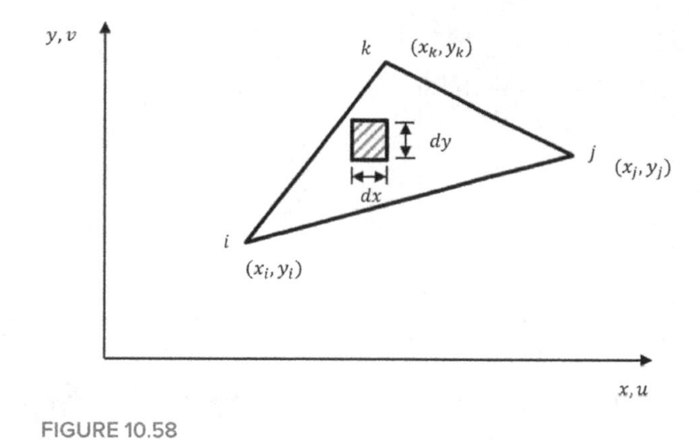

FIGURE 10.58

For plane stress, $\sigma_z = \tau_{xz} = \tau_{yz} = 0$

$$\Rightarrow \qquad \begin{Bmatrix} \sigma_x \\ \sigma_y \\ \tau_{xy} \end{Bmatrix} = \frac{E}{1-\nu^2} \begin{bmatrix} 1 & \nu & 0 \\ \nu & 1 & 0 \\ 0 & 0 & \frac{1-\nu}{2} \end{bmatrix} \begin{Bmatrix} \varepsilon_x \\ \varepsilon_y \\ \gamma_{xy} \end{Bmatrix},$$

which can be written as:

$$\{\sigma\} = [\bar{K}]\{\varepsilon\},$$

where

$$[\bar{K}] = \frac{E}{1-\nu^2} \begin{bmatrix} 1 & \nu & 0 \\ \nu & 1 & 0 \\ 0 & 0 & \frac{1-\nu}{2} \end{bmatrix}$$

$$\{\sigma\} = [B]\,\{d\}$$

$$(3\times 1) \quad (3\times 6) \quad (6\times 1)$$

$$u = c_1 + c_2 x + c_3 y$$

$$v = c_4 + c_5 x + c_6 y$$

$$u_i = c_1 + c_2 x_i + c_3 y_i$$

$$u_j = c_1 + c_2 x_j + c_3 y_j$$

$$u_k = c_1 + c_2 x_k + c_3 y_k$$

or

$$\begin{Bmatrix} u_i \\ u_j \\ u_k \end{Bmatrix} = \begin{bmatrix} 1 & x_i & y_i \\ 1 & x_j & y_j \\ 1 & x_k & y_k \end{bmatrix} \begin{Bmatrix} c_1 \\ c_2 \\ c_3 \end{Bmatrix}$$

$$\Rightarrow \quad \begin{Bmatrix} c_1 \\ c_2 \\ c_3 \end{Bmatrix} = \frac{1}{2A} \begin{bmatrix} x_j y_k - x_k y_j & x_k y_i - x_i y_k & x_i y_j - x_j y_i \\ y_j - y_k & y_k - y_i & y_i - y_j \\ x_k - x_j & x_i - x_k & x_j - x_i \end{bmatrix} \begin{Bmatrix} u_i \\ u_j \\ u_k \end{Bmatrix}$$

$$\Rightarrow \quad u = \frac{1}{2A}\Big\{\big[(x_j y_k - x_k y_j) + (y_j - y_k)x + (x_k - x_j)y\big]u_i$$
$$+\big[(x_k y_i - x_i y_k) + (y_k - y_i)x + (x_i - x_k)y\big]u_j$$
$$+\big[(x_i y_j - x_j y_i) + (y_i - y_j)x + (x_j - x_i)y\big]u_k\Big\}.$$

Similarly, we obtain

$$\Rightarrow \quad v = \frac{1}{2A}\Big\{\big[(x_j y_k - x_k y_j) + (y_j - y_k)x + (x_k - x_j)y\big]v_i$$
$$+\big[(x_k y_i - x_i y_k) + (y_k - y_i)x + (x_i - x_k)y\big]v_j$$
$$+\big[(x_i y_j - x_j y_i) + (y_i - y_j)x + (x_j - x_i)y\big]v_k\Big\}$$

$$\varepsilon_x = \frac{\partial u}{\partial x}; \quad \varepsilon_y = \frac{\partial v}{\partial y}; \quad \gamma_{xy} = \frac{\partial u}{\partial y} + \frac{\partial v}{\partial x}$$

$$\Rightarrow \quad \begin{Bmatrix} \varepsilon_x \\ \varepsilon_y \\ \gamma_{xy} \end{Bmatrix} = \frac{1}{2A} \begin{bmatrix} y_j - y_k & y_k - y_i & y_i - y_j & 0 & 0 & 0 \\ 0 & 0 & 0 & x_k - x_j & x_i - x_k & x_j - x_i \\ x_k - x_j & x_i - x_k & x_j - x_i & y_j - y_k & y_k - y_i & y_i - y_j \end{bmatrix} \begin{Bmatrix} u_i \\ u_j \\ u_k \\ v_i \\ v_j \\ v_k \end{Bmatrix}$$

or

$$\{\varepsilon\} = [B]\{d\}.$$

Finally, we obtain:

$$\underset{(6 \times 6)}{[K]} = At \underset{(6 \times 3)}{[B]^T} \underset{(3 \times 3)}{[\bar{K}]} \underset{(3 \times 6)}{[B]}$$

and

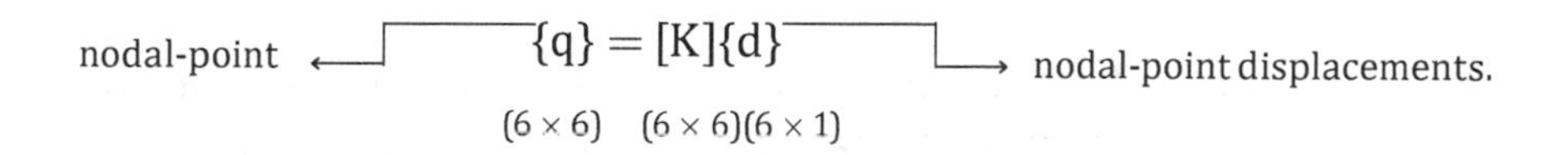

[K] is the (6 × 6) stiffness matrix.

Problems

10.1. The structure shown below is statically indeterminate. Compute the axial displacement of C and the axial displacement of D. Portion CD has a cross section area A, while both AC and DB have a cross section area 3A. Assume E to be constant throughout.

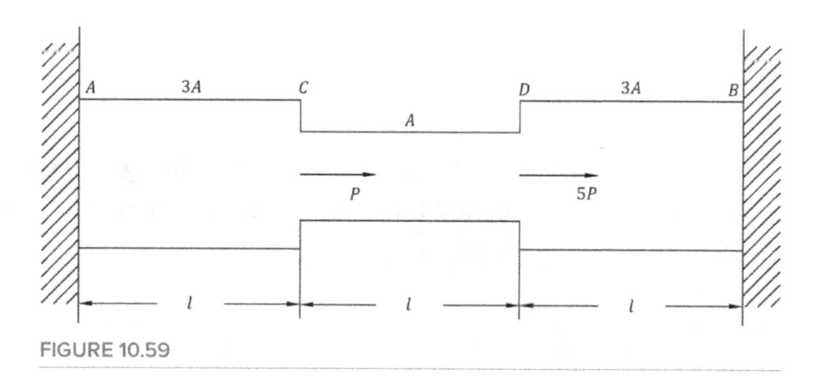

FIGURE 10.59

10.2. The structure shown below is statically indeterminate. Compute the axial displacement of C. Portion CB has a cross section area A, while portion AC has a cross section area 2A. Assume E to be constant throughout.

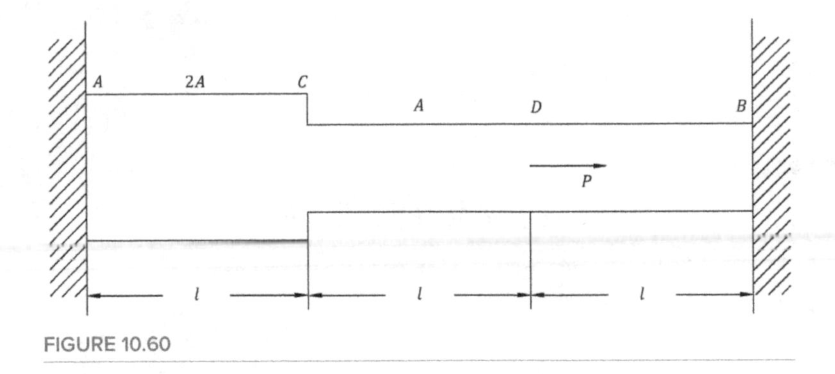

FIGURE 10.60

10.3. Compute the horizontal displacement and the vertical displacement of the free node D in the truss shown in the figure below. Assume AE to be constant throughout.

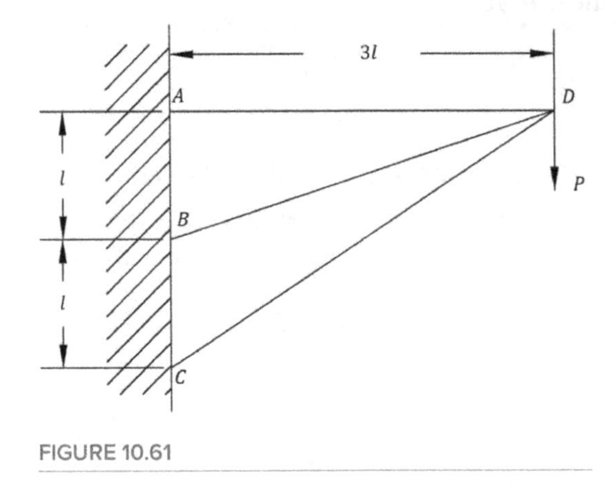

FIGURE 10.61

10.4. For the statically indeterminate plane truss shown in the figure below, compute the horizontal displacement and the vertical displacement of joint A. Assume that AE is constant throughout.

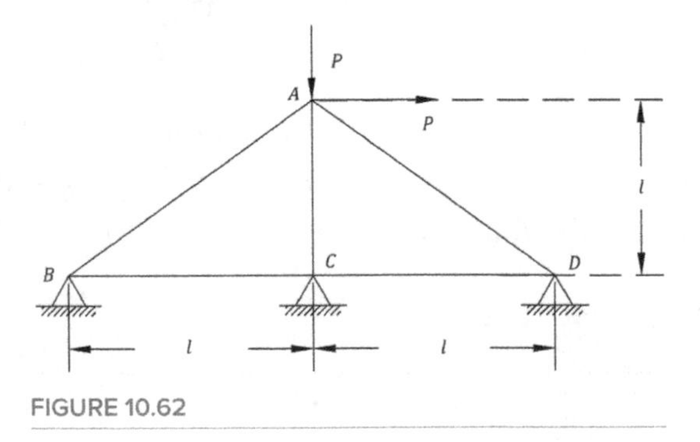

FIGURE 10.62

10.5. Determine the (2×2) stiffness matrix [K] for the statically indeterminate plane truss shown in the figure below. For each member, assume $A = 1 \text{ in}^2$ and $E = 30{,}000\ ksi$. Express your answer in Kips / in.

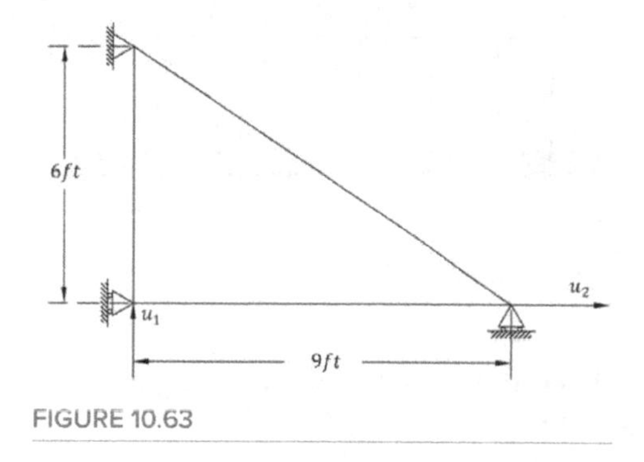

FIGURE 10.63

10.6. The statically determinate truss shown in the figure below has three degrees of freedom. Establish the (3×3) stiffness matrix for the truss. Assume that all three members have the same AE.

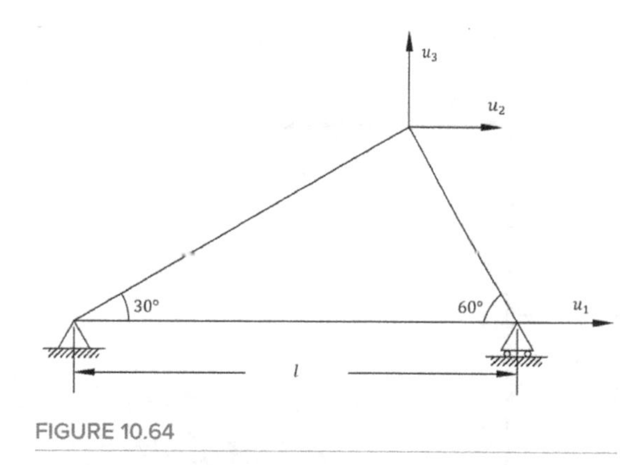

FIGURE 10.64

10.7. For the statically indeterminate beam shown in the figure below, compute the vertical displacement at C. Assume EI to be constant throughout.

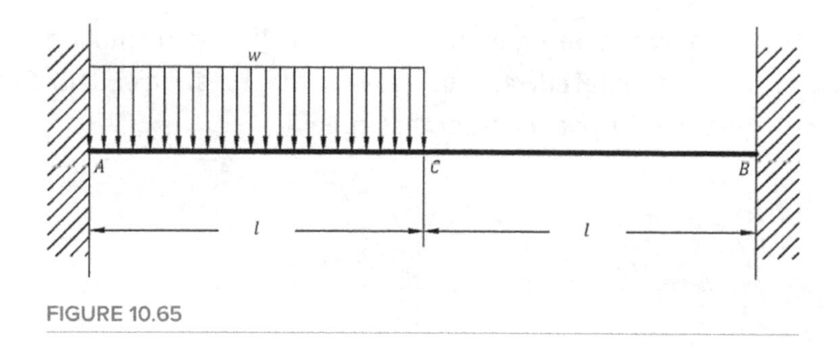

FIGURE 10.65

10.8. For the statically indeterminate beam shown in **figure 10.66**, compute the vertical displacement and rotation at midspan point. Assume EI to be constant throughout.

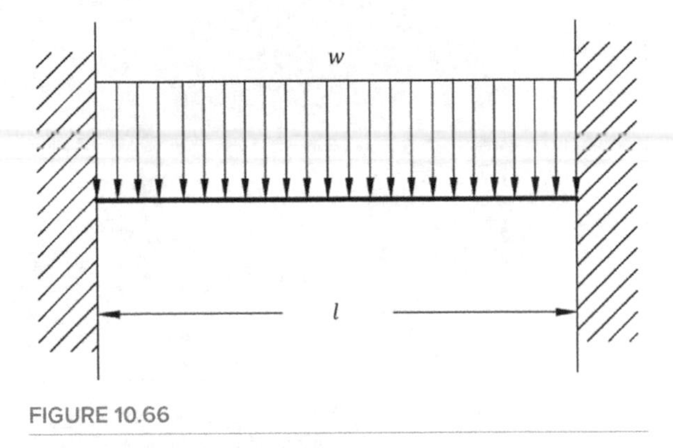

FIGURE 10.66

10.9. The frame shown in the figure below is statically indeterminate to the first degree. Ignoring axial effect, it has three degrees of freedom. Determine u_1, u_2, and u_3. Assume EI to be constant throughout.

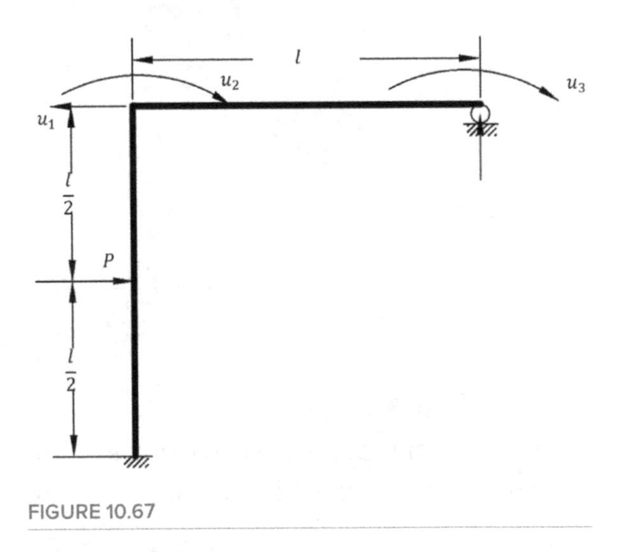

FIGURE 10.67

10.10. The frame shown in the figure below is statically indeterminate to the second degree. Ignoring axial effect, it has only two degrees of freedom. Determine u_1 and u_2. Assume *EI* to be constant throughout.

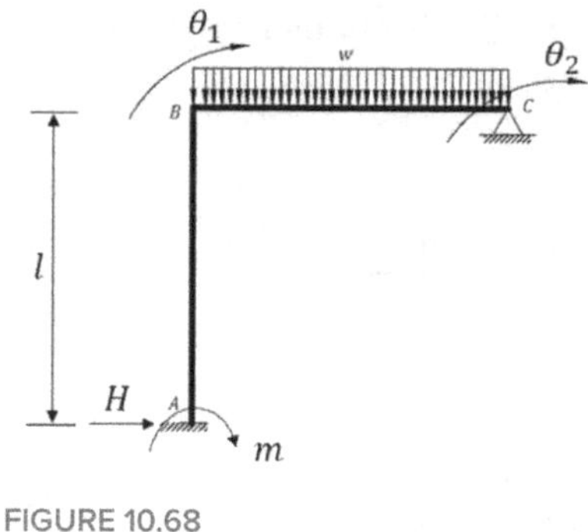

FIGURE 10.68

10.11. The frame shown in the figure below is statically indeterminate to the third degree. Ignoring axial effect, determine the reactions at A and B. Assume EI to be constant throughout.

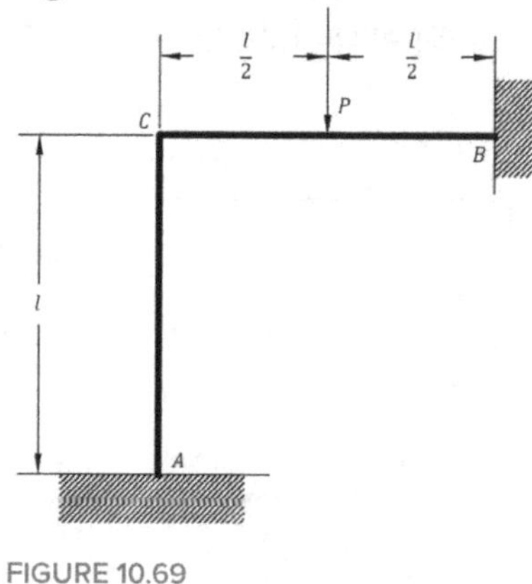

FIGURE 10.69

10.12. The frame shown in the figure below is statically indeterminate to the second degree. Compute the reactions at the supports. Ignore axial deformation. Assume EI to be constant throughout.

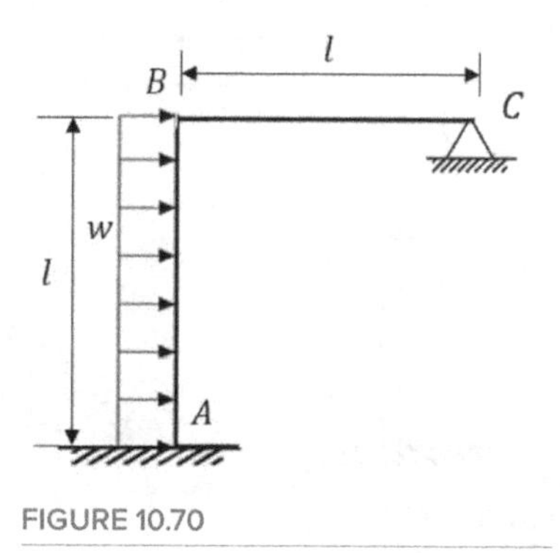

FIGURE 10.70

10.13. The structure shown in the figure below consists of two solid cylinders. It is fixed at both ends A and C. It is subject to a twisting moment T at B. Compute the angle of twist ϕ at B. Assume G to be constant throughout (the same material).

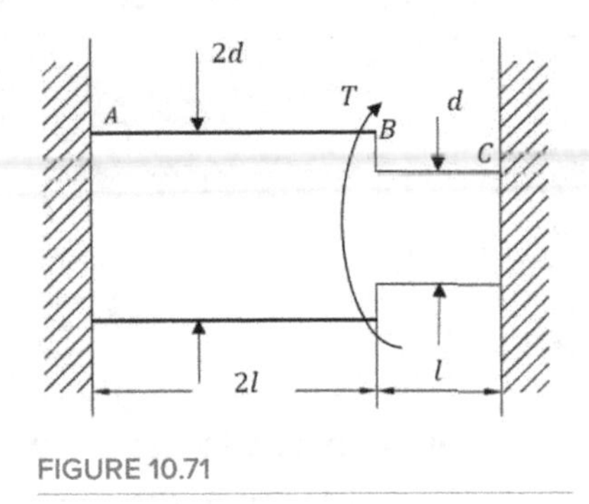

FIGURE 10.71

10.14. For the statically indeterminate frame shown in the figure below, compute the reactions at the supports. Ignore axial deformation. Assume EI to be constant throughout.

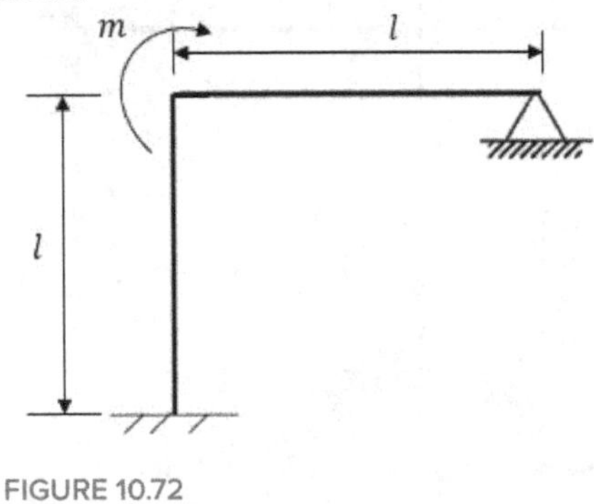

FIGURE 10.72

10.15. For the statically indeterminate frame shown in the figure below and ignoring axial effect, determine the reactions at A and C. Assume EI to be constant throughout.

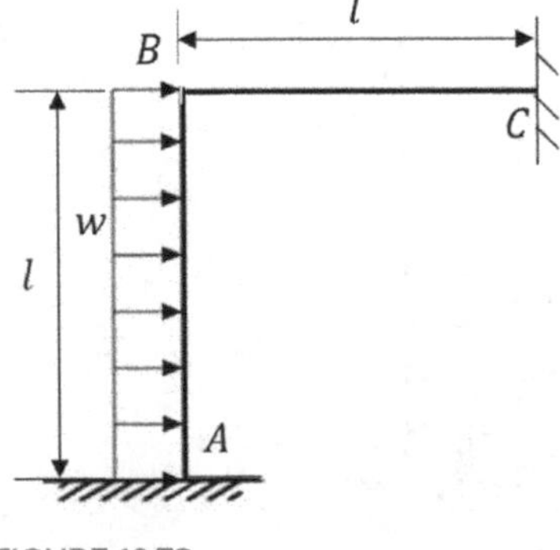

FIGURE 10.73

10.16. For the statically indeterminate plane frame shown in the figure below, compute all the reactions at supports A and D. Ignore axial deformation. Assume that EI is constant throughout.

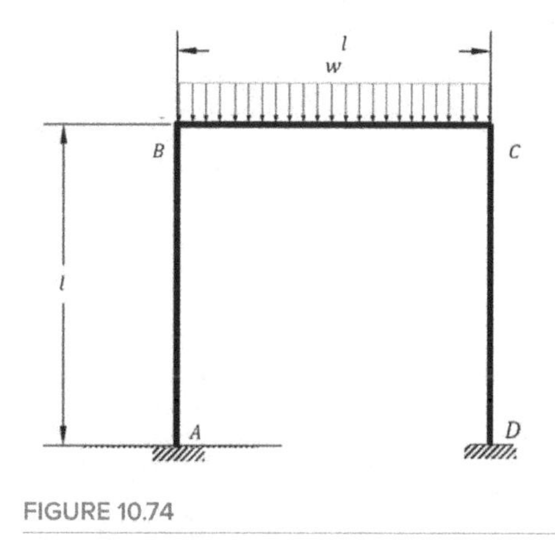

FIGURE 10.74

Reference

Courant, Richard "Variational methods for the solution of problems of equilibrium and vibrations." 1943. *Bulletin of the American Mathematical Society* 49: 1–23.

Further Reading

Ugural, Ansel. C. *Mechanical Design: An Integrated Approach.* New York City: McGraw-Hill, 2004.

Ugural, Ansel C., and Saul K. Fenster. *Advanced Mechanics of Materials and Applied Elasticity.* 5th ed. Upper Saddle River: Prentice Hall, 2012.

Curtis, H. D. *Fundamentals of Aircraft Structural Analysis.* McGraw-Hill, 1997.

Donaldson, B. K. *Analysis of Aircraft Structures: An Introduction.* McGraw-Hill, 1993.

Laursen, Harold I. *Structural Analysis.* 3rd ed. New York: McGraw-Hill, 1988.

Moaveni, S. *Finite Element Analysis Theory and Application with ANSYS.* 2nd ed. Upper Saddle River: Prentice Hall, 2003.

APPENDIX A

Review of Vector Algebra

A.1 Scalars and Vectors

In order to describe physical phenomena, we use physical quantities. A scalar is a quantity that can be completely defined by the mere assignment of a real number $s \in \mathbb{R}$. Examples of scalar quantities are time, mass, length, temperature, etc. Notice that a scalar quantity can be positive, negative, or zero. On the other hand, if I say I am applying a force of 1,000 *N* at the table, the 1,000 *N* is not enough to completely describe the force. Is it vertical? Is it horizontal? Is it oblique? If it is vertical, upward, or downward? A force is an example of a vector quantity. Indeed, four elements are required to completely describe a bound vector. These are:

- Point of application
- Line of action
- Direction
- Modulus[1] (or intensity or magnitude)

The 1,000 *N* in the example mentioned above refers only to the intensity or magnitude of the force.

1 "Modulus" means "measurement" in Latin.

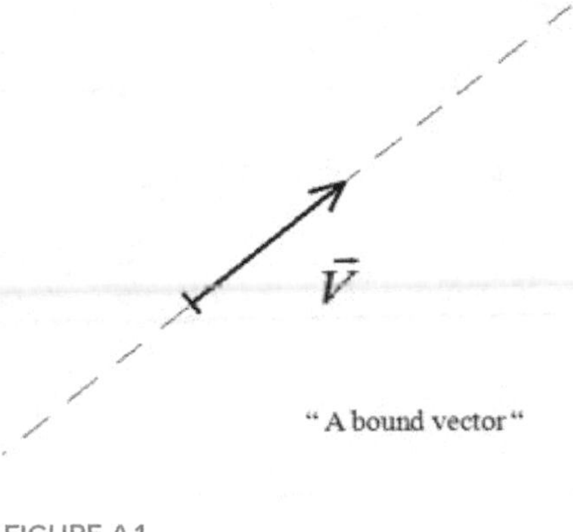

FIGURE A.1

From a physical point of view, vectors can be classified as bound vectors, sliding vectors, or free vectors. When both the point of application of the vector and the line of action are important to be specified, the vector is said to be a bound vector.

When the point of application is not important to be specified, the vector is said to be fixed. However, when the line of action is important to be specified, the vector is said to be a sliding vector. We are sliding the vector onto its line of action.

When neither the point of application nor the line of action is important to be specified, the vector is said to be a free vector. We can, thus, translate the vector anywhere in the space (keeping the same direction and intensity).

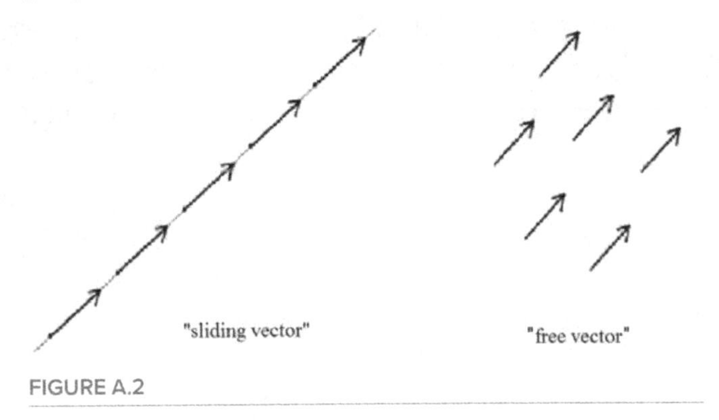

FIGURE A.2

Consider a prismatic bar loaded axially with a load *P*. In mechanics of rigid bodies, *P* can be treated as a sliding vector. The point of application is not important in order to determine the reaction at the fixed support. However, in mechanics of deformable bodies, *P* must be treated as a bound vector. The point of application is important in order to determine the axial deformation of the bar.

An example of a free vector: In dynamics, when a rigid body undergoes a pure translational motion, the velocity of each point of the rigid body is the same. Such velocity vector $\vec{V}$ is a free vector.

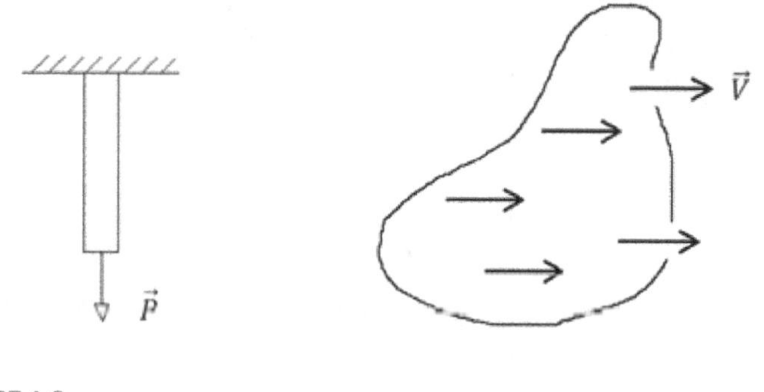

FIGURE A.3

The following is a brief review of vector algebra. All vectors, unless otherwise stated, will be treated as free vectors.

A.2 Addition of Two Vectors

Two vectors add up according to the parallelogram law of the addition of two vectors.

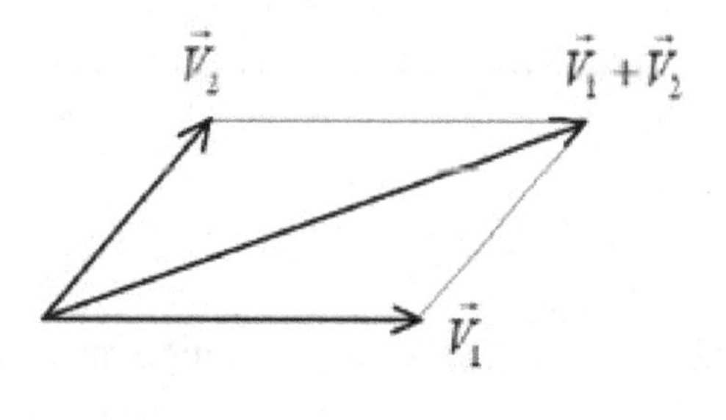

FIGURE A.4

It can be easily shown that

$$\left|\vec{V}_1 + \vec{V}_2\right| = \sqrt{\left|\vec{V}_1\right|^2 + \left|\vec{V}_2\right|^2 + 2\left|\vec{V}_1\right|\left|\vec{V}_2\right|\cos\measuredangle(\vec{V}_1, \vec{V}_2)}, \tag{A.1}$$

where $\left|\vec{V}_1 + \vec{V}_2\right|$ denotes the magnitude of vector $\vec{V}_1 + \vec{V}_2$.

Thus, when we add a 3 N force to a 4 N force, the resultant can be a 5 N force and not necessarily a 7 N force.

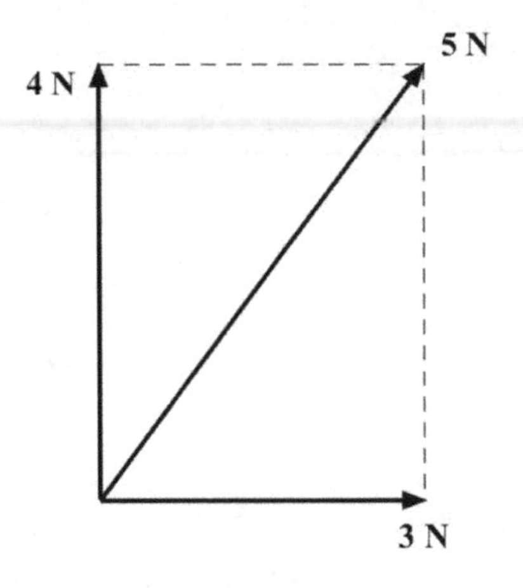

FIGURE A.5

Indeed, it can be shown that:

$$\left|\vec{V}_1 + \vec{V}_2\right| \leq \left|\vec{V}_1\right| + \left|\vec{V}_2\right| \text{ (triangular inequality).} \quad \text{(A.2)}$$

The magnitude of the sum is equal to the sum of the two magnitudes only when the two vectors are parallel to each other and have the same direction. Otherwise, the magnitude of the sum is less than the sum of the two magnitudes.

For the special case when $\theta = \measuredangle\left(\vec{V}_1, \vec{V}_2\right) = 0$, (A.1) becomes:

$$\left|\vec{V}_1 + \vec{V}_2\right| = \left|\vec{V}_1\right| + \left|\vec{V}_2\right|.$$

An alternative way of adding two vectors is the triangular way (see **figure A.6**).

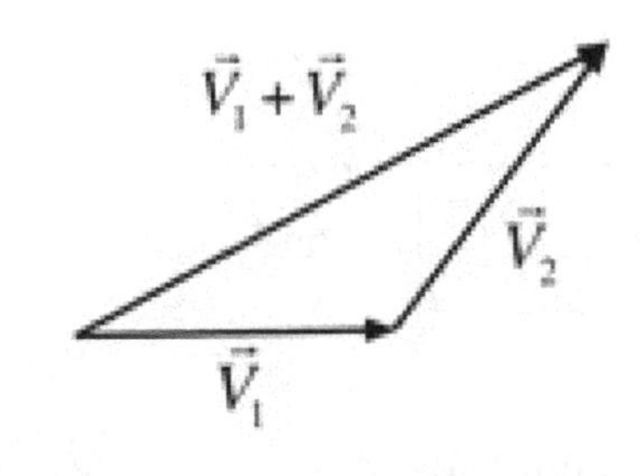

FIGURE A.6

In order to add $\vec{V}_1$ to $\vec{V}_2$, we place the origin of $\vec{V}_2$ at the terminus of $\vec{V}_1$. $(\vec{V}_1 + \vec{V}_2)$ will be the vector whose origin is the origin of $\vec{V}_1$ and whose terminus is the terminus of $\vec{V}_2$.

We can generalize the triangular way to more than two vectors: the polygonal way.

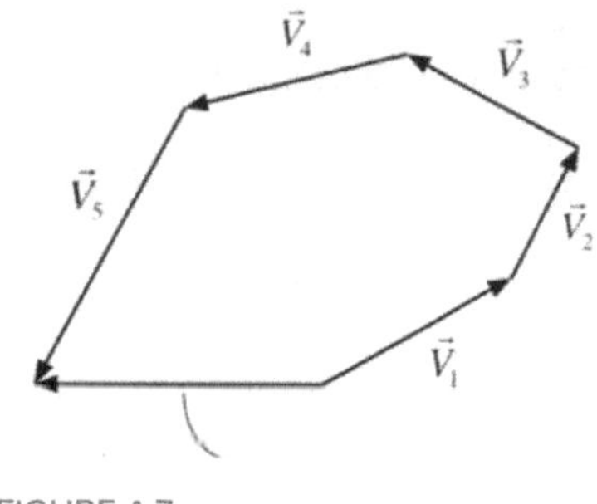

FIGURE A.7

$$\sum_{i=1}^{5} \vec{V}_i = \vec{V}_1 + \vec{V}_2 + \vec{V}_3 + \vec{V}_4 + \vec{V}_5$$

Thus, it can be easily seen that the seven forces shown below add up to $\vec{0}$ *(see* **figure A.8***)*, since the terminus of $\vec{F}_7$ coincides with the origin of $\vec{F}_1$.

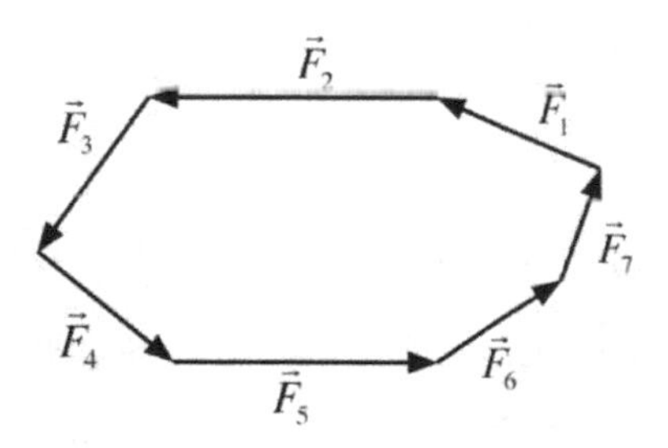

FIGURE A.8

$$\vec{F}_1 + \vec{F}_2 + \vec{F}_3 + \vec{F}_4 + \vec{F}_5 + \vec{F}_6 + \vec{F}_7 = \sum_{i=1}^{7} \vec{F}_i = \vec{0}$$

A.3 Scaling a Vector $\vec{v}$

Let k be a scalar ($k \in \mathbb{R}$), and let $\vec{v}$ be a non-zero vector ($\vec{v} \in \mathbf{V}$).

Then $k\vec{v} \in \mathbf{V}$ is defined the following way:

$$k\vec{v} \parallel \vec{v}$$

$$k\vec{v} \text{ and } \vec{v} \text{ have the same direction if } k > 0$$

$$k\vec{v} \text{ and } \vec{v} \text{ have opposite directions if } k < 0$$

$$k\vec{v} = \vec{0} \text{ if } k = 0$$

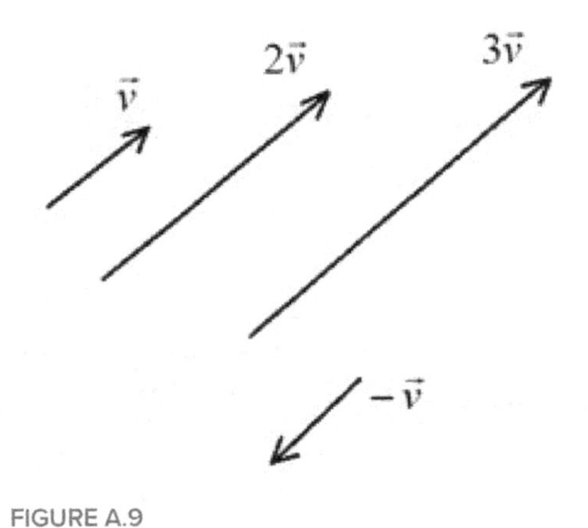

FIGURE A.9

It can be shown that:

$$\vec{A} + \vec{B} = \vec{B} + \vec{A} \text{ (commutativity)}$$

$$\vec{A} + (\vec{B} + \vec{C}) = (\vec{A} + \vec{B}) + \vec{C} \text{ (associativity)}$$

$$\vec{A} + \vec{0} = \vec{0} + \vec{A} = \vec{A} \text{ } (\vec{0} \text{ is a neutral element in vector addition})$$

$$\vec{A} + (-\vec{A}) = (-\vec{A}) + \vec{A} = \vec{0}.$$

V,+ is said to be a commutative group.

Also, it can be shown that:

$$k(\vec{A} + \vec{B}) = k\vec{A} + k\vec{B} \text{ (distributivity)}$$

$$(k_1 + k_2)\vec{A} = k_1\vec{A} + k_2\vec{A} \text{ (distributivity).}$$

A.4 Dot Product of Two Vectors (or Scalar Product)

Let $\vec{v}_1 \in \mathbf{V}$ and $\vec{v}_2 \in \mathbf{V}$.

The dot product of $\vec{v}_1$ and $\vec{v}_2$ is defined to be

$$\vec{v}_1 \cdot \vec{v}_2 = |\vec{v}_1||\vec{v}_2| \cos\theta,$$

where θ is the angle between these two vectors. Notice that $\vec{v}_1 \cdot \vec{v}_2 \in \mathbb{R}$. For this reason, the dot product is also called the scalar product. The geometrical interpretation of the dot product is $\vec{v}_1 \cdot \vec{v}_2$, which is the product of the magnitude of the first vector $\vec{v}_1$ and the magnitude of the orthogonal projection of $\vec{v}_2$ onto $\vec{v}_1$.

Alternatively, $\vec{v}_1 \cdot \vec{v}_2$ is the product of the magnitude of $\vec{v}_2$, and the magnitude of the orthogonal projection of $\vec{v}_1$ onto $\vec{v}_2$. The dot product is commutative.

$$\vec{A} \cdot \vec{B} = \vec{B} \cdot \vec{A} \text{ (commutativity)}$$

$$\vec{A} \cdot \vec{B} = 0$$

$$\Rightarrow \qquad \text{Either } \vec{A} = \vec{0}$$

$$\text{or} \qquad \vec{B} = \vec{0}$$

$$\textit{or} \qquad \vec{A} \perp \vec{B}$$

A classic example of scalar product is work. In dynamics, the work done by force $\vec{F}$ acting on a particle *P* upon displacing it from position ① to ② is:

$$U_{1\to 2} = \int_{①}^{②} \vec{F} \cdot d\vec{r}.$$

Thus, while $\vec{F}$ is a vector quantity, the work is a scalar quantity (it can be positive, negative, or zero). The work done by a force $\vec{F}$ acting on a particle *P* moving on a straight line is zero as long as $\vec{F}$ is constantly perpendicular to the straight path of the particle.

A.5 Vector Product of Two Vectors

Let $\vec{v}_1 \in \mathbf{V}$ and $\vec{v}_2 \in \mathbf{V}$.

Then, $\vec{v}_1 \times \vec{v}_2 \in \mathbf{V}$. $\vec{v}_1 \times \vec{v}_2$ is a vector quantity called the vector product of $\vec{v}_1$ and $\vec{v}_2$.

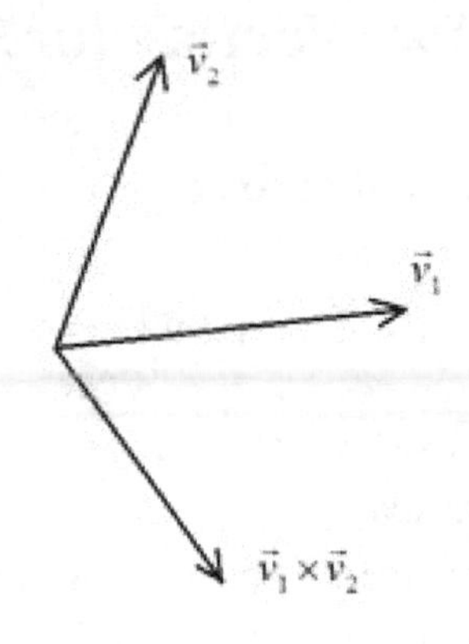

FIGURE A.10

The line of action of $\vec{v}_1 \times \vec{v}_2$ is perpendicular to the plane defined by $\vec{v}_1$ and $\vec{v}_2$. The direction is determined by the right-hand rule. You place the thumb along $\vec{v}_1$. The index along $\vec{v}_2$ and $\vec{v}_1 \times \vec{v}_2$ will be in the direction of the third finger (middle finger).

The magnitude of $\vec{v}_1 \times \vec{v}_2$ is:

$$\left|\vec{v}_1 \times \vec{v}_2\right| = \left|\vec{v}_1\right|\left|\vec{v}_2\right|\sin\theta$$

with θ being the angle between $\vec{v}_1$ and $\vec{v}_2$.

Obviously,

$$\overrightarrow{V_1} \times \overrightarrow{V_2} = -(\overrightarrow{V_2} \times \overrightarrow{V_1}) \text{ (anticommutativity).}$$

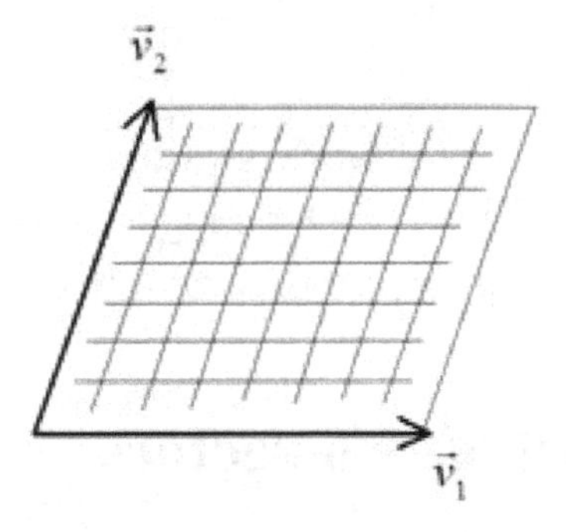

FIGURE A.11

$\left|\vec{v}_1 \times \vec{v}_2\right|$ measures the area of the parallelogram, having $\vec{v}_1$ and $\vec{v}_2$ as adjacent sides.

A classic example of vector product of two vectors is as follows. In mechanics, the moment of force $\vec{F}$ about point O in space is:

$$\vec{M}_0 = \vec{r} \times \vec{F},$$

where $\vec{r}$ is the position vector.

$$\vec{A} \times \vec{B} = \vec{0}$$

$\Rightarrow$ Either $\vec{A} = \vec{0}$

or $\vec{B} = \vec{0}$

or $\vec{A} \parallel \vec{B}$

A.6 Triple Mixed Product

Let: $\overrightarrow{A} \in \mathbf{V}, \overrightarrow{B} \in \mathbf{V}, \overrightarrow{C} \in \mathbf{V}$.

$\vec{A} \cdot (\vec{B} \times \vec{C})$ is called the triple mixed product or triple scalar product, since the outcome is a scalar quantity.

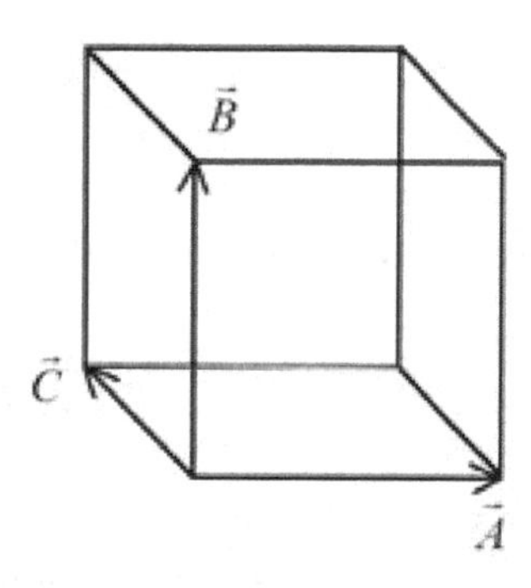

FIGURE A.12

$\left|\vec{A} \cdot (\vec{B} \times \vec{C})\right|$ (i.e., the absolute value of $\vec{A} \cdot (\vec{B} \times \vec{C})$) measures the volume of the parallelepiped, having $\vec{A}$, $\vec{B}$, and $\vec{C}$ as adjacent sides.

An important application of the above: Three nontrivial vectors are coplanar iff their triple mixed product vanishes. In other words, the necessary and sufficient condition for three nontrivial vectors to be coplanar is that their triple mixed product (or triple scalar product) vanishes.

It can be easily shown that:

$$\vec{A} \cdot (\vec{B} \times \vec{C}) = \vec{B} \cdot (\vec{C} \times \vec{A}) = \vec{C} \cdot (\vec{A} \times \vec{B}).$$

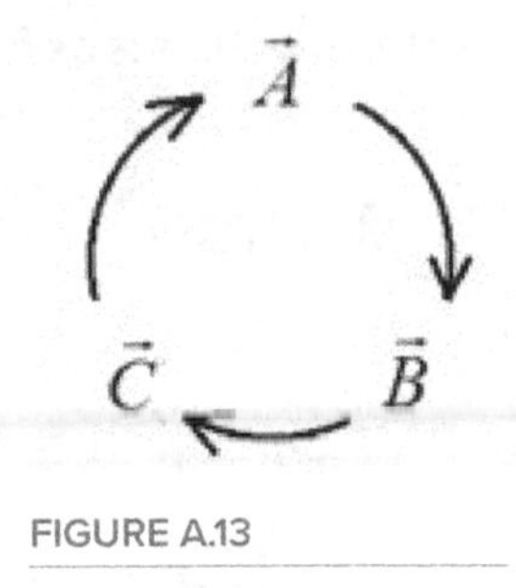

FIGURE A.13

The triple mixed product remains invariant under such a permutation.

A.7 Triple Vector Product

Let: $\vec{A} \in \mathbf{V}, \vec{B} \in \mathbf{V}, \vec{C} \in \mathbf{V}$.

Then $\vec{A} \times (\vec{B} \times \vec{C}) \in \mathbf{V}$. $\vec{A} \times (\vec{B} \times \vec{C})$ is called triple vector product, since $\vec{A} \times (\vec{B} \times \vec{C})$ is a vector quantity. The triple vector product is not associative. In other words, in general,

$$\vec{A} \times (\vec{B} \times \vec{C}) \neq (\vec{A} \times \vec{B}) \times \vec{C}.$$

It can be easily shown that:

$$\vec{A} \times (\vec{B} \times \vec{C}) = (\vec{A} \cdot \vec{C})\vec{B} - (\vec{A} \cdot \vec{B})\vec{C}.$$

It is worth mentioning here that in the triple vector product expression $\vec{A} \times (\vec{B} \times \vec{C})$, the parentheses are important and necessary to be specified, since the triple vector product is not associative, and both $\vec{A} \times (\vec{B} \times \vec{C})$ and $(\vec{A} \times \vec{B}) \times \vec{C}$ are meaningful.

On the other hand, the parentheses in the triple scalar product $\vec{A} \cdot (\vec{B} \times \vec{C})$ are not important. They are not necessary and can be omitted. $\vec{A} \cdot (\vec{B} \times \vec{C})$ is meaningful, while $(\vec{A} \cdot \vec{B}) \times \vec{C}$ is meaningless. In some textbooks, the parentheses in the triple mixed product are omitted:

$$\vec{A} \cdot (\vec{B} \times \vec{C}) = \vec{A} \cdot \vec{B} \times \vec{C}.$$

A.8 Right-Handed Cartesian Coordinate System *xyz*

Consider the right-handed Cartesian coordinate system *xyz* shown in the figure below. Let $\vec{i}$, $\vec{j}$, and $\vec{k}$ be three unit vectors along the *x*-, *y*-, and *z*-axes, respectively.

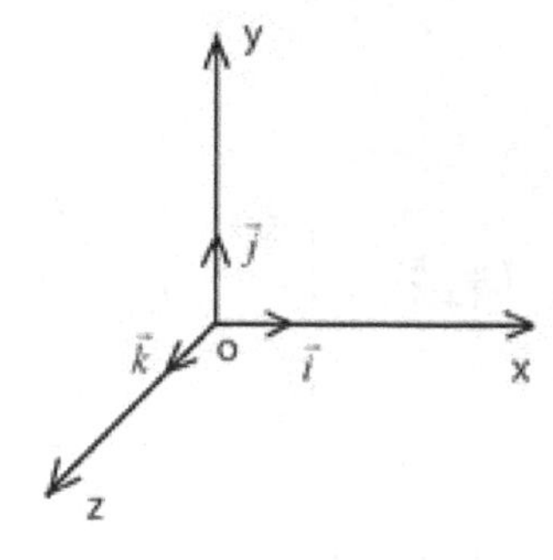

FIGURE A.14

$\vec{i}$ $\vec{j}$, and $\vec{k}$ can be chosen to be three unit vectors mutually perpendicular to each other. In other words,

$$\vec{i}\cdot\vec{i}=\vec{j}\cdot\vec{j}=\vec{k}\cdot\vec{k}=1$$

$$\vec{i}\cdot\vec{j}=\vec{j}\cdot\vec{k}=\vec{j}\cdot\vec{k}=0.$$

Any vector $\vec{V}$ in the space can be written in terms of its three Cartesian rectangular components along the x-, y-, and z-axes:

$$\vec{V}=V_x\vec{i}+V_y\vec{j}+V_z\vec{k}.$$

Let $\vec{A}$, $\vec{B}$, and $\vec{C}$ be three vectors in **V**:

$$\vec{A}=A_x\vec{i}+A_y\vec{j}+A_z\vec{k}$$

$$\vec{B}=B_x\vec{i}+B_y\vec{j}+B_z\vec{k}$$

$$\vec{C}=C_x\vec{i}+C_y\vec{j}+C_z\vec{k}.$$

It can be shown that:

$$\left|\vec{A}\right|=\sqrt{A_x^2+A_y^2+A_z^2}$$

$$\vec{A}\cdot\vec{B}=A_xB_x+A_yB_y+A_zB_z$$

$$\vec{A}\times\vec{B}=\begin{vmatrix}\vec{i} & \vec{j} & \vec{k}\\ A_x & A_y & A_z\\ B_x & B_y & B_z\end{vmatrix}=\left(A_yB_z-B_yA_z\right)\vec{i}+\left(A_zB_x-B_zA_x\right)\vec{j}+\left(A_xB_y-B_xA_y\right)\vec{k}.$$

Also,

$$\vec{A}\cdot\left(\vec{B}\times\vec{C}\right)=\begin{vmatrix} A_x & A_y & A_z \\ B_x & B_y & B_z \\ C_x & C_y & C_z \end{vmatrix}.$$

Below are several examples showing the power of vector algebra.

EXAMPLE A.1

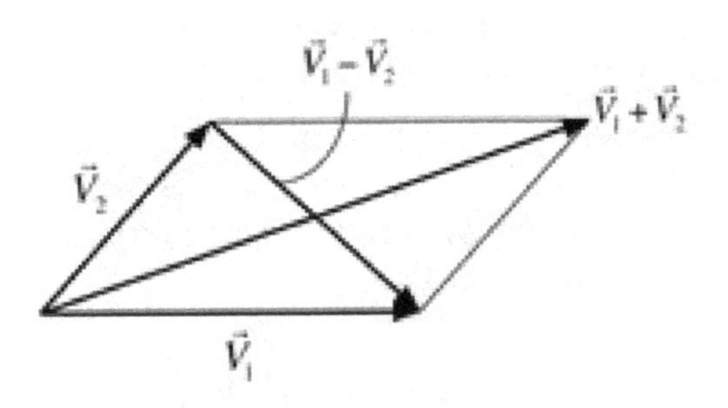

FIGURE A.15

$$\left|\vec{V}_1+\vec{V}_2\right|^2=(\vec{V}_1+\vec{V}_2)\cdot(\vec{V}_1+\vec{V}_2)$$

$$=\vec{V}_1\cdot\vec{V}_1+\vec{V}_1\cdot\vec{V}_2+\vec{V}_2\cdot\vec{V}_1+\vec{V}_2\cdot\vec{V}_2$$

$$=\left|\vec{V}_1\right|^2+\left|\vec{V}_2\right|^2+2\vec{V}_1\cdot\vec{V}_2$$

$$\left|\vec{V}_1-\vec{V}_2\right|^2=(\vec{V}_1-\vec{V}_2)\cdot(\vec{V}_1-\vec{V}_2)$$

$$=\vec{V}_1\cdot\vec{V}_1-\vec{V}_1\cdot\vec{V}_2-\vec{V}_2\cdot\vec{V}_1+\vec{V}_2\cdot\vec{V}_2$$

$$=\left|\vec{V}_1\right|^2+\left|\vec{V}_2\right|^2-2\vec{V}_1\cdot\vec{V}_2$$

Comparing the above two expressions, we conclude that

$$\left|\vec{V}_1+\vec{V}_2\right|=\left|\vec{V}_1-\vec{V}_2\right|\Leftrightarrow\vec{V}_1\perp\vec{V}_2,$$

and we have just proven a theorem in plane geometry. The necessary and sufficient condition for a parallelogram to become a rectangle is that its two diagonals are equal to each other. In other words, a parallelogram is a rectangle iff its two diagonals are equal to each other.

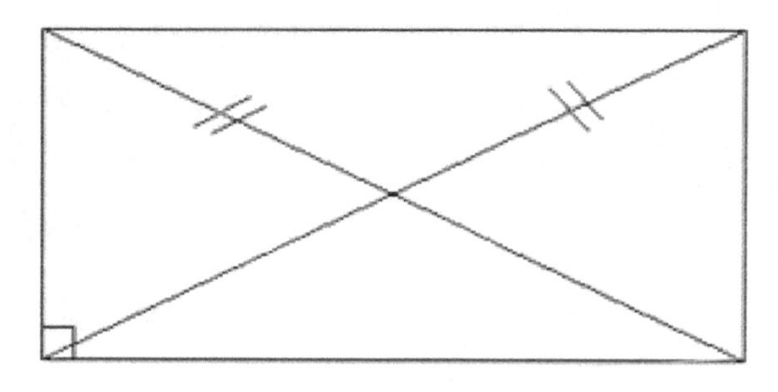

FIGURE A.16

EXAMPLE A.2

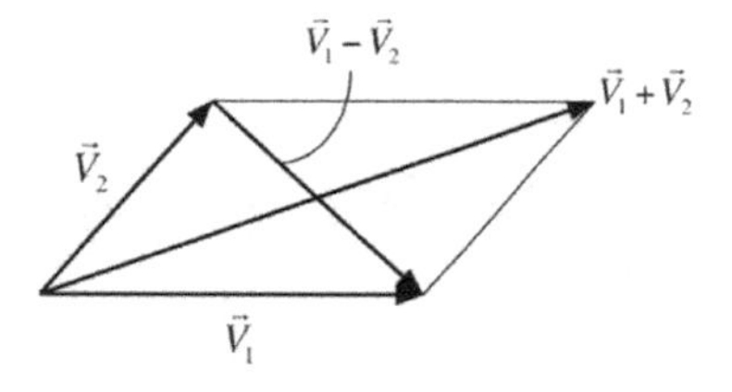

FIGURE A.17

$$(\vec{V}_1 + \vec{V}_2)\cdot(\vec{V}_1 - \vec{V}_2) = \vec{V}_1\cdot\vec{V}_1 - \vec{V}_1\cdot\vec{V}_2 + \vec{V}_2\cdot\vec{V}_1 - \vec{V}_2\cdot\vec{V}_2 = \left|\vec{V}_1\right|^2 - \left|\vec{V}_2\right|^2$$

Therefore,

$$\left|\vec{V}_1\right| = \left|\vec{V}_2\right| \Leftrightarrow (\vec{V}_1 + \vec{V}_2) \perp (\vec{V}_1 - \vec{V}_2),$$

and we have just proven another theorem in plane geometry. The necessary and sufficient condition for a parallelogram to become a rhombus is that its two diagonals are perpendicular to each other. In other words, a parallelogram is a rhombus iff its two diagonals are perpendicular to each other.

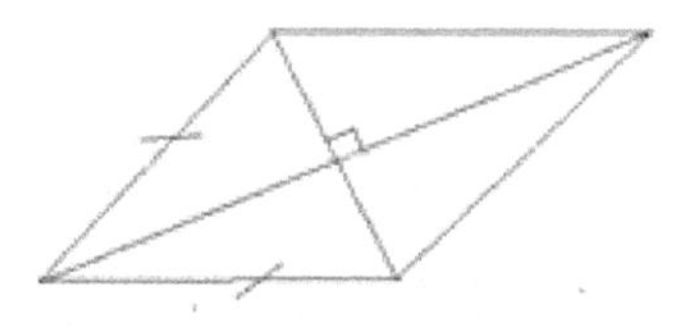

FIGURE A.18

Indeed, a square is a rectangle and a rhombus at the same time.

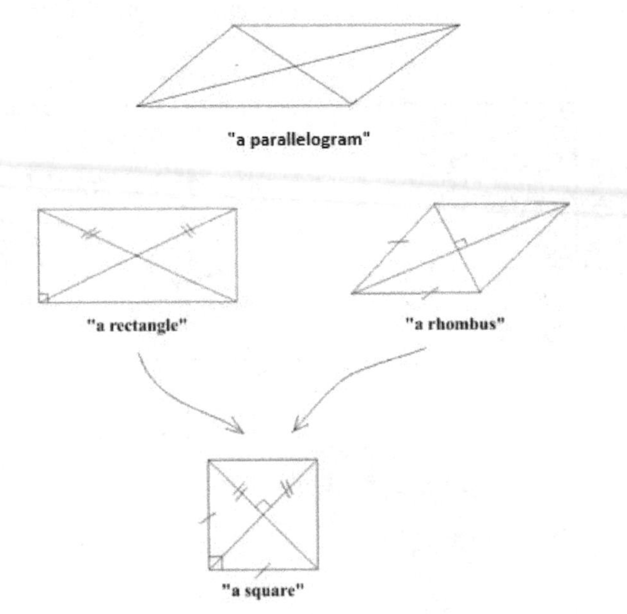

FIGURE A.19

In a square, the two diagonals are equal to each other and perpendicular to each other.

EXAMPLE A.3

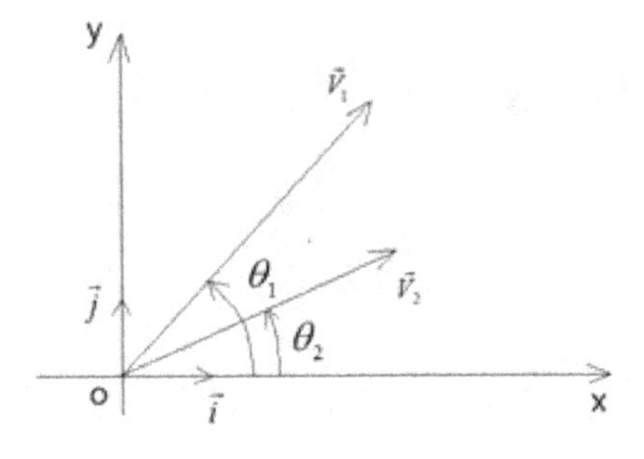

FIGURE A.20

Consider two vectors $\vec{V}_1$ and $\vec{V}_2$ in the xy-plane:

$$\vec{V}_1 = \left|\vec{V}_1\right| \cos\theta_1 \vec{i} + \left|\vec{V}_1\right| \sin\theta_1 \vec{j}$$

$$\vec{V}_2 = \left|\vec{V}_2\right| \cos\theta_2 \vec{i} + \left|\vec{V}_2\right| \sin\theta_2 \vec{j}.$$

Let us evaluate the dot product of $\vec{V}_1$ and $\vec{V}_2$:

$$\overrightarrow{V_1} \cdot \overrightarrow{V_2} = (|\overrightarrow{V_1}| \cos\theta_1 \vec{i} + |\overrightarrow{V_1}| \sin\theta_1 \vec{j}) \cdot (|\overrightarrow{V_2}| \cos\theta_2 \vec{i} + |\overrightarrow{V_2}| \sin\theta_2 \vec{j})$$

$$= |\overrightarrow{V_1}||\overrightarrow{V_2}|(\cos\theta_1 \cos\theta_2 + \sin\theta_1 \sin\theta_2).$$

On the other hand, from the definition of dot product:

$$\overrightarrow{V_1} \cdot \overrightarrow{V_2} = |\overrightarrow{V_1}||\overrightarrow{V_2}| \cos(\theta_1 - \theta_2).$$

Comparing the above expressions, we conclude that:

$$\cos(\theta_1 - \theta_2) = \cos\theta_1 \cos\theta_2 + \sin\theta_1 \sin\theta_2,$$

and we have just proven a well-known trigonometric identity!

EXAMPLE A.4

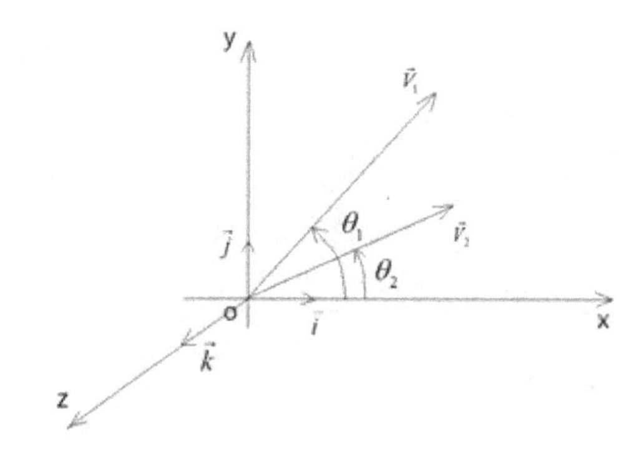

FIGURE A.21

Consider two vectors $\vec{V}_1$ and $\vec{V}_2$ in the xy-plane.

$$\vec{V}_1 = |\vec{V}_1| \cos\theta_1 \vec{i} + |\vec{V}_1| \sin\theta_1 \vec{j}$$

$$\vec{V}_2 = |\vec{V}_2| \cos\theta_2 \vec{i} + |\vec{V}_2| \sin\theta_2 \vec{j}$$

Let us evaluate the vector product of $\vec{V}_1$ and $\vec{V}_2$.

$$\vec{V}_1 \times \vec{V}_2 = \begin{vmatrix} \vec{i} & \vec{j} & \vec{k} \\ |\vec{V}_1| \cos\theta_1 & |\vec{V}_1| \sin\theta_1 & 0 \\ |\vec{V}_2| \cos\theta_2 & |\vec{V}_2| \sin\theta_2 & 0 \end{vmatrix}$$

$$= (|\vec{V}_1||\vec{V}_2|\cos\theta_1\sin\theta_2 - |\vec{V}_1||\vec{V}_2|\sin\theta_1\cos\theta_2)\vec{k}$$

$$= [|\vec{V}_1||\vec{V}_2|(\cos\theta_1\sin\theta_2 - \sin\theta_1\cos\theta_2)]\vec{k}$$

Alternatively, based on the definition of the vector product of two vectors, we can write:

$$\vec{V}_1 \times \vec{V}_2 = [|\vec{V}_1||\vec{V}_2|\sin(\theta_1 - \theta_2)](-\vec{k}).$$

Comparing the above two expressions, we conclude that

$$\sin(\theta_1 - \theta_2) = \sin\theta_1\cos\theta_2 - \cos\theta_1\sin\theta_2,$$

and we have just proven another well-known trigonometric identity!

EXAMPLE A.5

Compute the acute angle θ between the two diagonals of a cube.

Method 1: Without Vector Algebra)

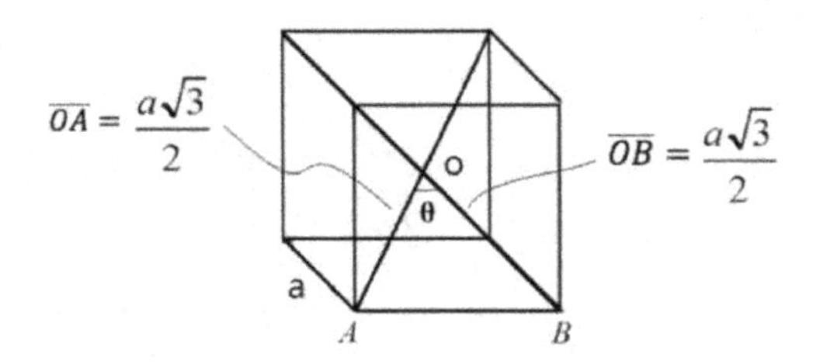

FIGURE A.22

The law of cosines in a triangle (triangle OAB):

$$a^2 = \left(\frac{a\sqrt{3}}{2}\right)^2 + \left(\frac{a\sqrt{3}}{2}\right)^2 - 2\left(\frac{a\sqrt{3}}{2}\right)\left(\frac{a\sqrt{3}}{2}\right)\cos\theta$$

$$\Rightarrow a^2 = \frac{3a^2}{4} + \frac{3a^2}{4} - (2)\left(\frac{3a^2}{4}\right)\cos\theta$$

$$\Rightarrow a^2 = \frac{3a^2}{2} - \frac{3a^2}{2}\cos\theta$$

$$\Rightarrow \cos\theta = \frac{1}{3} \Rightarrow \theta = \cos^{-1}\left(\frac{1}{3}\right) \approx 70.53°$$

Method 2: Using Vector Algebra

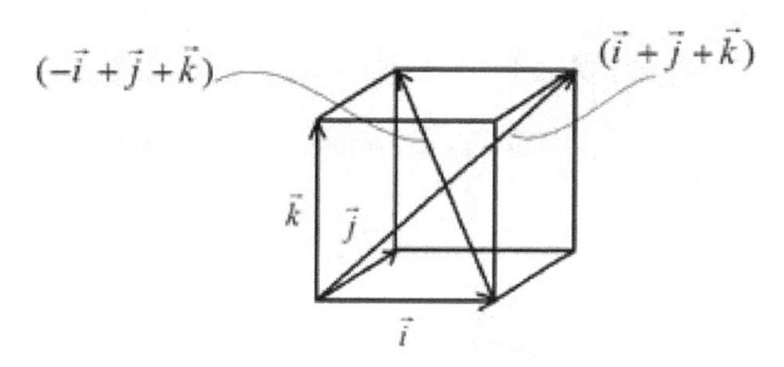

FIGURE A.23

Angle θ is the angle between the two vectors $(\vec{i}+\vec{j}+\vec{k})$ and $(-\vec{i}+\vec{j}+\vec{k})$

$$\Rightarrow \cos\theta = \frac{(\vec{i}+\vec{j}+\vec{k})\cdot(-\vec{i}+\vec{j}+\vec{k})}{\left|\vec{i}+\vec{j}+\vec{k}\right|\left|-\vec{i}+\vec{j}+\vec{k}\right|}$$

$$= \frac{-1+1+1}{\sqrt{3}\sqrt{3}} = \frac{1}{3}$$

$$\Rightarrow \theta = \cos^{-1}\left(\frac{1}{3}\right) \approx 70.53°.$$

This is exactly the same result obtained in method 1.

References

Beer, F. P., E. R. Johnston, Jr., J. T. DeWolf, and D. F. Mazurek. *Mechanics of Materials.* 7th ed. McGraw-Hill, 2015.

O'Neil, P. V. *Advanced Engineering Mathematics.* 7th ed. Cengage Learning, 2012.

Stewart, J. *Calculus: Early Transcendentals.* 5th ed. Brooks/Cole Publishing, 2003.

Problems

A.1. True or False?

For any two vectors $\vec{A}$ and $\vec{B}$, we have:

$$\left|\vec{A}-\vec{B}\right| \geq \left|\vec{A}\right| - \left|\vec{B}\right|.$$

A.2. True or False?

For any two vectors $\vec{A}$ and $\vec{B}$, we have:

$$\left|\vec{A} \times \vec{B}\right|^2 + \left|\vec{A} \cdot \vec{B}\right|^2 = \left|\vec{A}\right|^2 \left|\vec{B}\right|^2.$$

A.3. Find the area of triangle ABC. The Cartesian coordinates of the vertices in the xy-plane are:

$$A(1, 3), B(2, 4), C(-2, 5).$$

A.4. Find the volume of the parallelepiped with adjacent edges AB, AC and AD:

$$A(2, 0, -1), B(4, 1, 0), C(3, -1, 1), D(2, -2, 2).$$

A.5. Find the angle between a diagonal of a cube and one of its edges.

A.6. Show that the following holds true for any three vectors $\vec{a}$, $\vec{b}$ and $\vec{c}$:

$$\vec{a} \times \left(\vec{b} \times \vec{c}\right) + \vec{b} \times \left(\vec{c} \times \vec{a}\right) + \vec{c} \times \left(\vec{a} \times \vec{b}\right) = \vec{0}.$$

A.7. Show that the following holds true for any three vectors $\vec{a}$, $\vec{b}$ and $\vec{c}$:

$$\left(\vec{a} \times \vec{b}\right) \cdot \left[\left(\vec{b} \times \vec{c}\right) \times \left(\vec{c} \times \vec{a}\right)\right] = \left[\vec{a} \cdot \left(\vec{b} \times \vec{c}\right)\right]^2.$$

A.8. Show that the following holds true for any four vectors $\vec{A}$, $\vec{B}$, $\vec{C}$ and $\vec{D}$:

$$\left(\vec{A} \times \vec{B}\right) \cdot \left(\vec{C} \times \vec{D}\right) = \begin{vmatrix} \vec{A} \cdot \vec{C} & \vec{A} \cdot \vec{D} \\ \vec{B} \cdot \vec{C} & \vec{B} \cdot \vec{D} \end{vmatrix}.$$

A.9. If $\left(\vec{A} + \vec{B}\right) \cdot \left(\vec{B} + \vec{C}\right) \times \left(\vec{C} + \vec{A}\right) = 2$, compute $\vec{A} \cdot \vec{B} \times \vec{C}$.

A.10. In a parallelogram, the length of one side is 3 cm. The two diagonals are $\sqrt{37}$ cm and $\sqrt{13}$ cm. Determine the length of the second side.

A.11. True or False?

For any nontrivial vector $\vec{V}$ in the space, we can write: $\left|\frac{\vec{V}}{|\vec{V}|}\right| = 1.$

A.12. True or False?

For any two vectors in the space, we have: $(\vec{u} \times \vec{v}).\vec{u} = 0.$

A.13. Any vector $\vec{V}$ in the space can be written in terms of its three Cartesian rectangular components:

$$\vec{V} = V_x\vec{i} + V_y\vec{j} + V_z\vec{k}.$$

Normalizing $\vec{V}$, we obtain the unit vector $\vec{\lambda}$ in the direction of $\vec{V}$:

$$\vec{\lambda} = \frac{\vec{V}}{|\vec{V}|} = \lambda_x \vec{i} + \lambda_y \vec{j} + \lambda_z \vec{k} = (\cos\alpha)\vec{i} + (\cos\beta)\vec{j} + (\cos\gamma)\vec{k}.$$

$(\cos\alpha)$, $(\cos\beta)$, and $(\cos\gamma)$ are called the direction cosines of vector $\vec{V}$. α, β, and γ are called the direction angles of vector $\vec{V}$. A vector $\overrightarrow{OP}$ lies in the first octant. It has direction angles $\alpha = \frac{\pi}{4}, \beta = \frac{\pi}{3}$. Find the third direction angle γ.

A.14. Two vectors $\vec{a}$ and $\vec{b}$ lie in the xy-plane. If $(\vec{a} - \vec{b}) \times (\vec{a} + \vec{b}) = 25\vec{k}$, compute the area of the parallelogram having $\vec{a}$ and $\vec{b}$ as adjacent sides.

A.15. Determine whether the points $P(1,0,1)$, $Q(2,4,6)$, $R(3,-1,2)$, and $S(6,2,8)$ lie in the same plane.

APPENDIX B

Analytic Solution to a Cubic Equation

B.1 Fundamental Theorem in Algebra

The quest for a solution to polynomial algebraic equations has fascinated mathematicians. They have looked for such a solution since the birth of algebra. The fundamental theorem in algebra states that an nth degree polynomial algebraic equation with real coefficients

$$a_n x^n + a_{n-1} x^{n-1} \cdots + a_1 x + a_0 = 0 \tag{B.1}$$

has n roots in the complex field ₵. These roots do not have to be all real; they can be complex. However, when such an equation has complex roots, these occur as complex conjugates. For instance, a second-degree polynomial algebraic equation (quadratic equation) with real coefficients can have either two real distinct roots, one double real root, or two complex conjugate roots. A third-degree polynomial algebraic equation (a cubic equation) with real coefficients can have either three real roots or one real root and two complex conjugates.

(B.1) can have an analytic solution (closed form solution) only when n is small. We are all familiar with the analytic solution to a quadratic equation (the quadratic formula):

$$\begin{aligned} &ax^2 + bx + c = 0;\ a \neq 0 \\ &x = \frac{-b \mp \sqrt{b^2 - 4ac}}{2a}. \end{aligned} \tag{B.2}$$

An analytic solution does exist for a cubic equation and for a quartic equation. Abel[1] showed that Equation (B.1) does not have, in general, an analytic solution for $n \geq 5$. In that case, such polynomial equation can be solved numerically.

B.2 Analytic Solution to a Cubic Equation

Our objective is to solve the third-degree polynomial algebraic equation (cubic equation) with real coefficients:

$$ax^3 + bx^2 + cx + d = 0; (a \neq 0). \tag{B.3}$$

The following solution is credited to Cardano.[2]

Dividing by a, (B.3) becomes:

$$x^3 + \frac{b}{a}x^2 + \frac{c}{a}x + \frac{d}{a} = 0. \tag{B.4}$$

Let

$$x = y - \frac{b}{3a}. \tag{B.5}$$

Substituting in (B.4):

$$y^3 + \left(\frac{3ac - b^2}{3a^2}\right)y + \left(\frac{2b^3 - 9abc + 27a^2d}{27a^3}\right) = 0, \tag{B.6}$$

which can be written as

$$y^3 + py + q = 0, \tag{B.7}$$

1 Niels Henrik Abel was a Norwegian mathematician (August 5, 1802–April 6, 1829). He died at a very young age.

2 Gerolamo Cardano (September 24, 1501–September 21, 1576) was a mathematician, a famous physician, and an astrologer. He was the child of an Italian judge by the name of Fazio Cardano and a French mistress. He is credited as being the first to discover the existence of complex numbers. Cardano was a 16th-century mathematician (the pre-calculus era). He preceded Newton and Leibniz. He predicted the exact date of his death. He committed suicide!

where, obviously,

$$p = \frac{3ac - b^2}{3a^2}$$

$$q = \frac{2b^3 - 9abc + 27a^2d}{27a^3}. \qquad (B.8)$$

Let
$$y = u + v. \qquad (B.9)$$

Substituting in (B.7):

$$u^3 + v^3 + (3uv + p)(u + v) + q = 0. \qquad (B.10)$$

Let
$$uv = -\frac{p}{3}. \qquad (B.11)$$

Therefore,

$$u^3 + v^3 = -q$$

$$u^3v^3 = -\frac{p^3}{27}. \qquad (B.12)$$

From (B.12), we conclude that u^3 and v^3 are the two roots of the following quadratic equation:

$$z^2 + qz - \frac{p^3}{27} = 0. \qquad (B.13)$$

Solving the above quadratic equation will lead to u^3 and v^3. De Moivre's[3] formula can then be used to find u and v. Once u and v are computed, we can find y using (B.9) and x using (B.5).

3 The formula was named after Abraham de Moivre, a French mathematician who was born in France in 1667 and died in London in 1754. He was a friend of Isaac Newton. He is best known for de Moivre's formula.

EXAMPLE

Solve the following cubic equation analytically:

$$x^3 + 2x^2 - 13x + 10 = 0. \tag{B.14}$$

Let
$$x = y - \frac{2}{3}. \tag{B.15}$$

Substituting in (B.14):

$$\left(y - \frac{2}{3}\right)^3 + 2\left(y - \frac{2}{3}\right)^2 - 13\left(y - \frac{2}{3}\right) + 10 = 0.$$

Or
$$y^3 - \frac{43}{3}y + \frac{520}{27} = 0.$$

Let
$$y = u + v \tag{B.16}$$

$$\Rightarrow \quad (u + v)^3 - \frac{43}{3}(u + v) + \frac{520}{27} = 0.$$

Or
$$u^3 + v^3 + \left(3uv - \frac{43}{3}\right)(u + v) + \frac{520}{27} = 0.$$

Let $uv = \frac{43}{9}$

$$\Rightarrow \quad u^3 + v^3 = -\frac{520}{27},\ u^3v^3 = \frac{79507}{729}.$$

u^3 and v^3 must be the roots of the following quadratic equation:

$$z^2 + \frac{520}{27}z + \frac{79507}{729} = 0.$$

Or
$$z^2 + 19.259259z + 109.063100 = 0$$

$$\Rightarrow \quad z = -9.6296295 \mp 4.04145i$$

$$z = -9.6296295 + 4.04145i = 10.44335(\cos 157.23^\circ + i\sin 157.23^\circ)$$

$$\Rightarrow \quad \sqrt[3]{z} = 2.1858\left(\cos\frac{157.23^\circ + 360^\circ k}{3} + i\sin\frac{157.23^\circ + 360^\circ k}{3}\right); k = 0,1,2$$

$$k = 0 \rightarrow 2.1858(0.6100 + i0.7924) = 1.3333 + 1.7320i$$

$$k = 1 \rightarrow 2.1858(-0.9912 + i0.1321) = -2.1666 + 0.2887i$$

$$k = 2 \rightarrow 2.1858(0.3812 - i0.9245) = 0.8333 - 2.0208i$$

$$\Rightarrow \quad \sqrt[3]{z} = \begin{cases} 1.3333 + 1.7320i \\ -2.1666 + 0.2887i \\ 0.8333 - 2.0208i \end{cases}$$

$$z = -9.6296295 - 4.0415i = 10.44335(\cos 202.77^\circ + i\sin 202.77^\circ)$$

$$\Rightarrow \quad \sqrt[3]{z} = 2.1858\left(\cos\frac{202.77^\circ + 360^\circ k}{3} + i\sin\frac{202.77^\circ + 360^\circ k}{3}\right); k = 0,1,2$$

$$k = 0 \rightarrow 2.1858(0.3812 + i0.9245) = 0.8333 + 2.0208i$$

$$k = 1 \rightarrow 2.1858(-0.9912 - i0.1321) = -2.1666 - 0.2887i$$

$$k = 2 \rightarrow 2.1858(0.6100 - i0.7924) = 1.3333 - 1.7320i$$

$$\Rightarrow \quad \sqrt[3]{z} = \begin{cases} 0.8333 + 2.0208i \\ -2.1666 - 0.2887i \\ 1.3333 - 1.7320i \end{cases}$$

$$\Rightarrow \quad y = u + v = \begin{cases} 8/3 \\ -13/3. \\ 5/3 \end{cases}$$

Therefore, either $y = \frac{5}{3}$ or $y = \frac{8}{3}$ or $y = -\frac{13}{3}$.

$$\Rightarrow \quad \text{Either } x = \frac{5}{3} - \frac{2}{3} = 1$$

$$\text{or } x = \frac{8}{3} - \frac{2}{3} = 2$$

$$\text{or } x = -\frac{13}{3} - \frac{2}{3} = -5$$

Therefore, the roots of the equation are:

$$x = 1, x = 2, x = -5.$$

References

Ugural, A. C. *Mechanical Design: An Integrated Approach.* McGraw-Hill, 2004.

Ugural, A. C., and S. K. Fenster. *Advanced Mechanics of Materials and Applied Elasticity.* 5th ed. Prentice Hall, 2012.

Problems

B.1. For the stress matrix

$$[\sigma_{ij}] = \begin{bmatrix} \sigma_x & \tau_{xy} & \tau_{xz} \\ \tau_{yx} & \sigma_y & \tau_{yz} \\ \tau_{zx} & \tau_{zy} & \sigma_z \end{bmatrix},$$

the cubic characteristic equation that determines the principal stresses can be written as

$$\sigma^3 - I_1\sigma^2 + I_2\sigma - I_3 = 0,$$

where

$$I_1 = \sigma_x + \sigma_y + \sigma_z = \mathrm{Tr}[\sigma_{ij}]$$

$$I_2 = \sigma_x\sigma_y + \sigma_x\sigma_z + \sigma_y\sigma_z - \tau_{xy}^2 - \tau_{xz}^2 - \tau_{yz}^2$$

$$I_3 = \det[\sigma_{ij}].$$

I_1, I_2, and I_3 are called the stress invariants.

Using Cardano's method outlined in this appendix, show that the principal stresses can be written as

$$\sigma_a = 2S\left[\cos\left(\frac{\alpha}{3}\right)\right] + \frac{1}{3}I_1$$

$$\sigma_b = 2S\left\{\cos\left[\left(\frac{\alpha}{3}\right) + 120^\circ\right]\right\} + \frac{1}{3}I_1$$

$$\sigma_c = 2S\left\{\cos\left[\left(\frac{\alpha}{3}\right) + 240^\circ\right]\right\} + \frac{1}{3}I_1,$$

where

$$S = \sqrt{\frac{1}{3}R}$$

$$\alpha = \cos^{-1}\left(-\frac{Q}{2T}\right)$$

$$R = \frac{1}{3} I_1^2 - I_2$$

$$Q = \frac{1}{3} I_1 I_2 - I_3 - \frac{2}{27} I_1^3$$

$$T = \sqrt{\frac{1}{27} R^3}.$$

Notice that σ_a, σ_b, and σ_c are the principal stresses but not necessarily arranged in descending order like $\sigma_1 \geq \sigma_2 \geq \sigma_3$.

B.2. Outline an algorithm that will determine the direction cosines of the principal directions (corresponding eigenvectors).

APPENDIX C

Matrix Algebra

C.1 Introduction

Consider the following system of linear algebraic equations (n equations and n unknowns):

$$a_{11}x_1 + a_{12}x_2 + \cdots\cdots + a_{1n}x_n = b_1$$

$$a_{21}x_1 + a_{22}x_2 + \cdots\cdots + a_{2n}x_n = b_2$$

$$\vdots$$

$$a_{n1}x_1 + a_{n2}x_2 + \cdots\cdots + a_{nn}x_n = b_n.$$

The above system of equations can be written in a more compact and elegant fashion:

$$\begin{bmatrix} a_{11} & a_{12} & \cdots & a_{1n} \\ a_{21} & a_{22} & \cdots & a_{2n} \\ \vdots & \vdots & \ddots & \vdots \\ a_{n1} & a_{n2} & \cdots & a_{nn} \end{bmatrix} \begin{pmatrix} x_1 \\ x_2 \\ \vdots \\ x_n \end{pmatrix} = \begin{pmatrix} b_1 \\ b_2 \\ \vdots \\ b_n \end{pmatrix}$$

$$\text{or } AX = B,$$

where A is an $(n \times n)$ matrix. X and B are $(n \times 1)$ vectors.

C.2 Essentials of Matrix Algebra

Definition

Let $$A = \left[a_{ij}\right]_{(m\times n)} = \begin{bmatrix} a_{11} & a_{12} & \cdots & a_{1n} \\ a_{21} & a_{22} & \cdots & a_{2n} \\ \vdots & \vdots & \ddots & \vdots \\ a_{m1} & a_{m2} & \cdots & a_{mn} \end{bmatrix}_{(m\times n)}.$$

An $(m \times n)$ matrix A defined over the real set $\mathbb{R}$ is a rectangular array of real numbers a_{ij}. The size of matrix A is said to be $(m \times n)$. Also $(m \times n)$ are called the dimensions of matrix A. Notice that an $(m \times n)$ matrix has m rows and n columns. Also, notice that element a_{ij} corresponds to the ith row and j^{th} column. For simplicity, we will assume in this appendix that a_{ij} belongs to the real field $(\mathbb{R},+,.)$. However, the elements of a matrix can be chosen from any field, such as, for instance, the complex field $(\mathbb{C},+,.)$.

Special Cases

i. $n = 1 \Rightarrow A = \left[a_{ij}\right]_{(m\times 1)} = \begin{pmatrix} a_{11} \\ a_{21} \\ \vdots \\ a_{m1} \end{pmatrix}$ is called a column vector.

ii. $m = 1 \Rightarrow A = \left[a_{ij}\right]_{(1\times n)} = \left(a_{11}\ a_{12}\ \cdots\ a_{1n}\right)$ is called a row vector.

iii. $m = n \Rightarrow A = [a_{ij}]_{(n\times n)} = \begin{bmatrix} a_{11} & a_{12} & \cdots & a_{1n} \\ a_{21} & a_{22} & \cdots & a_{2n} \\ \vdots & \vdots & \ddots & \vdots \\ a_{n1} & a_{n2} & \cdots & a_{nn} \end{bmatrix}_{(n\times n)}$

In this case, the matrix is said to be a square matrix of dimensions $(n \times n)$. Or A is said to be a square matrix of order n.

iv. $$A = [a_{ij}]_{(m\times n)} = \begin{bmatrix} a_{11} & a_{12} & \cdots & a_{1n} \\ a_{21} & a_{22} & \cdots & a_{2n} \\ \vdots & \vdots & \ddots & \vdots \\ a_{m1} & a_{m2} & \cdots & a_{mn} \end{bmatrix}_{(m\times n)}$$

if $a_{ij} = 0 \; \forall \; i,j$, the matrix is said to be the null matrix.

v. $$A = [a_{ij}]_{(n\times n)} = \begin{bmatrix} a_{11} & a_{12} & \cdots & a_{1n} \\ 0 & a_{22} & \cdots & a_{2n} \\ \vdots & \vdots & \ddots & \vdots \\ 0 & 0 & \cdots & a_{nn} \end{bmatrix}_{(n\times n)}$$ is an upper triangular matrix.

vi. $$A = [a_{ij}]_{(n\times n)} = \begin{bmatrix} a_{11} & 0 & \cdots & 0 \\ a_{21} & a_{22} & \cdots & 0 \\ \vdots & \vdots & \ddots & \vdots \\ a_{n1} & a_{n2} & \cdots & a_{nn} \end{bmatrix}_{(n\times n)}$$ is a lower triangular matrix.

vii. $$A = [d_{ij}]_{(n\times n)} = \begin{bmatrix} d_{11} & 0 & \cdots & 0 \\ 0 & d_{22} & \cdots & 0 \\ \vdots & \vdots & \ddots & \vdots \\ 0 & 0 & \cdots & d_{nn} \end{bmatrix}_{(n\times n)}$$ is a diagonal matrix. Notice that in a diagonal matrix, $d_{ij} = 0$ when $i \neq j$.

viii. $$I_n = \begin{bmatrix} 1 & 0 & \cdots & 0 \\ 0 & 1 & \cdots & 0 \\ \vdots & \vdots & \ddots & \vdots \\ 0 & 0 & \cdots & 1 \end{bmatrix}_{(n\times n)}$$ is the identity matrix. The identity matrix is a special case of the diagonal matrix when all diagonal elements are equal to each other and equal to 1. It means that $d_{ii} = 1$ for every i.

Definition

Transposing a matrix will make its rows columns and its columns rows.

EXAMPLE C.1

$$A = \begin{bmatrix} 1 & 2 \\ 3 & 4 \\ 5 & 6 \\ 7 & 8 \end{bmatrix}_{(4\times2)} \Rightarrow A^T = \begin{bmatrix} 1 & 3 & 5 & 7 \\ 2 & 4 & 6 & 8 \end{bmatrix}_{(2\times4)}$$

Obviously, $(A^T)^T = A$.

A square matrix $A = [a_{ij}]_{(n\times n)}$ is said to be symmetric if $a_{ij} = a_{ji}$ $\forall$ i,j.

We conclude that for a symmetric matrix, we have $A = A^T$.

EXAMPLE C.2

$A = \begin{bmatrix} 1 & 2 & 4 \\ 2 & 6 & 7 \\ 4 & 7 & -1 \end{bmatrix}_{(3\times3)}$ is a (3×3) real symmetric matrix.

Determinant of a square matrix:

$$\text{Let } A = [a_{ij}]_{(n\times n)} = \begin{bmatrix} a_{11} & a_{12} & \cdots & a_{1n} \\ a_{21} & a_{22} & \cdots & a_{2n} \\ \vdots & \vdots & \ddots & \vdots \\ a_{n1} & a_{n2} & \cdots & a_{nn} \end{bmatrix}_{(n\times n)}.$$

The determinant of A, denoted by det(A), is defined the following way:

$$A = [a_{11}]_{(1\times1)}, \text{ then } \det(A) = a_{11}$$

$$A = \begin{bmatrix} a_{11} & a_{12} \\ a_{21} & a_{22} \end{bmatrix}_{(2\times2)}, \text{ then } \det(A) = a_{11}a_{22} - a_{12}a_{21}$$

$$A = \begin{bmatrix} a_{11} & a_{12} & a_{13} \\ a_{21} & a_{22} & a_{23} \\ a_{31} & a_{32} & a_{33} \end{bmatrix}_{(3\times3)}, \text{ then } \det(A) = a_{11}\begin{vmatrix} a_{22} & a_{23} \\ a_{32} & a_{33} \end{vmatrix} - a_{12}\begin{vmatrix} a_{21} & a_{23} \\ a_{31} & a_{33} \end{vmatrix} + a_{13}\begin{vmatrix} a_{21} & a_{22} \\ a_{31} & a_{32} \end{vmatrix}$$

$$= a_{11}(a_{22}a_{33} - a_{23}a_{32}) - a_{12}(a_{21}a_{33} - a_{23}a_{31}) + a_{13}(a_{21}a_{32} - a_{22}a_{31})$$

$$= a_{11}a_{22}a_{33} - a_{11}a_{23}a_{32} - a_{12}a_{21}a_{33} + a_{12}a_{23}a_{31} + a_{13}a_{21}a_{32} - a_{13}a_{22}a_{31}.$$

The process can be generalized in order to evaluate the determinant of any $(n \times n)$ matrix. For instance, the determinant of a (4×4) matrix can be written in terms of four determinants of order three.

Definition

A square matrix $A = [a_{ij}]_{(n\times n)}$ is said to be singular iff $\det(A) = 0$.

Operations on Matrices

Let $A = [a_{ij}]_{(m\times n)}$ and $B = [b_{ij}]_{(m\times n)}$. Two matrices A and B of the same size (i.e., the same dimensions) are said to be equal to each other iff $a_{ij} = b_{ij}, \forall\, i, j$.

A and B must have the same size to be equal. For this reason,

$$\begin{bmatrix} 1 & 1 \\ 1 & 1 \end{bmatrix} \neq \begin{bmatrix} 1 & 1 & 1 \\ 1 & 1 & 1 \\ 1 & 1 & 1 \end{bmatrix} \neq [1].$$

Let $A = [a_{ij}]_{(m\times n)}$ and $B = [b_{ij}]_{(m\times n)}$. Since A and B have the same size (i.e., the same dimensions), A and B are said to be conformable for addition.

$$C = [c_{ij}]_{(m\times n)} = A + B$$

is defined such that $c_{ij} = a_{ij} + b_{ij}$.

EXAMPLE C.3

$$\begin{bmatrix} 1 & -1 \\ 2 & 4 \end{bmatrix}_{(2\times 2)} + \begin{bmatrix} 3 & 0 \\ 7 & 8 \end{bmatrix}_{(2\times 2)} = \begin{bmatrix} 4 & -1 \\ 9 & 12 \end{bmatrix}_{(2\times 2)}$$

Let $A = [a_{ij}]_{(m\times n)}$, and let $k \in \mathbb{R}$. $B = kA = [b_{ij}]_{(m\times n)}$ is defined such that: $b_{ij} = ka_{ij}$.

EXAMPLE C.4

$$2\begin{bmatrix} 1 & 5 & 6 \\ -1 & 3 & 1 \end{bmatrix} = \begin{bmatrix} 2 & 10 & 12 \\ -2 & 6 & 2 \end{bmatrix}$$

Let $A = [a_{ij}]_{(m\times p)}$, and let $B = [b_{ij}]_{(p\times n)}$. We say that matrices A and B are conformable for multiplication and in this order.

$$C = [c_{ij}]_{(m\times n)} = AB$$

is defined such that:

$$c_{ij} = \sum_{k=1}^{p} a_{ik} b_{kj}.$$

We call it a RoCo multiplication. Notice that AB ≠ BA in general. Matrix multiplication is not commutative. Indeed AB can be defined. Yet, BA cannot be defined. Even when both AB and BA are defined, in general they are not equal to each other.

EXAMPLE C.5

$$A = \begin{pmatrix} 2 & 5 \\ 1 & -3 \end{pmatrix}; B = \begin{pmatrix} 1 & 7 \\ 5 & 6 \end{pmatrix}$$

$$AB = \begin{pmatrix} 2 & 5 \\ 1 & -3 \end{pmatrix} \begin{pmatrix} 1 & 7 \\ 5 & 6 \end{pmatrix} = \begin{pmatrix} 27 & 44 \\ -14 & -11 \end{pmatrix}$$

$$BA = \begin{pmatrix} 1 & 7 \\ 5 & 6 \end{pmatrix} \begin{pmatrix} 2 & 5 \\ 1 & -3 \end{pmatrix} = \begin{pmatrix} 9 & -16 \\ 16 & 7 \end{pmatrix}$$

Notice that $AB \neq BA$.

EXAMPLE C.6

$$\text{Let } A = [a_{ij}]_{(3\times5)}, \text{ and let } B = [b_{ij}]_{(5\times2)}.$$

AB is defined. It is a (3×2) matrix; however, BA is not defined. Although matrix multiplication is not commutative, it is associative. In other words,

$$A(BC) = (AB)C.$$

The inverse of a nonsingular $(n\times n)$ matrix A, denoted by A^{-1}, is defined by:

$$AA^{-1} = A^{-1}A = I_n = \begin{bmatrix} 1 & 0 & \cdots & 0 \\ 0 & 1 & \cdots & 0 \\ \vdots & \vdots & \ddots & \vdots \\ 0 & 0 & \cdots & 1 \end{bmatrix}_{(n\times n)}.$$

Several techniques exist that enable us to establish the inverse of a given nonsingular matrix A. Below is a step-by-step algorithm that illustrates how to compute A^{-1}.

Given an $(n\times n)$ matrix A:

1) First, evaluate det(A). If det(A) = 0, then A is singular. Stop. A does not have an inverse. If det(A) ≠ 0, then A is nonsingular, and you can continue.
2) Write down matrix A.

3) Construct a new $(n \times n)$ matrix obtained the following way: For each element in A, suppress its corresponding row and corresponding column. Evaluate the determinate of the resulting $(n-1 \times n-1)$ matrix, and that will be the corresponding element in the new matrix. Obviously, this process must be repeated n^2 times (the number of elements of A).
4) Multiply each element in the new matrix by its signature $(-1)^{i+j}$.

$$(-1)^{i+j} = \begin{cases} 1, \text{ if } (i+j) \text{ is even} \\ -1, \text{ if } (i+j) \text{ is odd} \end{cases}$$

5) Transpose the matrix in step 4.
6) Divide by det(A).
7) The result is A^{-1}.

EXAMPLE C.7

Let $A = \begin{bmatrix} 2 & 1 \\ 5 & 3 \end{bmatrix}_{(2\times 2)}$. Find A^{-1}.

$$\det(A) = (2)(3) - (1)(5) = 1 \neq 0$$

Therefore,

$$\begin{bmatrix} 2 & 1 \\ 5 & 3 \end{bmatrix} \rightarrow \begin{bmatrix} 3 & 5 \\ 1 & 2 \end{bmatrix} \rightarrow \begin{bmatrix} 3 & -5 \\ -1 & 2 \end{bmatrix} \rightarrow \begin{bmatrix} 3 & -1 \\ -5 & 2 \end{bmatrix} \rightarrow \frac{1}{1}\begin{bmatrix} 3 & -1 \\ -5 & 2 \end{bmatrix} = \begin{bmatrix} 3 & -1 \\ -5 & 2 \end{bmatrix} = A^{-1}.$$

As verification:

$$\begin{bmatrix} 2 & 1 \\ 5 & 3 \end{bmatrix}\begin{bmatrix} 3 & -1 \\ -5 & 2 \end{bmatrix} = \begin{bmatrix} 1 & 0 \\ 0 & 1 \end{bmatrix} \checkmark$$

$$\begin{bmatrix} 3 & -1 \\ -5 & 2 \end{bmatrix}\begin{bmatrix} 2 & 1 \\ 5 & 3 \end{bmatrix} = \begin{bmatrix} 1 & 0 \\ 0 & 1 \end{bmatrix} \checkmark.$$

Therefore, $A^{-1} = \begin{bmatrix} 3 & -1 \\ -5 & 2 \end{bmatrix}$.

EXAMPLE C.8

Let $A = \begin{bmatrix} 1 & 2 & 3 \\ -1 & 5 & 4 \\ 6 & 1 & 5 \end{bmatrix}_{(3\times 3)}$. Find A^{-1}

$$\det(A) = \begin{vmatrix} 1 & 2 & 3 \\ -1 & 5 & 4 \\ 6 & 1 & 5 \end{vmatrix} = (1)(25-4) - (2)(-5-24) + (3)(-1-30) = 21 + 58 - 93$$

$$= -14 \neq 0$$

Therefore,

$$\begin{bmatrix} 1 & 2 & 3 \\ -1 & 5 & 4 \\ 6 & 1 & 5 \end{bmatrix} \rightarrow \begin{bmatrix} 21 & -29 & -31 \\ 7 & -13 & -11 \\ -7 & 7 & 7 \end{bmatrix} \rightarrow \begin{bmatrix} 21 & 29 & -31 \\ -7 & -13 & 11 \\ -7 & -7 & 7 \end{bmatrix} \rightarrow \begin{bmatrix} 21 & -7 & -7 \\ 29 & -13 & -7 \\ -31 & 11 & 7 \end{bmatrix} \rightarrow$$

$$-\frac{1}{14}\begin{bmatrix} 21 & -7 & -7 \\ 29 & -13 & -7 \\ -31 & 11 & 7 \end{bmatrix} = \begin{bmatrix} -\frac{21}{14} & \frac{7}{14} & \frac{7}{14} \\ -\frac{29}{14} & \frac{13}{14} & \frac{7}{14} \\ \frac{31}{14} & -\frac{11}{14} & -\frac{7}{14} \end{bmatrix} = A^{-1}.$$

As verification:

$$\begin{bmatrix} 1 & 2 & 3 \\ -1 & 5 & 4 \\ 6 & 1 & 5 \end{bmatrix}\begin{bmatrix} -\frac{21}{14} & \frac{7}{14} & \frac{7}{14} \\ -\frac{29}{14} & \frac{13}{14} & \frac{7}{14} \\ \frac{31}{14} & -\frac{11}{14} & -\frac{7}{14} \end{bmatrix} = \begin{bmatrix} 1 & 0 & 0 \\ 0 & 1 & 0 \\ 0 & 0 & 1 \end{bmatrix} \checkmark$$

$$\begin{bmatrix} -\frac{21}{14} & \frac{7}{14} & \frac{7}{14} \\ -\frac{29}{14} & \frac{13}{14} & \frac{7}{14} \\ \frac{31}{14} & -\frac{11}{14} & -\frac{7}{14} \end{bmatrix}\begin{bmatrix} 1 & 2 & 3 \\ -1 & 5 & 4 \\ 6 & 1 & 5 \end{bmatrix} = \begin{bmatrix} 1 & 0 & 0 \\ 0 & 1 & 0 \\ 0 & 0 & 1 \end{bmatrix} \checkmark.$$

$$\text{Therefore, } A^{-1} = \begin{bmatrix} -\frac{21}{14} & \frac{7}{14} & \frac{7}{14} \\ -\frac{29}{14} & \frac{13}{14} & \frac{7}{14} \\ \frac{31}{14} & -\frac{11}{14} & -\frac{7}{14} \end{bmatrix}.$$

C.3 System of Linear Algebraic Equations

A system of n equations and n unknowns $AX = B$ has a unique solution when it is linearly independent (i.e, $\det(A) \neq 0$).

$$AX = B \Rightarrow X = A^{-1}B$$

Alternatively, such a system can be solved using Cramer's rule.[1]

EXAMPLE C.9

Consider the following system of linear algebraic equation

$$8x_1 - x_2 - x_3 = 4$$

$$x_1 + 2x_2 - 3x_3 = 0$$

$$2x_1 - x_2 + 4x_3 = 5.$$

Find the unique solution of the system.

SOLUTION

Method (1)

The given system can be written in matrix form:

$$\begin{bmatrix} 8 & -1 & -1 \\ 1 & 2 & -3 \\ 2 & -1 & 4 \end{bmatrix} \begin{pmatrix} x_1 \\ x_2 \\ x_3 \end{pmatrix} = \begin{pmatrix} 4 \\ 0 \\ 5 \end{pmatrix}$$

or

$$AX = B \Rightarrow X = A^{-1}B.$$

Therefore,

$$X = \begin{pmatrix} x_1 \\ x_2 \\ x_3 \end{pmatrix} = \begin{bmatrix} 8 & -1 & -1 \\ 1 & 2 & -3 \\ 2 & -1 & 4 \end{bmatrix}^{-1} \begin{pmatrix} 4 \\ 0 \\ 5 \end{pmatrix} = \frac{1}{55} \begin{bmatrix} 5 & 5 & 5 \\ -10 & 34 & 23 \\ -5 & 6 & 17 \end{bmatrix} \begin{pmatrix} 4 \\ 0 \\ 5 \end{pmatrix} = \frac{1}{55} \begin{pmatrix} 45 \\ 75 \\ 65 \end{pmatrix}$$

$$\Rightarrow \quad x_1 = \frac{45}{55} = \frac{9}{11}$$

$$x_2 = \frac{75}{55} = \frac{15}{11}$$

---

1 Gabriel Cramer was a Swiss mathematician. He was born in Geneva, Switzerland and died in France in 1752. He published his work in 1750.

$$x_3 = \frac{65}{55} = \frac{13}{11}.$$

Method (2)
Using Cramer's rule:

$$x_1 = \frac{\begin{vmatrix} 4 & -1 & -1 \\ 0 & 2 & -3 \\ 5 & -1 & 4 \end{vmatrix}}{\begin{vmatrix} 8 & -1 & -1 \\ 1 & 2 & -3 \\ 2 & -1 & 4 \end{vmatrix}}$$

$$x_2 = \frac{\begin{vmatrix} 8 & 4 & -1 \\ 1 & 0 & -3 \\ 2 & 5 & 4 \end{vmatrix}}{\begin{vmatrix} 8 & -1 & -1 \\ 1 & 2 & -3 \\ 2 & -1 & 4 \end{vmatrix}}$$

$$x_3 = \frac{\begin{vmatrix} 8 & -1 & 4 \\ 1 & 2 & 0 \\ 2 & -1 & 5 \end{vmatrix}}{\begin{vmatrix} 8 & -1 & -1 \\ 1 & 2 & -3 \\ 2 & -1 & 4 \end{vmatrix}}$$

$$\Rightarrow \qquad x_1 = \frac{45}{55} = \frac{9}{11}$$

$$x_2 = \frac{75}{55} = \frac{15}{11}$$

$$x_3 = \frac{65}{55} = \frac{13}{11},$$

which are exactly the same results obtained in method (1).

C.4 Properties of Determinants

1. $\det(A) = \det(A^T)$ (i.e., the determinant of a matrix is equal to the determinant of its transpose).
2. A is singular iff $\det(A) = 0$.

3. If all the elements of a single row (or a single column) of a matrix are multiplied by a scalark, the determinant of the new matrix is equal to k det(A).
4. If $A = [a_{ij}]_{(n\times n)}$, then $\det(kA) = k^n \det(A)$ where k is a scalar.
5. If we interchange any two rows (or two columns) of a square matrix, the determinant will be off by -1.
6. Let $A = [a_{ij}]_{(n\times n)} = \begin{bmatrix} a_{11} & a_{12} & \cdots & a_{1n} \\ 0 & a_{22} & \cdots & a_{2n} \\ \vdots & \vdots & \ddots & \vdots \\ 0 & 0 & \cdots & a_{nn} \end{bmatrix}_{(n\times n)}$ be an upper-triangular matrix. Then,

$$\det(A) = a_{11}a_{22}\cdots a_{nn} = \prod_{i=1}^{n} a_{ii}.$$

7. Let $A = [a_{ij}]_{(n\times n)} = \begin{bmatrix} a_{11} & 0 & \cdots & 0 \\ a_{21} & a_{22} & \cdots & 0 \\ \vdots & \vdots & \ddots & \vdots \\ a_{n1} & a_{n2} & \cdots & a_{nn} \end{bmatrix}_{(n\times n)}$ be a lower triangular matrix. Then,

$$\det(A) = a_{11}a_{22}\cdots a_{nn} = \prod_{i=1}^{n} a_{ii}.$$

8. Let $D = \lfloor d_{ij} \rfloor_{(n\times n)} = \begin{bmatrix} d_{11} & 0 & \cdots & 0 \\ 0 & d_{22} & \cdots & 0 \\ \vdots & \vdots & \ddots & \vdots \\ 0 & 0 & \cdots & d_{nn} \end{bmatrix}_{(n\times n)}$ be a diagonal matrix. Then,

$$\det(D) = d_{11}d_{22}\cdots d_{nn} = \prod_{k=1}^{n} d_{kk}.$$

9. $\det(AB) = \lfloor \det(A) \rfloor \lfloor \det(B) \rfloor$
10. If all the elements of any row (or any column) in a matrix are zero, then the determinant of the matrix is zero.
11. If any two rows (or two columns) in a matrix are identical, then the determinant of the matrix is zero.
12. For any nonsingular square matrix A, we can write:

$$\det(A^{-1}) = \frac{1}{\det(A)}.$$

13. The determinant of a matrix is unchanged if a scalar multiple of any row (or any column) is added to another row (or to another column).

C.5 Eigenvalues and Eigenvectors of a Matrix

Consider a square matrix $A = [a_{ij}]_{(n\times n)}$ defined over the real field $\mathbb{R}$:

$$A = [a_{ij}]_{(n\times n)} = \begin{bmatrix} a_{11} & a_{12} & \cdots & a_{1n} \\ a_{21} & a_{22} & \cdots & a_{2n} \\ \vdots & \vdots & \ddots & \vdots \\ a_{n1} & a_{n2} & \cdots & a_{nn} \end{bmatrix}_{(n\times n)}.$$

We are looking for a nontrivial $(n \times 1)$ vector V such that

$$\underset{(n\times n)}{A} \quad \underset{(n\times 1)}{V} = \lambda \quad \underset{(n\times 1)}{V},$$

where λ is a scalar quantity. λ is called an eigenvalue[2] of A, and the nontrivial $(n \times 1)$ vector is called the corresponding eigenvector.

The above equation can be rewritten as

$$(A - \lambda I)V = 0,$$

where $I = \begin{bmatrix} 1 & 0 & \cdots & 0 \\ 0 & 1 & \cdots & 0 \\ \vdots & \vdots & \ddots & \vdots \\ 0 & 0 & \cdots & 1 \end{bmatrix}_{(n\times n)}$ is the identity matrix.

The above set of equations is a homogeneous system of linear algebraic equations. Such system will always have the trivial solution (i.e., $V = 0$).

In order to have a nontrivial solution, the system must be linearly dependent. Therefore,

$$\det(A - \lambda I) = 0$$

---

2 Eigenvalues and eigenvectors were coined by German mathematicians at the beginning of the 20th century, notably by Hilbert in 1904. "Eigen" in German can be translated to "own." For this reason, eigenvalues, proper values, characteristic values, principal values, and intrinsic values have been used interchangeably in the literature.

or

$$\begin{vmatrix} (a_{11}-\lambda) & a_{12} & \cdots & a_{1n} \\ a_{21} & (a_{22}-\lambda) & \cdots & a_{2n} \\ \vdots & \vdots & \ddots & \vdots \\ a_{n1} & a_{n2} & \cdots & (a_{nn}-\lambda) \end{vmatrix} = 0,$$

and this will lead to an nth degree polynomial algebraic equation called the characteristic equation. The roots of the characteristic equation are called the eigenvalues. The word "eigenvalues" comes from German. It was coined by German mathematicians. Instead of eigenvalues, we can use proper values, principal values, characteristic values, or intrinsic values. Also, eigenvectors, proper vectors, principal vectors, characteristic vectors, and intrinsic vectors have been used interchangeably in the literature.

For an $(n \times n)$ real matrix, the eigenvalues can be real or complex. If the matrix has complex eigenvalues, they will occur as complex conjugates.

For an $(n \times n)$ real and symmetric matrix, all the eigenvalues (and eigenvectors) will be real.

C.6 Orthogonal Matrices

A nonsingular matrix A is said to be orthogonal iff $A^{-1} = A^T$.

C.7 Similar Matrices

Two real square matrices A and B are said to be similar over the real set R iff there exists a nonsingular matrix P such that

$$B = P^{-1}AP$$

Two matrices that are similar to each other over the real set R will have the same characteristic equation and, therefore, will have the same eigenvalues.

C.8 Diagonalization of a Matrix

A square real symmetric matrix is always diagonalizable even when the matrix has repeating eigenvalues.

A square real unsymmetric matrix does not necessarily have to be diagonalizable.

C.9 Positive Definite Matrix

A real $(n \times n)$ square matrix is called positive definite if for any nontrivial $(n \times 1)$ real vector V we have

$$\underbrace{\underset{(1\times n)}{V^T} \quad \underset{(n\times n)}{A} \quad \underset{(n\times 1)}{V}}_{(1\times 1)} > 0.$$

The eigenvalues of a positive definite real matrix are all positive.

Problems

C.1. True or False?

The eigenvalues of a matrix are the same as the eigenvalues of its transpose.

C.2. True or False?

If A is any $(n \times n)$ square real matrix, and I_n is the $(n \times n)$ identity matrix, then we can write:

$$A = I_n \Leftrightarrow A^2 = I_n.$$

C.3. Consider:

$$A = \begin{pmatrix} 1 & 2 \\ -1 & 5 \end{pmatrix}; B = \begin{pmatrix} 7 & -1 \\ 3 & 4 \end{pmatrix}; C = \begin{pmatrix} 1 & 0 \\ -2 & 8 \end{pmatrix}.$$

Determine AB, BA, A(BC), and (AB)C.

C.4. Consider the following nonhomogeneous system of linear algebraic equations:

$$\begin{aligned} x_1 - x_2 + x_3 &= 4 \\ 2x_1 + 5x_2 - x_3 &= 0. \\ x_1 - 2x_2 - 5x_3 &= 1 \end{aligned}$$

Find the unique solution of the system.

C.5. Evaluate the following determinant:

$$\begin{vmatrix} 0 & 0 & 0 & 0 & 0 & 1 \\ 0 & 0 & 0 & 0 & 2 & 1 \\ 0 & 0 & 0 & 3 & 2 & 1 \\ 0 & 0 & 4 & 3 & 2 & 1 \\ 0 & 5 & 4 & 3 & 2 & 1 \\ 6 & 5 & 4 & 3 & 2 & 1 \end{vmatrix}.$$

C.6. Evaluate the following determinant of order 5

$$\begin{vmatrix} 2a & -a & 0 & 0 & 0 \\ -a & 2a & -a & 0 & 0 \\ 0 & -a & 2a & -a & 0 \\ 0 & 0 & -a & 2a & -a \\ 0 & 0 & 0 & -a & 2a \end{vmatrix}.$$

C.7. The following characteristic equation appears in engineering vibrations

$$\begin{vmatrix} 1 & 0 & 1 & 0 \\ 0 & 1 & 0 & 1 \\ \cosh\beta l & \sinh\beta l & \cos\beta l & \sin\beta l \\ \sinh\beta l & \cosh\beta l & -\sin\beta l & \cos\beta l \end{vmatrix} = 0.$$

Expand the determinant, and simplify the equation.

C.8. Show that $\begin{vmatrix} a & b & b & b \\ b & a & b & b \\ b & b & a & b \\ b & b & b & a \end{vmatrix} = (a-b)^3(a+3b).$

C.9. Determine the eigenvalues and corresponding eigenvectors of the following matrix:

$$A = \begin{bmatrix} 1 & 4 \\ 1 & 1 \end{bmatrix}.$$

C.10. If $A = \begin{bmatrix} 0 & 1 \\ 2 & 0 \end{bmatrix}$, compute A^{10}.

C.11. Knowing that $\begin{bmatrix} 0.5 & 1.5 & 1.5 \\ 0.5 & 1.5 & 2 \\ 0.5 & 2 & 1.5 \end{bmatrix}^{-1} = \begin{bmatrix} 14 & -6 & -6 \\ -2 & 0 & 2 \\ -2 & 2 & 0 \end{bmatrix}$, compute

$$\begin{bmatrix} 1 & 3 & 3 \\ 1 & 3 & 4 \\ 1 & 4 & 3 \end{bmatrix}^{-1}.$$

C.12. An $(n \times n)$ square matrix A is said to be diagonalizable if there exists a nonsingular $(n \times n)$ matrix P such that $P^{-1}AP = \tilde{A}$ where $\tilde{A}$ is a diagonal matrix.

If $A = \begin{bmatrix} 1 & 0 \\ 1 & 4 \end{bmatrix}$, show that A is diagonalizable. Find a matrix P. Notice that P is not unique.

C.13. If $A = \begin{bmatrix} 1 & 0 \\ 1 & 4 \end{bmatrix}$, compute A^{16}.

C.14. A square root of a square matrix is another square matrix of the same order that will produce the original matrix when multiplied by itself. Hence, B is a square root of A if $BB = B^2 = A$. We can also write that $B = \sqrt{A} = A^{\frac{1}{2}}$.

Find a square root of the (2×2) identity matrix $I = \begin{bmatrix} 1 & 0 \\ 0 & 1 \end{bmatrix}$.

How many square roots does the identity matrix I have?

C.15. Show that the (2×2) real symmetric matrix

$$A = \begin{bmatrix} 13 & -4\sqrt{3} \\ -4\sqrt{3} & 21 \end{bmatrix}$$

is a positive definite matrix.

References

Gere, J. M., and W. Weaver, Jr. *Matrix Algebra for Engineers.* 2nd ed. Brooks/Cole Publishing, 1983.

O'Neil, P. V. *Advanced Engineering Mathematics.* 7th ed.; Cengage Learning, 2012.

APPENDIX D

Area Moments and Product of Inertia

D.1 Definition

Consider an area in the xy-plane as shown in the figure below.

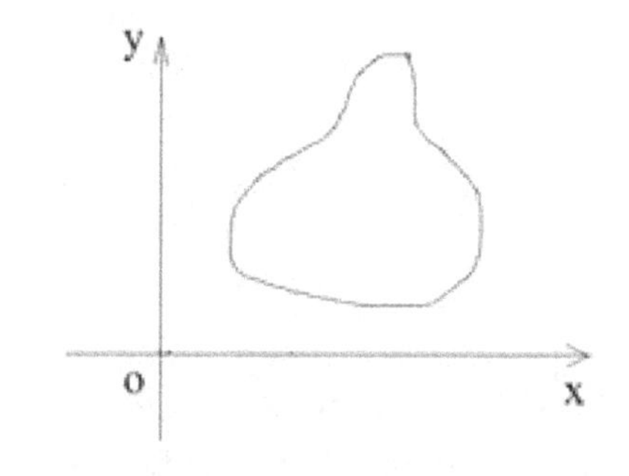

FIGURE D.1

$$I_x = \int_A y^2 dA$$

$$I_y = \int_A x^2 dA$$

$$I_{xy} = -\int_A xy dA$$

Also, define the (2×2) real symmetric matrix $[I_{ij}] = \begin{bmatrix} I_x & I_{xy} \\ I_{yx} & I_y \end{bmatrix}_{(2\times2)}$.

I_x is called the area moment of inertia with respect to the x-axis. I_y is called the area moment of inertia with respect to the y-axis. I_{xy} is called the area product of inertia with respect to the xy-axes.

Notice that the above integrals are double integrals. The dimension of I_x, I_y, and I_{xy} is (length)^4 with the units: m4, mm4, in4, ft4, etc. Whereas I_x and I_y are always positive, I_{xy} can be positive, negative, or zero. Notice also that I_{xy} is defined here as $I_{xy} = -\int_A xydA$. Some textbooks define it as $\int_A xydA$ (without the negative sign). Both versions are encountered in the literature.

The version used here (with the negative sign) has certain advantages, especially in dynamics.

D.2 Rotation of the Coordinate System

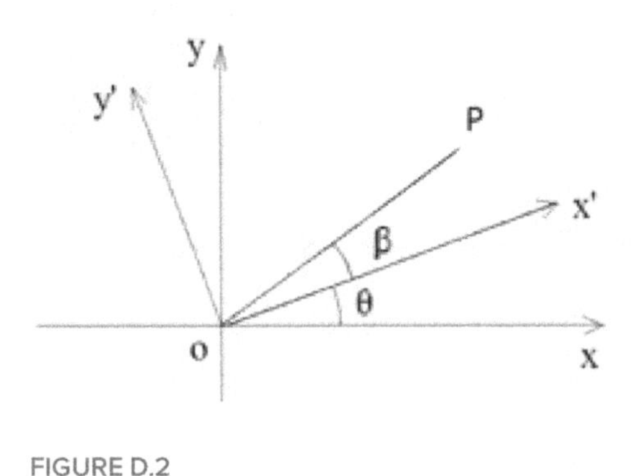

FIGURE D.2

Our objective is to establish a relationship between (x,y) the rectangular Cartesian coordinates of a point P in the plane in the old unprimed coordinate system and (x',y') the rectangular Cartesian coordinates of the same point P in the new primed coordinate system obtained by rotating the old one through an angle θ counterclockwise about O as shown in **figure D.2**.

$$x = \overline{OP}\cos(\theta + \beta)$$

$$= \overline{OP}(\cos\theta\cos\beta - \sin\theta\sin\beta)$$

$$= \overline{OP}\cos\theta\cos\beta - \overline{OP}\sin\theta\sin\beta$$

$$= x'\cos\theta - y'\sin\theta$$

$$y = \overline{OP}\sin(\theta + \beta)$$

$$= \overline{OP}(\sin\theta\cos\beta + \cos\theta\sin\beta)$$

$$= \overline{OP}\sin\theta\cos\beta + \overline{OP}\cos\theta\sin\beta$$

$$= x'\sin\theta + y'\cos\theta$$

Therefore,

$$x = x'^{\cos\theta} - y'^{\sin\theta}$$

$$y = x'\sin\theta + y'\cos\theta.$$

The above transformation relations can be written, more elegantly, in matrix form:

$$\begin{pmatrix} x \\ y \end{pmatrix} = \begin{pmatrix} \cos\theta & -\sin\theta \\ \sin\theta & \cos\theta \end{pmatrix} \begin{pmatrix} x' \\ y' \end{pmatrix}.$$

$\begin{pmatrix} \cos\theta & -\sin\theta \\ \sin\theta & \cos\theta \end{pmatrix}$ is an orthogonal matrix (i.e., its inverse is equal to its transpose).

Therefore, thc abovc transformation relations can be easily inverted:

$$\begin{pmatrix} x \\ y \end{pmatrix} = \begin{pmatrix} \cos\theta & -\sin\theta \\ \sin\theta & \cos\theta \end{pmatrix} \begin{pmatrix} x' \\ y' \end{pmatrix} \Leftrightarrow \begin{pmatrix} x' \\ y' \end{pmatrix} = \begin{pmatrix} \cos\theta & \sin\theta \\ -\sin\theta & \cos\theta \end{pmatrix} \begin{pmatrix} x \\ y \end{pmatrix}.$$

The (2×2) real matrix $\begin{pmatrix} \cos\theta & \sin\theta \\ -\sin\theta & \cos\theta \end{pmatrix}$ is an orthonormal transformation matrix.

We conclude that:

$$x' = x\cos\theta + y\sin\theta$$

$$y' = -x\sin\theta + y\cos\theta.$$

D.3 Establishing $\left[I'_{ij}\right] = \begin{bmatrix} I_{x'} & I_{x'y'} \\ I_{y'x'} & I_{y'} \end{bmatrix}_{(2\times2)}$

$$
\begin{aligned}
I_{x'} &= \int_A y'^2 dA \\
&= \int \left(-x\sin\theta + y\cos\theta\right)^2 dA \\
&= \int \left(x^2\sin^2\theta + y^2\cos^2\theta - 2xy\sin\theta\cos\theta\right) dA \\
&= I_x(\cos^2\theta) + I_y(\sin^2\theta) + 2I_{xy}\sin\theta\cos\theta \\
&= I_x\left(\frac{1+\cos2\theta}{2}\right) + I_y\left(\frac{1-\cos2\theta}{2}\right) + I_{xy}\sin2\theta \\
&= \frac{I_x + I_y}{2} + \frac{I_x - I_y}{2}\cos2\theta + I_{xy}\sin2\theta
\end{aligned}
$$

Similarly,

$$
\begin{aligned}
I_{y'} &= \int_A x'^2 dA \\
&= \int (x\cos\theta + y\sin\theta)^2 dA \\
&= \int \left(x^2\cos^2\theta + y^2\sin^2\theta + 2xy\sin\theta\cos\theta\right) dA \\
&= I_x(\sin^2\theta) + I_y(\cos^2\theta) - 2I_{xy}\sin\theta\cos\theta \\
&= I_x\left(\frac{1-\cos2\theta}{2}\right) + I_y\left(\frac{1+\cos2\theta}{2}\right) - I_{xy}\sin2\theta \\
&= \frac{I_x + I_y}{2} - \frac{I_x - I_y}{2}\cos2\theta - I_{xy}\sin2\theta.
\end{aligned}
$$

Similarly, we can write:

$$I_{x'y'} = -\int_A x'y'dA$$

$$= -\int (x\cos\theta + y\sin\theta)(-x\sin\theta + y\cos\theta)dA$$

$$= -\int \left(-x^2\sin\theta\cos\theta + xy\cos^2\theta - xy\sin^2\theta + y^2\sin\theta\cos\theta\right)dA$$

$$= I_{xy}\cos 2\theta - \frac{I_x - I_y}{2}\sin 2\theta.$$

Therefore, we can conclude that:

$$I_{x'(\theta)} = \frac{I_x + I_y}{2} + \frac{I_x - I_y}{2}\cos 2\theta + I_{xy}\sin 2\theta$$

$$I_{y'(\theta)} = \frac{I_x + I_y}{2} - \frac{I_x - I_y}{2}\cos 2\theta - I_{xy}\sin 2\theta \quad \text{(D.1)}$$

$$I_{x'y'(\theta)} = I_{xy}\cos 2\theta - \frac{I_x - I_y}{2}\sin 2\theta.$$

The above equations are the transformation equations that relate $[I_{ij}]$ to $[I'_{ij}]$. Such transformation equations are characteristic of a second rank (or second order) tensor in physics.

D.4 Discussion of the Above Transformation Equations

i. First, notice that $I_{x'} + I_{y'} = I_x + I_y$, which means that the trace of $[I_{ij}]$ is equal to the trace of $[I'_{ij}]$. The sum of the two diagonal elements in the (2×2) matrix remains invariant. This should not be surprising here, since both $I_x + I_y$ and $I_{x'} + I_{y'}$ refer to the same area polar moment of inertia about point O, I_o.

ii. Obviously $I_{x'}$ is a function of θ. Let us look for angle θ that will extremize $I_{x'}$. In order to extremize $I_{x'}$, we set $\frac{dI_{x'(\theta)}}{d\theta} = 0$

$$\Rightarrow \quad 2I_{xy}\cos 2\theta - (I_x - I_y)\sin 2\theta = 0$$

$$\Rightarrow \quad \frac{\sin 2\theta}{\cos 2\theta} = \frac{2I_{xy}}{I_x - I_y}$$

$$\Rightarrow \quad \tan 2\theta = \frac{2I_{xy}}{I_x - I_y}. \tag{D.2}$$

iii. Let us now find angle θ that will extremize $I_{y'\theta}$. In order to extremize $I_{y'}$, we set $\frac{dI_{y'(\theta)}}{d\theta} = 0$

$$\Rightarrow \quad (I_x - I_y)\sin 2\theta - 2I_{xy}\cos 2\theta = 0$$

$$\Rightarrow \quad \frac{\sin 2\theta}{\cos 2\theta} = \frac{2I_{xy}}{I_x - I_y}$$

$$\Rightarrow \quad \tan 2\theta = \frac{2I_{xy}}{I_x - I_y},$$

which is the same expression (D.2) obtained in (ii).

iv. Let us now look for angle θ that will make $I_{x'y'(\theta)} = 0$

$$\frac{I_x - I_y}{2}\sin 2\theta = I_{xy}\cos 2\theta$$

$$\Rightarrow \quad \tan 2\theta = \frac{2I_{xy}}{I_x - I_y},$$

which is the same expression in (D.2)!

It is interesting that the same angle θ that extremizes $I_{x'(\theta)}$ will also extremize $I_{y'(\theta)}$ and, furthermore, make the product of inertia I_{xy} vanish.

Such an angle corresponds to the principal axes and the extrema for area moment of inertia (one maximum and the other minimum) are called principal area moments of inertia.

Principal Area Moments of Inertia

Let us find the extrema of the area moment of inertia.

$$\tan 2\theta = \frac{2I_{xy}}{I_x - I_y}$$

$$\sec^2 2\theta = \frac{1}{\cos^2 2\theta} = 1 + \tan^2 2\theta = \frac{(I_x - I_y)^2 + 4I_{xy}^2}{(I_x - I_y)^2}$$

$$\Rightarrow \qquad \cos 2\theta = \mp \frac{I_x - I_y}{\sqrt{(I_x - I_y)^2 + 4I_{xy}^2}}$$

$$\sin 2\theta = (\cos 2\theta)(\tan 2\theta) = \mp \frac{2I_{xy}}{\sqrt{(I_x - I_y)^2 + 4I_{xy}^2}}$$

Therefore,

$$I_{x'} = \frac{I_x + I_y}{2} + \left(\frac{I_x - I_y}{2}\right)\left[\mp \frac{I_x - I_y}{\sqrt{(I_x - I_y)^2 + 4I_{xy}^2}}\right] + I_{xy}\left[\mp \frac{2I_{xy}}{\sqrt{(I_x - I_y)^2 + 4I_{xy}^2}}\right]$$

$$\Rightarrow \qquad I_{x'} = \frac{I_x + I_y}{2} \mp \frac{1}{2}\sqrt{(I_x - I_y)^2 + 4I_{xy}^2}.$$

The plus sign corresponds to I_{max}, and the negative sign corresponds to I_{min}.

We conclude that:

$$I_{max}^{min} = \frac{I_x + I_y}{2} \mp \frac{1}{2}\sqrt{(I_x - I_y)^2 + 4I_{xy}^2}. \qquad \text{(D.3)}$$

I_{max} and I_{min} are the principal area moments of inertia.

D.5 An Alternative Way for Determining I_{max} and I_{min}

The principal area moments of inertia are the eigenvalues of the (2×2) real symmetric matrix

$$[I_{ij}] = \begin{bmatrix} I_x & I_{xy} \\ I_{yx} & I_y \end{bmatrix}_{(2\times2)}.$$

The principal directions are the corresponding eigenvectors.

In order to determine the eigenvalues of $[I_{ij}] = \begin{bmatrix} I_x & I_{xy} \\ I_{yx} & I_y \end{bmatrix}$, we set:

$$\begin{vmatrix} (I_x - I) & I_{xy} \\ I_{yx} & (I_y - I) \end{vmatrix} = 0$$

$$\Rightarrow \qquad (I_x - I)(I_y - I) - I_{xy}^2 = 0$$

$$\Rightarrow \qquad I^2 - (I_x + I_y)I + I_x I_y - I_{xy}^2 = 0.$$

The above quadratic equation is the characteristic equation.

$$\Delta = (I_x + I_y)^2 - (4)(1)(I_x I_y - I_{xy}^2) = (I_x - I_y)^2 + 4I_{xy}^2$$

Notice that the discriminant of the characteristic equation cannot be negative, which guarantees real roots. Indeed, the eigenvalues and corresponding eigenvectors of an (2×2) real symmetric matrix are always real.

We conclude that

$$I_{max}^{min} = \frac{I_x + I_y}{2} \mp \frac{1}{2}\sqrt{(I_x - I_y)^2 + 4I_{xy}^2},$$

which is the same result obtained in (D.3).

D.6 Graphical Solution of the Problem

The above result can also be obtained using Mohr's circle (see **figure D.3**).[1]

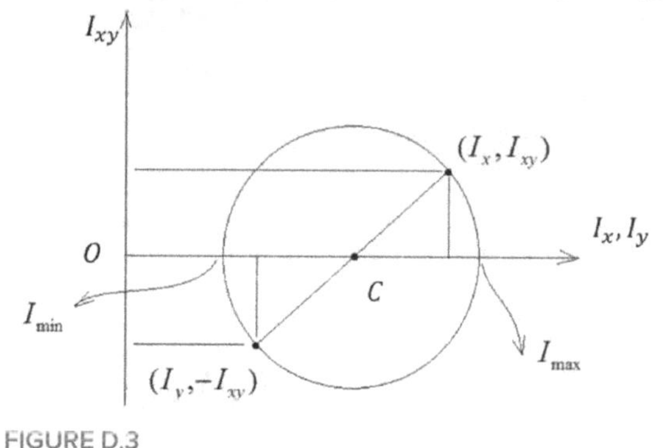

FIGURE D.3

Mohr's circle is a very clever method that was popular and important in the 20th century before electronic calculators became cheap and available. Nowadays, it is certainly unwise to use it instead of cheap scientific calculators.

D.7 Area Moments and Product of Inertia of Common Geometric Shapes

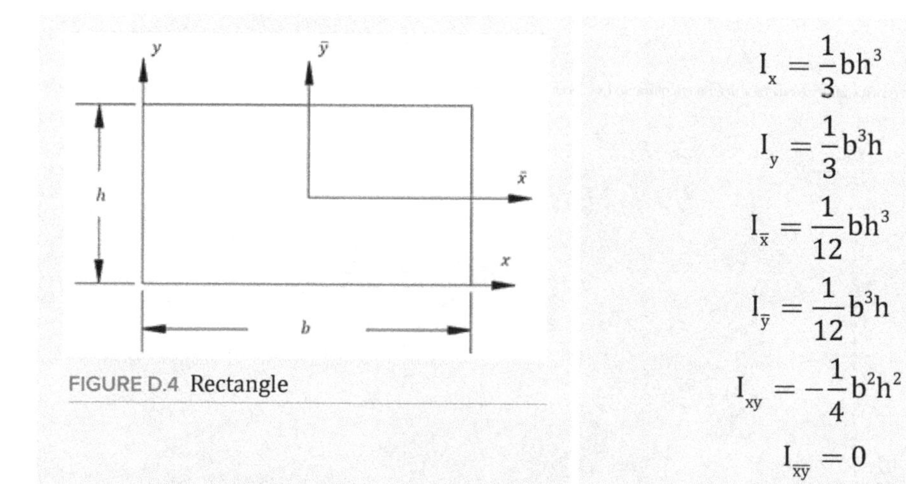

FIGURE D.4 Rectangle

$$I_x = \frac{1}{3}bh^3$$

$$I_y = \frac{1}{3}b^3h$$

$$I_{\bar{x}} = \frac{1}{12}bh^3$$

$$I_{\bar{y}} = \frac{1}{12}b^3h$$

$$I_{xy} = -\frac{1}{4}b^2h^2$$

$$I_{\overline{xy}} = 0$$

1 Otto Mohr (October 8, 1835–October 2, 1918) was a German professor of engineering who came up with a graphical solution to the problem in 1905.

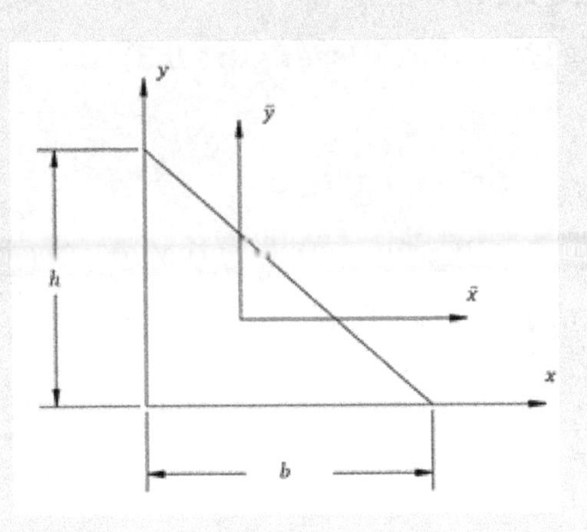

FIGURE D.5 Triangle

$$I_x = \frac{1}{12}bh^3$$

$$I_y = \frac{1}{12}b^3h$$

$$I_{\bar{x}} = \frac{1}{36}bh^3$$

$$I_{\bar{y}} = \frac{1}{36}b^3h$$

$$I_{xy} = -\frac{1}{24}b^2h^2$$

$$I_{\bar{x}\bar{y}} = \frac{1}{72}b^2h^2$$

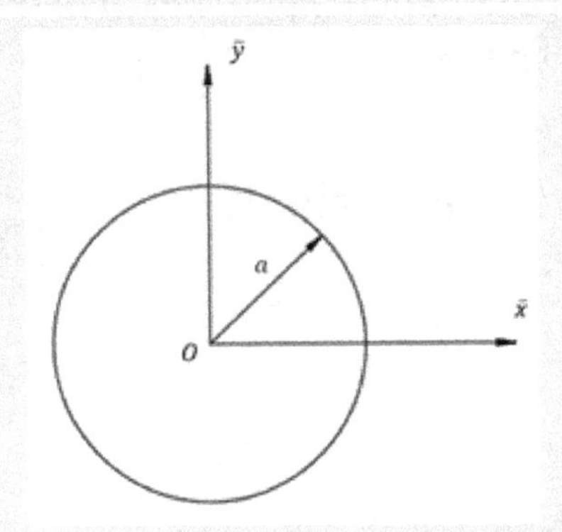

FIGURE D.6 Circle

$$I_{\bar{x}} = I_{\bar{y}} = \frac{\pi}{4}a^4$$

$$I_O = \frac{\pi}{2}a^4$$

$$I_{\bar{x}\bar{y}} = 0$$

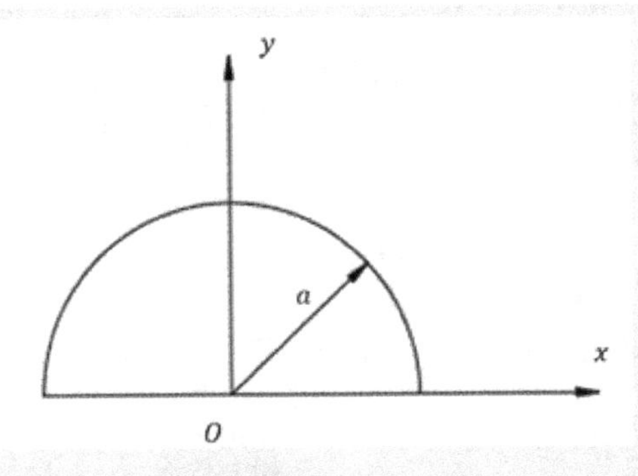

FIGURE D.7 Semicircle

$$I_x = I_y = \frac{\pi}{8}a^4$$

$$I_O = \frac{\pi}{4}a^4$$

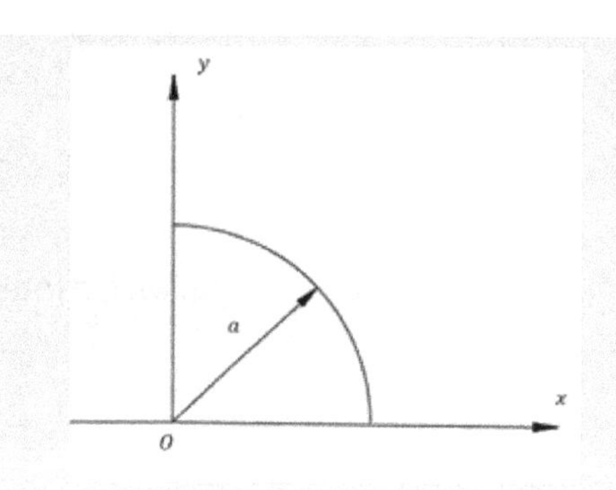

FIGURE D.8 Quarter-circle

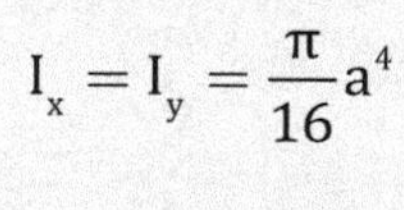

$$I_x = I_y = \frac{\pi}{16}a^4$$

$$I_0 = \frac{\pi}{8}a^4$$

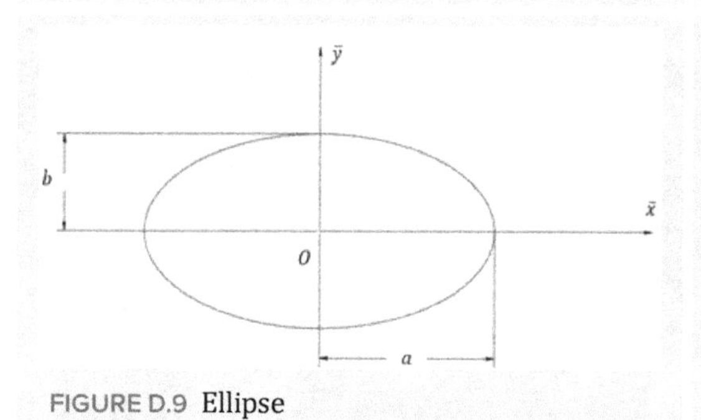

FIGURE D.9 Ellipse

$$I_{\bar{x}} = \frac{\pi}{4}ab^3$$

$$I_{\bar{y}} = \frac{\pi}{4}a^3b$$

$$I_{\overline{xy}} = 0$$

Problem

D.1.

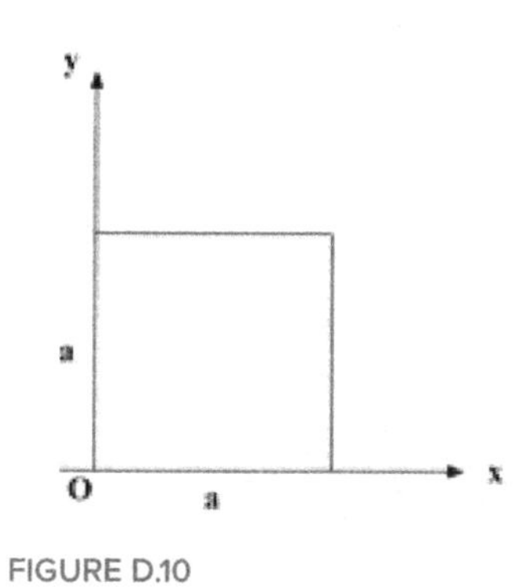

FIGURE D.10

For the square shown in the figure above, establish the (2×2) real symmetric matrix:

$$[I_{ij}] = \begin{bmatrix} I_x & I_{xy} \\ I_{yx} & I_y \end{bmatrix}_{(2\times2)}.$$

Also, determine the principal area moments of inertia and the principal directions.

Reference

Beer, F. P., E. R. Johnston Jr., and D. F. Mazurek. *Vector Mechanics for Engineers: Statics*. 11th ed. McGraw Hill Education, 2016.

APPENDIX E

Systems of Units

E.1 Introduction

Physical quantities are encountered in engineering and other disciplines. We have to use a system of units when measuring and expressing such quantities. There are numerous systems of units, and by far, the most widely used is the SI system of units. There have been several recommendations by the US government, in particular in the early 1980s, to switch to the SI system of units. However, until now, in the United States, we sell gasoline by the gallon, and your driver's license lists your height in feet and inches and your weight in pounds. Although the SI system of units has been increasingly used in this country, and most engineering textbooks are now published in the SI system, it is still necessary and important for engineers in the US to master both the SI system of units and the US customary units. Engineering is a practical and applied field, and whether in industry or academia, getting the right and correct answer is very important and crucial. Indeed, it is sometimes more important than understanding the theory, techniques, and methods used in design or analysis. It is impossible to obtain the right answer until the systems of units are mastered and properly used. I have noticed that undergraduate students, graduate students, and even professional engineers make errors when using the systems of units. Some of these errors are very costly and catastrophic. In 1999, NASA lost a $125 million Mars orbiter because systems of units were not properly used. In this appendix, we will review the SI system of units, the CGS system of units, and the technical English system of units.

E.2 SI System of Units

In the SI (Système International) system, the modern form of the metric system, we use:

- meter* (m) as a unit of length
- kilogram (kg) as a unit of mass
- second (s) as a unit of time

The above three units are called basic, or fundamental, units, since all other units (derived units) can be derived from them. For instance, in this system:

- Force is measured in Newton (N). $1\text{N} = 1\text{kg m} / \text{s}^2$
- Work (or energy) is measured in Joule (J). $1\text{J} = 1\text{Nm} = 1\text{kg m}^2 / \text{s}^2$
- Power is measured in Watt (W). $1\text{W} = 1\text{ J} / \text{s} = 1\text{kg m}^2 / \text{s}^3$
- Area is measured in m^2.
- Volume is measured in m^3.
- Speed is measured in m / s.
- Acceleration is measured in m / s^2.
- Volumetric rate is measured in m^3 / s.

In this appendix, we will focus on units relevant to Newtonian mechanics and widely used in stress analysis. For example, in this appendix we will skip units such as ampere for electric current measurement.

E.3 CGS System of Units

In the CGS system of units, we use:

- centimeter (cm) as a unit of length
- gram (g) as a unit of mass
- second (s) as unit of time

The above three units are called basic, or fundamental, units. Other units, called derived units, can be expressed in terms of these three basic units. In this system:

---

* Either meter (American spelling) or metre (British spelling) are acceptable.

- The unit of force is dyne. $1 \text{ dyne} = 1\text{g cm} / \text{s}^2$
- The unit of work (or energy) is erg. $1 \text{ erg} = 1(\text{dyne})(\text{cm}) = 1\text{g cm}^2 / \text{s}^2$
- The unit of area is cm^2.
- The unit of volume is cm^3.
- The unit of speed is cm / s.
- The unit of acceleration is cm / s^2.
- The unit of volumetric rate is cm^3 / s.

EXAMPLES

$$1 \text{ m}^2 = 10^4 \text{ cm}^2 = 10{,}000 \text{ cm}^2$$

$$1 \text{ m}^3 = 10^6 \text{ cm}^3 = 1{,}000{,}000 \text{ cm}^3$$

$$1 \text{ N} = 1\frac{\text{kg m}}{\text{s}^2} = \frac{(1{,}000 \text{ g})(100 \text{ cm})}{\text{s}^2} = 10^5 \text{ dyne}$$

$$1\text{J} = 1 \text{ Nm} = 10^7 \, erg$$

E.4 Technical English System of Units

In this system, still used in the United States, we use:

- foot (ft) as a unit of length
- pound force (lb_f) as a unit of force
- second (s) as a unit of time

The above three units are called basic, or fundamental, units. All other units can be expressed in terms of these basic units. Notice, first, that the technical English system differs fundamentally from the previous two systems. In the SI and CGS systems, mass was chosen to be a basic unit and force became a derived unit. The SI and CGS systems are called absolute systems of units. On the contrary, in the technical English system, the force was chosen to be a basic unit, and in this case, mass becomes a derived unit. This system is not an absolute system of units. In this system:

- Mass is measured in slug. $1 \text{ slug} = 1 \text{ lb}_\text{f} \text{ s}^2 / \text{ft}$
- Work (or energy) is measured in $\text{lb}_\text{f} \cdot \text{bk}$.
- Power is measured in $\text{lb}_\text{f} \cdot \text{ber}$.
- Area is measured in ft^2.

- Volume is measured in ft^3.
- Speed is measured in ft / s.
- Acceleration is measured in ft / s^2.
- Volumetric rate is measured in ft^3 / s.

There is a big advantage, especially in physics, to use an absolute system of units. 1 kg of mass remains the same (1 kg of mass) everywhere in the universe. However, the weight of 1 kg of mass is not the same in the universe. The weight of 1 kg of mass on the moon is 1/6 of its weight on earth.

E.5 Dimensions and Dimensional Analysis

Although meter, centimeter, and foot belong to different systems of units, they have something essential in common. They are all units of length. We say that m, cm, ft, in, km, mile, etc. have the same dimension, which is the dimension of length. Similarly, s, ms, μs, min, hr, etc. have the dimension of time. kg, g, slug, lb_m, mg, etc. have the dimension of mass. N, dyne, lb_f, kg_f, kN, etc. have the dimension of force.

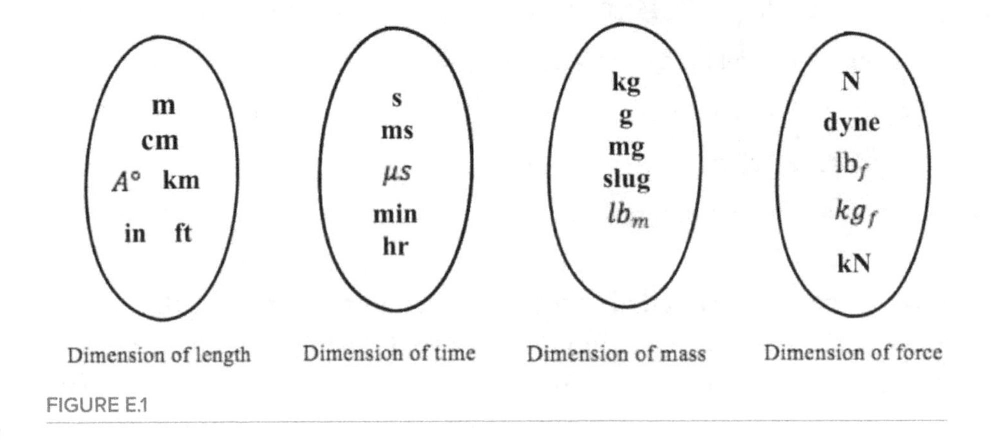

FIGURE E.1

Given any two units in the same bag (i.e., having the same dimension), we should be able to find a conversion factor that takes us from one to the other:

- How many cm in 1m? $1\text{ m} = 10^2\text{ cm}$
- How many in in 1ft? $1\text{ ft} = 12\text{ in}$
- How many A° in 1 m? $1\text{ m} = 10^{10}\text{ A}^\circ$
- How many ft in 1 km? $1\text{ km} \approx 3{,}280.8\text{ ft}$

Obviously, we cannot find a conversion factor for two units belonging to two separate bags (i.e., having two different dimensions). A question such as, "How many seconds are in one meter?" is wrong and meaningless. Similarly, a question such as, "How many N are in one kg?" is meaningless and wrong. Instead, we should say that:

- The weight of 1 kg of mass on earth is 1 kg_f.
- The weight of 1 kg of mass on earth is 9.81 N.
- Therefore, 1 kg_f= 9.81 N.

Similarly:

- The weight of 1 slug of mass on earth is 32.2 lb_f.
- The weight of 1 lb_m of mass on earth is 1 lb_f.
- Therefore, 1 slug = 32.2 lb_m.

Only terms having the same dimension can be added to each other. For example, we can add m^4 to m^4, but we cannot add m^4 to m^5. Checking the dimensional homogeneity of a formula in engineering or physics is important in order to verify the validity of such a formula. For instance, without being able to derive the formula that gives us the period T of a simple pendulum of length L, we should be able to conclude that a formula such as $T = 2\pi\sqrt{Lg}$ is certainly wrong, since it is dimensionally inhomogeneous. On the other hand, $T = 2\pi\sqrt{L / g}$ is dimensionally homogeneous. Obviously, the dimensional homogeneity of a formula does not guarantee its correctness and accuracy. However, a dimensionally inhomogeneous formula is guaranteed to be incorrect. Dimensional analysis is used in some engineering fields such as fluid dynamics and fracture mechanics to derive practical and important formulas that cannot be derived in a rigorous way.

E.6 Example

In physics, mass density ρ is defined to be: $\rho = \frac{m}{V}$. Thus, the unit of ρ in the SI system is kg/m^3; in the CGS system the unit is g/cm^3; and in the technical English system the unit is $\frac{slug}{ft^3}$.

Specific weight γ is defined to be: $\gamma = \frac{weight}{Volume}$.

Thus, the unit of γ in the SI system is N / m^3; in the CGS system it is $\frac{dyne}{cm^3}$; and in the technical English system it is $\frac{lb_f}{ft^3}$.

Specific gravity sp.gr. for a solid or liquid is defined to be: $sp.gr. = \frac{\rho}{\rho_{water}}$

Below is a table illustrating ρ, γ and sp.gr. for water in different systems of units.

	SI system	CGS system	Technical English system
ρ_w	$1000\ kg / m^3$	$1\ g / cm^3$	$1.94\ \frac{slug}{ft^3}$
γ_w	$9{,}810\ N / m^3$	$981\ \frac{dyne}{cm^3}$	$62.4\ \frac{lb_f}{ft^3}$
$Sp.gr._w$	1	1	1

Notice that specific gravity is unitless or dimensionless. The numerical value of a dimensionless quantity does not depend on the system of units used. The specific gravity of mercury is 13.6. It means that mercury is 13.6 times heavier than water, and this is true in any system of units. It is advantageous in engineering to define unitless quantities. Another example of a dimensionless quantity is Mach number. In fluid dynamics, a Mach number is defined to be the ratio of the flow speed to the local speed of sound.

Problems

E.1. True or False?

$\frac{N\ cm}{hr}$, $\frac{dyne \cdot cm}{min}$, $\frac{lb_f \cdot in}{s}$, $Watt$, and $\frac{lb_f \cdot ft}{s}$ have the same dimension.

E.2. In fluid dynamics, the dynamic viscosity μ is defined to be

$$F = \mu A \frac{u}{y},$$

where F is force, μ is dynamic viscosity, A is area, u is speed, and y is length. The kinematic viscosity ν is defined to be

$$\nu = \frac{\mu}{\rho},$$

where ν is the kinematic viscosity, μ is the dynamic viscosity, and ρ is the mass density.

What is the unit of μ and the unit of ν in the SI system of units?

Reference

Beer, F. P., E. R. Johnston Jr., and D. F. Mazurek. Vector Mechanics for Engineers: Statics. 11th ed. McGraw Hill Education, 2016.

CPSIA information can be obtained
at www.ICGtesting.com
Printed in the USA
LVHW050013250622
722073LV00003B/14